Contents

ENGLISH HERITAGE
STEP INTO ENGLAND'S STORY

KU-350-821

Welcome and thank you

In this year of the Queen's Diamond Jubilee and of the London Olympic Games there is much to be proud of, not least our amazing national story. English Heritage, as the proud custodian of the National Collection of heritage sites, is in a unique position to celebrate England's history this year. That's why this year's Members' Handbook has taken on a new look. Over the next few pages, we look at the story of England, a narrative of our history told through the remarkable places in our care.

When my predecessors started to collect prehistoric monuments in the Victorian age they founded a collection of historic places that now illustrates the most important events in our national story. This year's handbook brings out the connections between our sites and I hope will help people enjoy them more fully, seeing the role they played in our history.

English Heritage has in its care many churches and this year we are proud to be launching a new collaboration with the Churches Conservation Trust (CCT), a national charity that helps to save redundant parish churches. We have included 53 of the most important and interesting CCT churches in this handbook, many of which are conveniently close to popular English Heritage properties. Do visit as many of them as you can.

Exciting things are happening at Stonehenge too. We have secured permission to close the A344, the road which blights visits to Britain's most famous monument. This is part of the work we are doing to move the current ugly car park and facilities away from the stones. In April work will start on building a new museum and car park with really high quality visitor facilities. This will open to the public towards the end of 2013.

I am also excited about the opening of Queen Victoria and Prince Albert's private beach at Osborne House on the Isle of Wight. Since the house was given to the Nation this has never been open to the public; come along this summer and enjoy a paddle or lunch in our new beach café. A slightly more rugged, but none the less beautiful experience can be found at Housesteads on Hadrian's Wall. This summer we will open a new museum there with exhibitions showing what life was really like for the soldiers billeted on the Roman Empire's northern frontier.

If you didn't get to Wrest Park last year I do hope you will make the trip this summer. Work has continued over the winter on the parterre in front of the house and much of last year's planting is maturing nicely. I'm really grateful to our volunteer gardeners there who have worked so hard.

I hope you like our new-look handbook. This year it has been sponsored by our long-term supporters, Ecclesiastical. Thanks to them it contains more pages of useful information than ever and we have divided the listings into counties to make it easier to find what you are looking for. Above all, I hope it will encourage you to visit as many of our sites as possible.

Thank you so much for your support.

Simon Thurley
Chief Executive

1 St Peter's Church, Sandwich, Kent, one of the CCT properties
2 Osborne House
3 Wrest Park
4 Stonehenge

LOTTERY FUNDED

The Heritage Lottery Fund exists to support a wide range of heritage organisations through innovative investment in projects which have a lasting impact on people and places. The support of the Heritage Lottery Fund is key to many of the most ambitious projects that English Heritage undertakes, including the highly successful Revitalisation Project at Wrest Park.

Photo: © Roger Clegg

STEP INTO ENGLAND'S STORY

Our National Collection of over 400 sites has no equal for variety, breadth and time-coverage. Ranging from prehistoric stone circles via medieval castles and monasteries, Jacobean country houses, and Georgian gardens to Victorian servants' wings and a 1960s nuclear bunker, the properties we care for tell the story of England.

Some of our sites – like *Hadrian's Wall*, *Battle Abbey*, and *Apsley House* in the heart of London – are linked with famous events and personalities from the nation's story. Others, sometimes in little-visited corners, have unexpected twists in their histories or associations with eccentrics, such as the horse-hirer who originated 'Hobson's Choice' at *Denny Abbey*. Many more recall the ordinary people who also played their own small but vital parts in the story of England.

We hope the following period summaries will help you to trace this story at our sites.

Prehistory Before AD 43

The oldest human remains in England – found during the Boxgrove, Sussex excavation supported by English Heritage – are about 500,000 years old. But continuous human occupation began only after the end of the last Ice Age, around 14,000 years ago.

The First Farmers
Early 'hunter-gatherer' people left few visible traces: but with the arrival of farming in the Neolithic (New Stone Age) period, people began constructing monuments. Among the earliest are communal tombs like *West Kennet Long Barrow* and ritual enclosures like *Windmill Hill*.

Henges, Stone Circles and Ritual Landscapes
Circular earthwork 'henges' appear from about 3000 BC, when *Stonehenge* was begun and *Grime's Graves* flint mines were in use. The later Neolithic and early Bronze Ages saw massive stone circles like *Castlerigg Stone Circle* and *Avebury Stone Circle* raised, sometimes as elements of 'ritual landscapes'. The construction of mysterious *Silbury Hill* followed, and individuals were buried in 'round barrows' like *Flowerdown Barrows*. Though monuments like *Hurlers Stone Circles* later attracted legends, their original purpose remains enigmatic.

Wealth, Conflict and Trade
Bronze Age sites provide evidence of greater wealth, but also more conflict, apparently worsening in the Iron Age – when pressure on land produced many defensive hill forts, like *Maiden Castle*. *Chysauster Ancient Village* reflects locally more peaceful conditions, while *Stanwick Iron Age Fortifications* herald the growth of town-like tribal power centres – a development interrupted by the Roman Conquest.

7

Top: Maiden Castle
Left: Castlerigg Stone Circle
Right: Stonehenge

c.500,000 years ago	c.4000–2500 BC	c.2500–750 BC	AD 43
Oldest human remains in England	*Neolithic period (First Farmers)*	*Bronze Age*	*Roman Conquest begins*

c.14,000 years ago	c.3000 BC	from c.750 BC
Continuous human settlement begins	*Stonehenge begun*	*Iron Age*

The Romans   AD 43–c.410

Roman Britain lasted for over three and a half centuries – the span which separates us from the Civil Wars. English Heritage's Roman sites reflect the era from its violent beginning to its obscure end.

Conquest

Though Julius Caesar raided Britain in 55 and 54 BC, permanent conquest began when Roman forces landed near *Richborough Roman Fort* in AD 43.

Despite resistance by Boudica (Boadicea) and others, Roman armies had reached northern Scotland by AD 84, before retiring to the permanent frontier of *Hadrian's Wall*. Incomparably the most impressive Roman monument in Britain, the Wall's defensive system includes major forts like *Birdoswald, Chesters* and *Housesteads*.

Civilisation

Away from the frontiers, Roman Britain was for long periods peaceful and prosperous. 'Country houses' like *Lullingstone Roman Villa* flourished, bath-houses and amphitheatres were built, and many towns were founded – including large *Silchester* and *Wroxeter* and smaller *Aldborough* and *Corbridge* – often at existing British tribal centres. Most were eventually walled against increasing external threats.

The Saxon Shore

Towards the end of the 3rd century, attacks by seaborne Germanic raiders prompted the creation of 'Saxon Shore' coastal fortifications like *Burgh Castle*: further trouble saw the system strengthened in the next century, and *Pevensey Castle* added. Garrisons were by now mainly British-born, and little distinguished 'Romans' from 'Britons' when imperial rule petered out: there was no clearly definable end of Roman Britain.

Among the 52 Roman sites in English Heritage's care are:

- Birdoswald Roman Fort
- Burgh Castle
- Chesters Roman Fort
- Corbridge Roman Town
- Hadrian's Wall
- Housesteads Roman Fort
- Lullingstone Roman Villa
- Pevensey Castle
- Richborough Roman Fort and Amphitheatre
- Wroxeter Roman City

Top left: Corbridge lion
Top right: Genii Cucullati relief carving from Housesteads
Centre: Mosaic at Lullingstone Roman Villa
Bottom right: bust from Corbridge
Bottom centre: Hadrian's Wall
Bottom left: coins from Richborough and Stanwick

8

© Roger Clegg

AD 43
Roman Conquest begins

AD 84
Furthest extent of Roman rule in Britain

AD 122
Hadrian's Wall begun

c.AD 260–360
Saxon Shore defences built

c.AD 410–425
Imperial rule by Rome fades

Britons, English & Vikings   c.400–1066

The centuries between the end of Roman Britain and the Norman Conquest saw the gradual emergence of an English nation, and its narrow escape from Scandinavian domination.

The English Conquest
Even before its severance from the Roman Empire, Britain was threatened by sea-borne Germanic peoples – Angles, Saxons, Jutes and Frisians. Though long delayed by Romano-British resistance (perhaps inspired by a fabled 'Arthur') these 'Anglo-Saxon' invaders had conquered most of lowland England by the mid-600s, establishing several independent kingdoms. Tantalising hints about this shadowy period have emerged from sites like *Birdoswald Roman Fort*, *Tintagel Castle* and *Wroxeter Roman City*.

Christian Culture Blossoms
Increasingly called 'English', the pagan conquerors were converted to Christianity by missionaries from Rome – including St Augustine – and Ireland. Christian culture blossomed: *Lindisfarne Priory* produced its illuminated manuscript Gospels, while Bede's writings at *St Paul's Monastery, Jarrow* fostered the concept of an English nation. Through their architecture and craftsmanship, *St Peter's Church, Barton-Upon-Humber* and *Sandbach Crosses* likewise reflect the English Church's vitality.

The Viking Threat
Towards the end of the 3rd century, soon after *Offa's Dyke* defined its western boundary, the development of England was imperilled as Viking raids became invasions. King Alfred of Wessex turned the tide, and his descendants reconquered Viking-held lands: his grandson Aethelstan became the first ruler of a unified English state. But Danish pressure revived – King Cnut subsumed England into his Scandinavian empire – and it was a weakened England which faced the Normans in 1066.

Among the 19 sites within this period in English Heritage's care are:

- 1066 Battle of Hastings, Abbey and Battlefield
- Lindisfarne Priory
- Lydford Castle and Saxon Town
- Offa's Dyke
- St Augustine's Abbey
- St Paul's Monastery, Jarrow
- St Peter's Church, Barton-on-Humber
- Sandbach Crosses
- Tintagel Castle
- Whitby Abbey

9

Above: Viking stone at Lindisfarne
Left: reconstruction of a cross at Sandbach, Cheshire
Below: St Peter's Church, Barton-upon-Humber

c.410–25	597–625	871–900	1066
End of Imperial Roman rule in Britain	*Principal Christian missions*	*Alfred the Great reigns*	*Norman Conquest begins*

c.550–c.620	787–9	927
Anglo-Saxons conquer lowland England	*Viking raids begin*	*Aethelstan becomes first king of all England*

The Middle Ages   1066–1485

'The Middle Ages', as G. K. Chesterton observed, 'did not all happen at the same time'. The five centuries between the battles of Hastings in 1066 and Bosworth in 1485 witnessed considerable changes in England, including language – from the Anglo-Saxon, Danish and Norman-French spoken here at the beginning of the period to the recognisable ancestor of modern English used by its end. Nearly half of all English Heritage sites date from this era, and their variety mirrors its developing character: but many reflect two constants – the importance of castles and the dominance of the Church.

The Land Filled with Castles

Earthwork and timber 'motte and bailey' castles were the instruments and symbols of the Norman Conquest: many, like *Clifford's Tower* and *Totnes Castle*, were later refortified in stone. The great stone keeps of the Norman and Angevin kings and their barons formed the core of major early fortresses like *Dover Castle, Orford Castle* and *Richmond Castle*, before the focus shifted to many-towered enclosure walls with powerful gatehouses, as at *Framlingham Castle* and *Goodrich Castle*. Equipped with halls, chapels and many domestic buildings, some strongholds like *Beeston Castle* or *Kenilworth Castle* were immense in scale. More compact fortresses – including *Farleigh Hungerford Castle* and *Nunney Castle* – developed towards the end of the era, some (like *Berry Pomeroy* and *Kirby Muxloe* castles) equipped for artillery defence.

Manor Houses, Town Houses and Barns

Only a tiny minority of medieval people lived in castles. English Heritage's collection also includes lightly fortified or undefended manor houses like *Stokesay Castle* or *Old Soar Manor*; and urban houses like Southampton's *Medieval Merchant's House*. Country life is represented by *Wharram Percy Deserted Medieval Village* and farm buildings like imposing *Harmondsworth Great Barn*.

Oases of Peace

Whether in castle, town or country, medieval life was dominated by the Church: in the 14th century about one in fifteen Englishmen were clergy of some kind. English Heritage cares for parish churches like *St Mary's Kempley* with its wonderful wall-paintings, and bishops' mansions including *Lincoln Medieval Bishops Palace*: and the evocative remains of many monasteries, from big, prosperous *Castle Acre Priory* to tiny *Mattersey Priory*.

1066
Norman Conquest

1215
Magna Carta

1277–1307
Edward I's wars in Wales and Scotland

1066–1154
Norman Kings

1154–1485
Angevin/Plantagenet Kings

Each reflects the characteristics of the monastic order which inhabited it: 'mainstream' Benedictines at *Binham Priory* and *Whitby Abbey*; solitude-seeking Cistercians at *Furness Abbey* and *Rievaulx Abbey*; decoration-loving Cluniacs at *Wenlock Priory*; Augustinian canons at lovely *Lanercost Priory*; hermit-like Carthusians at *Mount Grace Priory* or the urban friars of Gloucester's *Blackfriars* and *Greyfriars*.

Memories of Conflict

Many of English Heritage's medieval sites, by contrast, recall the foreign or internal wars of medieval England.

Some – like *Carlisle Castle* – guarded land borders against Scots or Welsh, or like *Carisbrooke Castle* and *Dartmouth Castle* defended coasts against sea-borne invasion and raiding. Others, including *Rochester Castle*, endured conflicts between monarchs and barons, or like *Dunstanburgh Castle* or *Warkworth Castle* witnessed the dynastic Wars of the Roses, ended by the Battle of Bosworth which began the Tudor age.

Among the 202 sites within this period in English Heritage's care are:

- Beeston Castle
- Binham Priory
- Carisbrooke Castle
- Carlisle Castle
- Castle Acre Priory
- Clifford's Tower
- Conisbrough Castle
- Dover Castle
- Eleanor Cross, Geddington
- Eltham Palace
- Framlingham Castle
- Goodrich Castle
- Harmondsworth Great Barn
- Kenilworth Castle
- Lanercost Priory
- Old Sarum
- Rievaulx Abbey
- St Mary's Church, Kempley
- Scarborough Castle
- Stokesay Castle

Left page top to bottom: William the Conqueror from Battle Abbey and a reconstruction drawing of Dover Castle's Great Tower

Right page top to bottom: Roof boss from Hailes Abbey; Goodrich Castle; detail of Eleanor Cross at Geddington; Rievaulx Abbey

11

1337–1453
Hundred Years War with France

1349
Black Death

1381
Peasants' Revolt

1455–85
Wars of the Roses

1476–7
First books printed in England

The Tudors   1485–1603

The crucial pivot of medieval and modern history, the Tudor era saw strong central government established; England transformed from a Catholic to a Protestant nation; and the flowering of a distinctively English culture and the English country house.

Among the 50 sites within this period in English Heritage's care are:

- Blackfriars, Gloucester
- Deal Castle
- Hailes Abbey
- Hardwick Old Hall
- Kenilworth Castle and Elizabethan Garden
- Kirby Hall
- Norham Castle
- Pendennis Castle
- Rushton Triangular Lodge
- Titchfield Abbey

The Triumph of Monarchy

Ending the Wars of the Roses, Henry VII curtailed aristocratic power and castle-building, and his successors strengthened the grip of monarchy. Henceforth fortresses would be raised only by the crown, most notably Henry VIII's coastal artillery forts – the first co-ordinated system of national defence – including *Deal Castle* and *Pendennis Castle*.

Religious Upheavals

Henry's new-style forts defended England against European Catholic reaction to the religious changes he initiated: English Heritage's outstanding collection of monastic ruins bear witness to his Dissolution of the Monasteries. After swinging from Edward VI's radical Protestantism to Mary's revived Catholicism, the nation settled down to religious compromise under Queen Elizabeth.

The Flowering of English Culture

Elizabeth's long and glorious reign witnessed the expansion of English sea power (reinforced by her defeat of the Spanish Armada) and the flowering of English culture epitomised by Shakespeare. It also saw the burgeoning of the great English country house – some converted monasteries or adapted medieval fortresses like *Kenilworth Castle and Elizabethan Garden*, but most built from new like *Kirby Hall*. All these developments expressed new-found English self-confidence.

Top left: A reconstruction drawing of the Long Gallery at Kirby Hall as it might have appeared in the early 17th century
Top right: Deal Castle
Bottom left: Queen Elizabeth I
Bottom centre: Kirby Hall
Below: Rushton Triangular Lodge

1485
Battle of Bosworth

1536–40
Dissolution of Monasteries

1558–1603
Elizabeth I reigns

1564–1616
Shakespeare living

1509–47
Henry VIII reigns

1532–59
Religious changes

1588
Spanish Armada

The Stuarts   1603–1714

Following a long period of peace, the intense political and religious conflicts of the Stuart era transformed the government of England. Developments in artistic styles and living standards are also reflected in this era's English Heritage sites.

Among the 39 sites within this period in English Heritage's care are:

- Abingdon County Hall
- Audley End House and Gardens
- Berry Pomeroy Castle
- Bolsover Castle
- Boscobel House and the Royal Oak
- Carisbrooke Castle
- Great Yarmouth Row Houses
- Langley Chapel
- Pendennis Castle
- Tilbury Fort

13

Gracious Living

The earlier ('Jacobean') part of the period saw many lavish mansions like *Audley End House* and *Bolsover Castle* built, and fine interiors created in more modest dwellings like *Bessie Surtees House* and *Great Yarmouth Row Houses*.

Civil Wars and Republic

The Civil Wars between Charles I and Parliament (1642–51) brought much devastation; epic sieges of *Pendennis Castle* and many other places; and (after his imprisonment at *Carisbrooke Castle*) the king's execution and the creation (1649–60) of the Commonwealth, the only republic in English history. Young Charles II narrowly escaped capture near *Boscobel House*.

Restoration and New Styles

Epitomised by Pepys's diary, the reign of the restored Charles II brought continuing scientific advances, but also plague and fire in London and humiliating Dutch attack, provoking the building of defences like *Tilbury Fort*. The 'English Baroque' style of *Abingdon County Hall* came increasingly into fashion towards the end of the period.

England and Britain

The era's long-simmering religious disputes were addressed in 1689, after the Catholic James II was deposed by the Protestant William and Mary. Under Queen Anne, the Acts of Union with Scotland made England part of 'Great Britain'.

Top: Oliver Cromwell
Left top: Audley End
Left centre: Boscobel House
Left bottom: Reconstruction of Tilbury Fort
Bottom: Little Castle at Bolsover

1603–25	1649–60	1688
James I (Jacobean period)	Commonwealth and Cromwell's Protectorate	William and Mary crowned

1642–51	1660–69	1706–7
Civil Wars	Pepys's diary written	Acts of Union with Scotland

The Georgians 1714–1837

An age of elegant country houses and glittering town mansions, the Georgian era also saw Britain become the world's first industrial nation, at the hub of a rapidly growing empire.

Among the 42 sites within this period in English Heritage's care are:

- Apsley House
- Belsay Hall, Castle and Gardens
- Chiswick House
- Derwentcote Steel Furnace
- Iron Bridge
- Kenwood House
- Marble Hill House
- The Grange at Northington
- Wellington Arch
- Wrest Park

Elegant Mansions
English Heritage's outstanding collection of Georgian and Regency mansions reflect the period's progression of fashionable styles, from the Palladian of *Chiswick House* via Robert Adam's *Kenwood* to the 'Regency' Greek Revival of *Belsay Hall* and *The Grange at Northington*. Tasteful interiors (as at *Marble Hill House*) were counterpointed by formal or 'landscaped' gardens – an English gift to the world – often adorned (as at *Audley End House* and *Wrest Park*) with charming garden architecture.

Industrial Revolution
The wealth which financed these mansions was increasingly founded on England's pioneering Industrial Revolution. Built in the 1730s, *Derwentcote Steel Furnace* produced steel for springs and cutting tools, while the *Iron Bridge* was the world's first of its kind, and the world's first steam trains ran in England in 1825.

War and Empire
International trade boomed alongside an expanding empire, particularly in India and the Americas. Yet as *Dover Castle* and *Dymchurch Martello Tower* demonstrate, Britain's growing

Top left: Marble Hill House
Left: Iron Bridge
Top right: artillery barracks in Dover Castle tunnels
Below: wine cooler from Apsley House

military and especially naval power did not go unchallenged, notably during the long wars with Revolutionary and Napoleonic France. Wellington, greatest military hero of these wars, is remembered at *Apsley House, Walmer Castle* and *Wellington Arch.*

14

1715 & 1745/6
Jacobite Risings

1779
Industrial Revolution: Iron Bridge completed

1811–20
Regency period

1754–63
'Seven Years War' expands British Empire

1793–1815
Napoleonic Wars

1825
First public steam railway opens

The Victorians & Edwardians   1837–1910

The long reign of Queen Victoria, with the Edwardian 'Indian Summer' that followed, saw Britain at the zenith of her international power and status, and the greatest manufacturing nation in the world.

Masters and Servants
The Queen's strong personality is reflected at *Osborne House*. Her wealthier subjects also continued to build great mansions like *Brodsworth Hall* and *Witley Court*, operated by armies of servants – as *Audley End*'s service wing and stables demonstrate.

A Hive of Industry
J.W. Evans Silver Factory and *Stott Park Bobbin Mill* reflect Victorian England as a hive of manufacturing industry: rural life was also being transformed by machinery, as seen in English Heritage's collection of windmills.

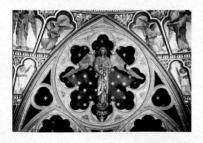

Doubt and Certainty
The publication of Charles Darwin's ideas on evolution (matured and written down at *Down House*) shook Victorian religious certainty, but did not stem the period's flood of chapel and church building – the latter almost always in the ubiquitous 'Gothic Revival' style. *St Mary's Church, Studley Royal* is a flamboyant example.

An Imperial Power
Despite the 1860s French invasion scare which produced new fortifications like *Fort Brockhurst* and the updating of older defences like *Dartmouth Castle*, Britannia's fleets continued to rule the waves and her armies to fight far-flung colonial wars. The Boer War of 1899–1902 dented 'Imperial' confidence, but at the death of Edward VII (a very 'un-Victorian' monarch) the British Empire was nearing its greatest extent.

Left: Gothic Revival decoration at St Mary's Church, Studley Royal

Among the 30 sites within this period in English Heritage's care are:

- *Audley End House*
- *Brodsworth Hall*
- *The Home of Charles Darwin, Down House*
- *Fort Brockhurst*
- *Mount Grace Priory*
- *Osborne House*
- *St Mary's Church, Studley Royal*
- *Sibsey Trader Windmill*
- *Stott Park Bobbin Mill*
- *Witley Court*

15

Top: Charles Darwin and Beagle voyage notebook
Left: Osborne House
Below: Perseus and Andromeda Fountain at Witley Court

1837	1895	1901
Accession of Queen Victoria	First motor cars in England	Death of Victoria

1859	1897	1910
Darwin's 'Origin of Species' published	Victoria's Diamond Jubilee	Death of Edward VII: British Empire nears greatest extent

The Modern Age   1910–present

The two World Wars which dominate the modern age of British history also acted as catalysts for previously unimaginable changes.

Two World Wars – and a Third?
The First World War, with its terrible carnage, and the Second World War – whose far greater impact on the civilian population is underlined at *Great Yarmouth Row Houses* – are both reflected in many English Heritage properties. Old fortifications like *Calshot Castle* were updated for new types of warfare, and the Secret Wartime Tunnels beneath *Dover Castle* played a crucial role in saving the nation in 1940. The dead of both wars are remembered by the London war memorials cared for by English Heritage, among them the poignant Royal Artillery Memorial at Hyde Park Corner. But *York Cold War Bunker* is a chilling reminder that the threat of even greater mass destruction remained ever-present.

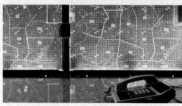

An Ongoing Revolution
The post-World War II creation of the Welfare State made life easier for the many: and the advent of radio and TV and more recently of affordable computer technology have fostered a still greater (and still continuing) revolution in lifestyles.

Social Transformation
Both World Wars transformed the social structure of England: *Brodsworth Hall* tracks the decline of the country house and its servant-dependent lifestyle – though remodelled *Eltham Palace* glitteringly displays the stylish living still enjoyed by the millionaire few.

English Heritage cares for 23 sites with major features of this period – including the following – and several London war memorials

- Brodsworth Hall and Gardens
- Calshot Castle
- Dover Castle (Secret Wartime Tunnels)
- Eltham Palace
- Great Yarmouth Row Houses
- J. W. Evans Silver Factory
- Richmond Castle
- Royal Garrison Church
- Tynemouth Priory and Castle
- York Cold War Bunker

Top: WWII hospital in Dover Castle Tunnels and Operations Room at York Cold War Bunker
Bottom left: from the Royal Artillery Memorial, London
Bottom right: Entrance Hall at Eltham Palace

16

1914–18
First World War

1930
First regular TV broadcasting

1948
National Health Service established

1977 *Personal computers* and **1990** *mobile phones widely available*

1922
First BBC radio broadcast

1939–45
Second World War

1946–1989
'Cold War'

The Churches Conservation Trust

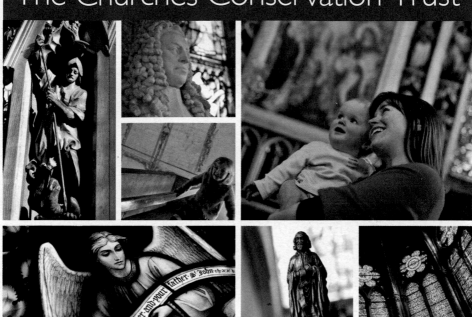

Explore the beauty and history of some of the most wonderful churches imaginable

The Churches Conservation Trust (CCT) is the national charity protecting historic churches at risk. We've saved over 340 beautiful buildings, which attract almost 2 million visitors a year. With our help and with your support they are kept open and in use – living once again at the heart of their communities.

We care for and open to the public one of the greatest collections of ecclesiastical architecture and art in the world. Trust churches are scattered throughout the length and breadth of England,

in town and country, ranging from ancient, rustic buildings to others of great richness and splendour. Each has been saved because it represents something remarkable.

Our work both in conservation and new uses of churches wins national and international awards. Over 4,000 cultural and community events take place in Trust churches across England each year.

We warmly welcome visitors and entry is free. A thousand years of English history awaits you within their walls.

To discover more about this great heritage go to www.visitchurches.org.uk where you will find descriptions, directions, photos and much more of interest about the historic churches in CCT's care.

THE CHURCHES CONSERVATION TRUST

Registered charity no: 258612

I West Smithfield, London EC1A 9EE
Tel: 020 7213 0660
Email: central@tcct.org.uk

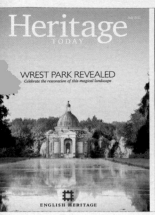

Your membership and events programme

Thank you for supporting English Heritage – your membership really does make a difference to our work – and helps us look after more than 400 properties, ranging from historic castles to grand palaces, inspiring abbeys to lavish gardens. We look foward to welcoming you on your next visit soon.

Your membership gives you:

- Free and unlimited entry to all our sites.
- Free entry for up to six accompanied children (under 19) within your family group per member.
- Free or reduced price admission to over 100 associated attractions.
- Your free handbook worth £10.95 to help you get the most out of your visits.
- Our award-winning magazine – *Heritage Today* – packed with ideas, inspiration and news of events and activities.
- Access to exclusive members' events and behind the scenes tours.

READ ALL ABOUT IT

Our superb magazine *Heritage Today* is packed with inspiration and ideas for making the most of your membership, including a full list of our events. What's more, it's completely FREE to members and is delivered direct to you, so look out for it. You can also be the first to hear about special events and the latest news by signing up to receive our regular e-newsletter. Go to **www.english-heritage.org.uk/newsletter**

MORE VALUE, MORE PROPERTIES

Your English Heritage membership card opens doors to many other associated attractions and properties – often at no extra cost. Check details in this handbook or visit **www.english-heritage. org.uk/members** to see offers and check terms and conditions.

EVENTS

Every year we offer a whole host of fantastic days out. There's something for everyone, from live action spectaculars to ghost tours, arts and crafts fairs, talks, tours, exhibitions and children's quests and trails.

If you have a passion for history or are just looking for a great day out we recommend you visit at least one of our unmissable family event weekends: St George's Day Festival at Wrest Park (21-22 Apr); 1066 Battle of Hastings (13-14 Oct) – this year featuring 1,066 re-enactors; and the unbeatable Festival of History (14-15 Jul) **www.twitter.com/festivalhistory**

Members' Events

There is so much more to our properties than you might think, and as a member you have access to behind the scenes tours guided by our experts, who will share their unique knowledge and insight with you. We have over 100 member-only events throughout the year, across the country.

See page 309 for more information, or visit **www.english-heritage.org.uk/events** or check *Heritage Today* for a full programme of events.

KEEP IN TOUCH

Tell other members about your visit to one of our properties. Post your message and photos on **www.flickr.com/groups/ englishheritagedaysout** and subscribe to our YouTube channel to check our latest videos **www.youtube.com/user/ englishheritagefilm**

THE IDEAL GIFT
FOR FRIENDS AND FAMILY

Give the Gift of Membership – and help a great cause.

Birthdays, Christmas, just because – call us now on

0870 333 1182

and set up your Gift of Membership today.

CONTACT US

Telephone
0870 333 1182

Lines open 8.30am-5pm Mon-Fri (6.30pm in summer) and 9am-5pm Sat

Email
members@english-heritage. org.uk

 www.facebook.com/ englishheritage

 www.twitter.com/ englishheritage

Planning your visit

We want you to enjoy every moment of your visit, and so please read the following section carefully. Each property listing will contain symbols to help you assess its suitability for your visiting party. We hope you will find all the information you will need to plan your perfect day, but if you have any questions please do not hesitate to call us on 0870 333 1181.

Access

We want as many people as possible to enjoy a day out with English Heritage. The handbook listings indicate areas of properties accessible to disabled visitors and visitors with babies and younger children – with the use of the ♿ symbol. Remember that if you are disabled your carer is always admitted free and many of our sites have parking spaces for the disabled.

For more detailed information, our free *Access Guide* offers an up-to-date and honest assessment about which properties and gardens are most suited to families and disabled people. There's information about parking and drop-off points, and about properties that have special features such as scented gardens or tactile objects for those with impaired sight.

For your free copy, call 0870 333 1181, minicom 0800 015 0516, or email customers@english-heritage.org.uk. You can also download it from our website.

ADMISSIONS

Admission charges apply to non-members, and prices are given in this handbook as follows: Adult; Concession (senior citizens, jobseekers and students with relevant ID); Child (age 5-16, under 5s go free).

Where available, Family tickets normally admit two adults and three children (may vary at properties not managed by us).

For groups of 11 or more visitors paying together, discounts of 15% (10% at Stonehenge) are available. We recommend that groups book in advance. Call 0870 333 1181 for a copy of our Group Visits Guide.

If you are a visitor from overseas and are planning to visit a number of properties an **Overseas Visitors Pass** (OVP) may make financial sense. As well as other benefits, this allows unlimited free access to all English Heritage properties marked with the OVP symbol over a 7 or 14 day period. Call 0870 333 1181 or visit **www.english-heritage.org.uk/ovp**

P CAR PARKING

There is free parking at most of our properties. In cases where any parking charges apply, you will be reimbursed on admission (except Battle Abbey, Kenwood and Marble Hill). Any revenue raised from car parking will be re-invested back into our properties. Disabled parking is available at many of our sites.

APPS

Make sure you download our free App to help you plan your days out. Simple and intuitive to use, it features:

- Events at places to visit
- Don't miss tips for when you arrive
- Times, prices, directions and more
- Picture galleries
- Favourites – build your own list
- Scalable maps

www.english-heritage.org.uk/daysout/app

CATERING AND PICNICS

Many of our properties offer delicious home-made food and drink. Visitors are welcome to picnic in the grounds of most of our properties.

DOGS

Dogs on leads usually are welcome but please see individual property listings. No restrictions on assistance dogs.

EDUCATIONAL VISITS

There is nothing more inspiring or educational than visiting an English Heritage property. We believe that experiencing the local historic environment should be central to the national curriculum of every school in England, and actively encourage groups for this purpose, offering a

range of resources to help teachers and students of all ages. For safety purposes, we require a ratio of one adult to every 6 children for Years 1 to 3, one adult to every 10-15 children for Years 4 to 6, and one adult for every 15 children from Year 7 up. English Heritage Education is a lead partner in Engaging Places, which encourages teachers and students to work creatively with the historic built environment. Visit **www.engagingplaces.org.uk**

🖼 FAMILIES AND CHILDREN

Many of our properties are fascinating for children. We put on special exhibitions catering to children's needs, and at well over 50 properties we offer free activity sheets, back-packs, book boxes and Very Big Books. Our interactive Discovery Centres will keep younger visitors absorbed for hours. Please note that you will be responsible for the safety and supervision of your children at all times at our sites, so please ensure a sensible ratio of adults to children.

🎧🖼 GUIDES AND TOURS

Guidebooks and audio tours help bring sites to life at more and more of our properties. We also provide audio-guides for children and people with learning difficulties, as well as in different languages. Specialist tours are available at certain sites for pre-booked groups of 11 or more. Many of our properties have dedicated guidebooks – including 50 or so in the 'Red Guide' series with their distinctive red spines. Written by leading experts, these feature a tour of the site together with a more in-depth history of the people who lived and worked there. Packed with plans,

reconstruction drawings, eyewitness accounts and beautiful photography, they make essential reading as well as brilliant souvenirs of your visit. Short histories and descriptions of our free sites are also available online.

PHOTOGRAPHY

Taking pictures is not permitted in some properties due to the sensitive nature of some materials. Non-commercial photography is welcome in the gardens and grounds of all our sites.

⚠ SAFETY AND SMOKING

Due to their historic nature, some of our sites have potentially hazardous features – please pay attention to all safety notices on site. If you have any doubts, our staff can always advise on safety issues. Please wear suitable footwear to avoid accidents, and do not climb on walls or monuments. In areas of woodland/deer pasture there may be slight risk of ticks, so keep vulnerable parts of your body covered and/or use insect repellent. Note that smoking is not permitted inside any of our properties.

TRAVEL AND TRANSPORT

Where possible in the property listings, we have provided public transport information which has kindly been supplied by the Confederation of Passenger Transport (**www.cpt-uk.org**). These details were correct at time of going to press. For cycle routes, call 0845 113 0065 or visit sustrans. org.uk. OS LandRanger/Explorer map references have also been supplied for each property. A free Sat Nav download of our properties is available at **www.english-heritage.org.uk/satnav**

Ecclesiastical Insurance works in close partnership with English Heritage and is delighted to sponsor the production of the 2012/13 handbook, as well as a range of other exciting activities. We hope there will be opportunities to meet members at English Heritage events throughout the year.

Ecclesiastical is a unique commercial organisation owned by a charity. We have a distinctive culture and values that have guided us for 125 years. Giving a share of profits to charity is nothing new and lots of companies do it. What makes us different is that we all believe in it – and we are already one of the top 15 corporate donors in the UK*.

Established in 1887 to protect the Anglican Church, we are now one of the UK's largest British owned insurers offering honest advice, deep expertise and caring protection. We're big enough to be a serious player, offering outstanding insurance solutions, but also small enough to care.

We form strong partnerships with organisations that share our values. Ecclesiastical and English Heritage both have a vested interest in the heritage sector. We started working together over 20 years ago and four years ago we established a formal agreement to work together more closely.

Steve Wood, UK Managing Director, Ecclesiastical Insurance

* Source: UK Guide to Company Giving 2011/12

years making a difference
Ecclesiastical

Wellington Arch

LONDON

PROPERTIES

London properties consist of:

13	English Heritage
1	The Churches Conservation Trust
11	Associated Attractions

Remember to check opening times before you visit any of our properties www.english-heritage. org.uk/daysout

Details of local public transport information in England are available from Traveline www.traveline.org.uk or call 0871 200 2233.

For travel information in London you can also call Transport For London on 0843 222 1234 or visit www.tfl.gov.uk

Eltham Palace

Make the most of your membership and keep up to date with upcoming events, the latest news and special offers by subscribing to our e-newsletter. Register online now at **www.english-heritage.org.uk/ newsletter**

CAMDEN
Kenwood

GREENWICH
Eltham Palace and Gardens
Ranger's House –
   the Wernher Collection

HILLINGDON
Harmondsworth Great Barn

HOUNSLOW
Chiswick House and Gardens

KINGSTON-UPON-THAMES
Coombe Conduit

RICHMOND-UPON-THAMES
Marble Hill House

SOUTHWARK
Winchester Palace

TOWER HAMLETS
London Wall

WESTMINSTER
Apsley House
Chapter House and Pyx Chamber
Jewel Tower
Wellington Arch

LONDON

Enfield

Barnet

Harrow

Haringey Waltham Redbridge
Forest

Hillingdon Havering

Brent Hackney

Camden Islington Barking

Ealing Tower Newham
The City Hamlets

Hammersmith Kensington Westminster

Southwark

Hounslow Greenwich

Lambeth Bexley

Richmond Wandsworth

Lewisham

Merton

Kingston

Sutton Bromley

Croydon

HIGHLIGHTS FOR 2012/13 IN LONDON

- **Apsley House:** Regency history and one of the finest art collections in London.
- **Eltham Palace & Gardens:** immerse yourself in the glamour of the Art Deco period.
- **Wellington Arch:** an unmissable London landmark offering panoramic views.

Apsley House Hyde Park – W1J 7NT

Check opening times at www.english-heritage.org.uk

Apsley House, home of the first Duke of Wellington and his descendants, stands right in the heart of London at Hyde Park Corner. For over 200 years, this great metropolitan mansion has been known colloquially as 'Number 1 London', because it was the first house encountered after passing the tollgates at the top of Knightsbridge.

The Portico Room

Wellington enthusiasts may also be interested in visiting the spectacular Wellington Arch opposite Apsley House (see p.38), and elegant Walmer Castle (p.72), the duke's residence when he was Lord Warden of the Cinque Ports.

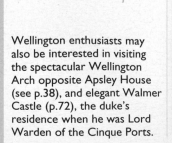

The Waterloo Gallery

The Wellington Shield

Apsley House was originally designed and built by Robert Adam between 1771 and 1778 for Baron Apsley – from whom it takes its name. It passed to the Wellesley family in 1807, being first owned by Richard and then his younger brother Arthur Wellesley – the Duke of Wellington.

Wellington is most famous for defeating Napoleon at the Battle of Waterloo in 1815, but this was only the culmination of a brilliant military career. He was also a major politician, rising from representing a small Irish constituency in 1790 to Prime Minister in 1828.

Redesigned to reflect the Duke of Wellington's rising status, Apsley House's dazzling interiors are magnificent examples of the Regency style. They provided the perfect backdrop for entertaining, particularly at the annual Waterloo Banquets which commemorated the great victory.

Inside Apsley House you will see many aspects of the first Duke's life and work, including his outstanding art collection. Paintings by many famous artists are hung throughout the first floor, many of them part of the Spanish Royal Collection which came into Wellington's possession after the Battle of Vitoria in 1813. A colossal nude statue of Napoleon by Canova dominates the stairwell at the centre of the house.

Throughout his military career, the Duke was presented with a vast collection of silver plate and unique porcelain as trophies from grateful nations. Many of these can be seen in the Plate and China Room. Wellington's

The Physician's Visit, by Jan Steen

victories are celebrated in the fine British craftsmanship of the magnificent Wellington Shield, designed by Thomas Stothard, and the impressive candelabra presented by the merchants and bankers of the City of London.

When the seventh Duke of Wellington gave the house to the nation in 1947, the family retained the private rooms, which they still use today. This makes Apsley House the last surviving great London town house open to the public.

Don't miss our 15-minute Walk and Talk Gallery Tours which take place twice daily throughout the year.

www.english-heritage.org.uk/apsleyhouse

 www.facebook.com/apsleyhouse

NEW FOR 2012

Meet the Keeper

Every Wednesday afternoon in May, come along to a special talk at 2pm by the Keeper of the Wellington Collection.

NON-MEMBERS

Apsley House

Adult	£6.50
Concession	£5.90
Child	£3.90
Family	£21.30

Joint ticket with Wellington Arch

Adult	£8.20
Concession	£7.40
Child	£4.90

OPENING TIMES

1 Apr-4 Nov, Wed-Sun & Bank Hols	11am-5pm
5 Nov-28 Mar, Sat-Sun	10am-4pm
24-26 Dec and 1 Jan	Closed

Free members' guided tours
8 Nov, 4 Dec, 8 Jan, 5 Feb, 5 Mar, 12 Mar   11.30am & 2.30pm

HOW TO FIND US

Direction: 149 Piccadilly, Hyde Park Corner

Train: Victoria ½ mile

Bus: From surrounding areas

Tube: Hyde Park Corner

Tel: 020 7499 5676

Disabled access very limited.
Please phone property for information

MAP Page 314 (4E)
OS Map 176, 161/173: TQ284799

'Ideal Head (Head of a Dancer)' bust by Antonio Canova

Chandos Mausoleum (St Lawrence's Church)
Little Stanmore
HA8 6RB

© CCT

Chandos Mausoleum was added to early 18th-century St Lawrence's Church (church not part of CCT's estate) in 1736. The Mausoleum contains a magnificent monument by master carver Grinling Gibbons and the walls and ceiling are lavishly decorated. There are also hatchments in the ante-room.

Owned and managed by The Churches Conservation Trust.

OPENING TIMES

Summer, Sun	2pm-5pm
Winter, Sun	2pm-4pm

For other times please call 020 8952 0019 to enquire

HOW TO FIND US

Train: Nearest ⧉ Mill Hill Broadway 1¾ miles

Bus: Route 30

Within 1 hour of Apsley House and Wellington Arch, Kenwood, and Chapter House and Pyx Chamber and Jewel Tower

MAP Page 314 (3E)
OS Map 176, 173: TQ186913

Don't forget to check opening times online before you visit

www.english-heritage.org.uk/ daysout/properties

Chapter House and Pyx Chamber
Westminster Abbey – SW1P 3PA

Built by the royal masons in 1250, the Chapter House of Westminster Abbey was used from the 13th to the 16th century by Benedictine monks for their daily meetings. It was also sometimes used as a meeting place of the King's Great Council and the Commons, predecessors of today's Parliament.

A beautiful octagonal building with a vaulted ceiling and delicate central column, it offers rarely seen examples of medieval sculpture, an original floor of glazed tiles and spectacular wall paintings. The 11th-century Pyx Chamber also has a medieval tiled floor, and was used as a monastic and royal treasury. It contains a 13th-century stone altar which survived the Reformation.

During 2009/10, English Heritage funded a major programme of conservation repairs to the external fabric of the Chapter House. This included repairs to the roof, gutters, stonework on the elevations and flying buttresses, and repairs to the lead light glazing – thus preserving this highly important building for future generations.

Chapter House free to EH members. Under the care and management of the Dean and Chapter of Westminster.
www.westminster-abbey.org

OPENING TIMES

Throughout the year, Mon-Sun	10am-4pm
Good Fri, 24-26 Dec and 1 Jan	Closed

May be closed at short notice on state and religious occasions

HOW TO FIND US

Direction: Through the cloister from Dean's Yard if you only want to visit the Chapter House. Turn into Dean's Yard off Broad Sanctuary. Turn left along the square and go through the entrance-way into the cloister

Please show your EH membership card to the Marshal at the gate

Train: Victoria and Charing Cross both ¾ mile, Waterloo 1 mile

Bus: From surrounding areas

Tube: Westminster and St James' Park stations both ¼ mile

Tel: 020 7654 4900

MAP Page 315 (4F)
OS Map 176/177, 161/173: TQ299795

Chiswick House and Gardens
See feature opposite

Chiswick House and Gardens Chiswick – W4 2QN

Chiswick House is among the most glorious examples of 18th-century British architecture. The third Earl of Burlington, who designed this noble Roman-style Palladian villa, drew inspiration from his 'grand tours' of Italy. The sumptuous interiors, created by William Kent, display a rich collection of Old Master paintings which complement the beautiful painted and gilded ceilings, and show the diversity of Burlington's collections.

Chiswick House Gardens are a site of international importance, both as the birthplace of the English Landscape Movement, and as the setting for one of the most beautiful houses in London. Spreading over 65 acres, they have inspired countless designed landscapes, from Blenheim Palace to Central Park in New York. Highlights of a £12m restoration unveiled in 2010 include the planting of over 1600 trees, including trees propagated from the original 18th-century cedars of Lebanon; the opening up of historic views from the Classic Bridge; and the complete refurbishment of the 19th-century conservatory, housing an

internationally important collection of camellias – possibly the oldest collection outside China and Japan.

Complete your day by visiting the acclaimed modern airy café. For more information including events and activities, visit www.chgt.org.uk

Managed by Chiswick House and Gardens Trust in partnership with English Heritage.

Don't miss the Camellia Festival, held here in Feb/Mar, where you can discover Chiswick's glorious camellias in the restored Conservatory and enjoy spectacular new spring flower displays in the 19th-century Italian Garden. Dates for 2013 can be found on www.chgt.org.uk. Pre-booking is advised.

🎞 *The Golden Compass.*

www.english-heritage.org.uk/chiswickhouse

⬛ Available for corporate and private hire – contact Chiswick House and Gardens Trust 020 8742 2762

⬛ Licensed for civil wedding ceremonies

 www.facebook.com/chiswickhouse

NON-MEMBERS

Adult	£5.70
Concession	£5.10
Child	£3.40
Family	£14.80

Members may be charged for special events

OPENING TIMES

1 Apr-4 Nov, Sun-Wed & Bank Hols	10am-5pm
5 Nov-31 Jan	Closed
1 Feb-28 Mar, Sat-Sun	10am-5pm

Free members' guided tours
15 Nov, 18 Dec, 17 Jan, 12 Feb, 14 Mar   11am & 2pm

HOW TO FIND US

Direction: Burlington Lane, W4

Train: Chiswick ½ mile

Bus: TfL 190, E3

Tube: Turnham Green ¾ mile

Tel: 020 8995 0508

Disabled access (ground floor; wheelchair stair-climber to first floor, please call to confirm use prior to visit).

Dogs on leads (restricted areas only).

Parking (charged – off westbound A4).

MAP Page 314 (4E)
OS Map 176, 161: TQ210775

Eltham Palace and Gardens

Greenwich – SE9 5QE

When millionaires Stephen and Virginia Courtauld built their 1930s Art Deco mansion adjoining the Great Hall of medieval Eltham Palace, they created a masterpiece of 20th-century design.

The Entrance Hall

The inclusive audio tour at Eltham Palace features the voice of actor David Suchet, best known for his role as Agatha Christie's Poirot.

Venetian 'tabernacle'

The Great Hall

View of the House from the gardens

The Entrance Hall stairs

Completed in 1936, the red brick exterior of the house was built in sympathy with the Great Hall. But the interior remains a glamorous 1930s showpiece, an eclectic mix of Art Deco, ultra-smart ocean-liner style and cutting-edge Swedish design.

The dining room is a tour de force, with pink leather upholstered chairs, bird's-eye maple veneered walls, a shimmering aluminium-leaf ceiling, and black-and-silver doors portraying animals and birds.

Even more exotic is Virginia Courtauld's vaulted bathroom, complete with onyx bath and sink and gold-plated bath taps. Luxury also emanates from the centrally-heated sleeping quarters of the Courtaulds' pet ring-tailed lemur, Mah-Jongg. Equipped with all the latest modern conveniences, the house featured underfloor heating, a centralised vacuum cleaner and a built-in audio system.

Upstairs is a display of discoveries from the Courtauld era, including original furniture and family photographs. Visitors can also enjoy a restored original 10-minute Courtauld home movie, giving an intimate glimpse of their family life. A display celebrating the Royal Army Education Corps' (RAEC)

post-World War II association with Eltham Palace highlights a further chapter in its fascinating history. It includes a recreation of an officer's bedroom of the 1960s, together with exhibition panels and a photograph album telling the story of the RAEC's time here.

The medieval palace presents a striking contrast to the opulent 1930s house. The Great Hall, with its stunning hammerbeam roof, was built for Edward IV in the 1470s, and Henry VIII spent much of his childhood here.

The palace's 19 acres of beautiful gardens feature both 20th-century and medieval elements. These include a rock garden sloping down to the moat, a medieval bridge, a stunning herbaceous border, and plenty of picnic areas. Striking at any time of year, garden highlights include the spring bulbs and the wisteria cascading over the classical pergola in summer.

Eltham Palace hosts a range of events throughout the year, including the popular Art Deco fairs in May and Sep. Look out for details in *Heritage Today* or on our website.

🎬 *The Gathering Storm*; *Bright Young Things*; *Brideshead Revisited*; *Shanghai*; *Revolver*; *Madonna's WE*.

www.english-heritage.org.uk/elthampalace

f www.facebook.com/elthampalace

⊤ Available for corporate and private hire

🔲 Licensed for civil wedding ceremonies

NON-MEMBERS

House and Garden

Adult	£9.60
Concession	£8.60
Child	£5.80
Family	£25.00

Garden only

Adult	£6.00
Concession	£5.40
Child	£3.60

OPENING TIMES

1 Apr-4 Nov, Sun-Wed	10am-5pm
5 Nov-17 Feb, Sun	10am-4pm
18-22 Feb, Mon-Wed	10am-4pm
23 Feb-28 Mar, Sun	10am-4pm
24-26 Dec	Closed

Events on Sat 12 May, 23 Jun and 15 Sep. Contact us for more information

The property may close at short notice, please ring in advance for details

Free members' guided tours
7 Nov, 5 Dec, 9 Jan, 6 Feb, 6 Mar   11am & 2pm

HOW TO FIND US

Direction: Off Court Rd SE9, Jct 3 on the M25, then A20 to Eltham

Train: Eltham and Mottingham, both ½ mile

Bus: TfL bus services 124, 126, 160 or 161 and then a short walk

Tel: 020 8294 2548

Disabled access (and parking via Court Yard entrance).

Parking (signed off Court Rd).

Pushchairs and large rucksacks need to be left at reception.

No photography allowed inside the house.

MAP Page 315 (4F)
OS Map 177, 162: TQ424740

Kenwood Hampstead – NW3 7JR

Kenwood House will be closed from April 2012 until autumn 2013 for major works, including urgent repairs to the roof and neo-classical house exteriors and a major re-presentation of the Robert Adam interiors.

The beautiful grounds around Kenwood and its café will remain open for visitors. Come and enjoy a lunch in the Brewhouse, which will complete its roof repair programme in summer 2012. A small exhibition about the works will be located in Mansion Cottage.

If you are interested in supporting the project, please contact the Development Department on 020 7973 3797 or foundation@english-heritage.org.uk.

The English Heritage Foundation is a registered charity, no. 1140351.

🎬 *Notting Hill; Mansfield Park; Scenes of a Sexual Nature; Venus*

www.english-heritage.org.uk/kenwoodhouse

 **www.facebook.com/EHKenwood**

OPENING TIMES

1 Apr-28 Mar	House closed
Re-opens Autumn 2013	
Estate open from 7am to dusk (see park entrance for closed time)	
Café open	9am-5pm

Entry to the grounds free; donations welcome.
Pre-booked group tours available

HOW TO FIND US

Direction: Hampstead Lane, NW3

Train: Gospel Oak or Hampstead Heath

Bus: Tfl 210 ⚉ Finsbury Park – Golders Green

Tube: Golders Green or Archway then bus 210

Tel: 020 8348 1286

Disabled access (ground floor only; toilets).

Dogs on leads (restricted areas only).

Café open, daily.

Parking (Charge applies. Disabled bays. Mobility service available on request).

MAP Page 314 (3E)
OS Map 176, 173: TQ271874

Coombe Conduit
Kingston-upon-Thames KT2 7HE

These two brick-walled chambers, connected by an underground passage, were once part of a system which collected water from nearby springs and channelled it to Hampton Court Palace.

Managed by the Kingston-upon-Thames Society.

OPENING TIMES
Apr-Sep,
every 2nd Sun   2pm-4pm

HOW TO FIND US
Direction: Coombe Lane on the corner of Lord Chancellor's Walk

Train: Norbiton ¾ mile or Raynes Park 1 mile then bus 57

Bus: Tfl 57 Kingston – Streatham

Tube: Wimbledon then bus 57

Tel: 020 8541 3108/020 8942 7387

www.kingstonuponthamessociety.co.uk

MAP Page 314 (4E)
OS Map 176, 161: TQ204698

Harmondsworth Great Barn
UB7 0AQ

Medieval timber framed barn built in 1426-7 by Winchester College. The Great Barn is one of the largest ever known to have been built in England, and one of the most complete and unaltered pre-Dissolution buildings in Britain.

OPENING TIMES
1 Apr-31 Oct, 2nd and 4th
Sun of each month   10am-5pm

1 Nov-28 Mar   Closed

Harmondsworth Great Barn

HOW TO FIND US
Direction: Located in High Street, Harmondsworth Village

Train: West Drayton 2 miles, Hayes & Harlington 4¼ miles, Uxbridge 5 miles

Bus: TfL U3 and 350

Tel: 0870 333 1181

MAP Page 314 (4E)
OS Map 176, 160: TQ056778

The Home of Charles Darwin, Down House
See feature – Page 62

Eltham Palace and Gardens
See feature – Page 32

Jewel Tower
Westminster – SW1P 3JX

The Jewel Tower, or 'King's Privy Wardrobe', was built c. 1365 to house Edward III's treasures. One of only two buildings from the medieval Palace of Westminster to survive the fire of 1834, the tower features a 14th-century ribbed vault. It displays *Parliament Past and Present*, a fascinating exhibition about the history of Parliament, and the second floor includes panels telling the story of this small but important building.

The remains of a moat and medieval quay are still visible outside.

Jewel Tower

NON-MEMBERS
Adult	£3.50
Concession	£3.20
Child	£2.10

OPENING TIMES
1 Apr-4 Nov, daily	10am-5pm
5 Nov-28 Mar, Sat-Sun	10am-4pm
24-26 Dec and 1 Jan	Closed

Last admission ½ hour before closing

Free members' guided tours
29 Nov, 27 Dec, 31 Jan,
28 Feb, 28 Mar   11am & 2pm

HOW TO FIND US
Direction: Located on Abingdon Street, opposite the southern end of the Houses of Parliament (Victoria Tower)

Train: Victoria and Charing Cross ¾ mile, Waterloo 1 mile

Bus: From surrounding areas

Tube: St James's Park and Westminster ¼ mile

Tel: 020 7222 2219

🔲🔲🔲🔲 OVP
Light refreshments available.
Disabled access (limited).

MAP Page 315 (4F)
OS Map 176/177, 161/173: TQ301793

Kenwood
See feature opposite

London Wall
Tower Hill

This is the best-preserved remnant of the Roman wall which once formed part of the eastern defences of Roman Londinium. Built c. AD 200, the wall defined the shape and size of London for over a millennium.

OPENING TIMES
Free access

HOW TO FIND US
Direction: Located outside Tower Hill Underground station, EC3

London Wall

Train: Fenchurch Street or London Bridge
Bus: From surrounding areas
Tube: Tower Hill or Tower Gateway

MAP Page 315 (3F)
OS Map 176/177, 173: TQ336807

Marble Hill House
See feature opposite

Ranger's House – The Wernher Collection
See feature opposite

Wellington Arch
See feature – Page 38

Winchester Palace
Southwark

Part of the great hall of Winchester Palace, built in the early 13th century as the London house of the Bishops of Winchester, including the striking rose window which adorns the west gable. Most of the palace was destroyed by fire in 1814.

OPENING TIMES
Free access

HOW TO FIND US
Direction: Next to Southwark Cathedral and the Golden Hinde replica ship; corner of Clink St and Storey St, SE1

Train/Tube: London Bridge ¼ mile
Bus: From surrounding areas

MAP Page 315 (4F)
OS Map 176/177, 173: TQ325803

Marble Hill House Richmond – TW1 2NL

A lovely Palladian villa still set in 66 acres of riverside parkland, Marble Hill House is the last complete survivor of the elegant villas which bordered the Thames between Richmond and Hampton Court in the 18th century. It was begun in 1724 for the remarkable Henrietta Howard, mistress of King George II and friend of some of the cleverest men in England. The house and gardens were planned by a coterie of fashionable connoisseurs, including the poet Alexander Pope.

The interiors of the house have been exquisitely restored and recreated, and there is also a fine collection of early Georgian paintings, including portraits of Mrs Howard and her circle. Marble Hill was intended as an Arcadian retreat from crowded 18th-century London, and there can be few places in England which better recall the atmosphere of Georgian fashionable life.

🎬 *Nanny MacPhee 2 The Big Bang*

www.english-heritage.org.uk/ marblehill

🍸 Available for corporate and private hire

💐 Licensed for civil wedding ceremonies

NON-MEMBERS

Adult	£5.50
Concession	£5.00
Child	£3.30
Family	£14.30

OPENING TIMES

1 Apr-4 Nov
Sat: Entry by guided tours only at 10.30am and 12pm
Sun: Entry by guided tours only at 10.30am, 12pm, 2.15pm and 3.30pm

Tours last around 1½ hours

Free members' guided tours
20 Nov, 22 Jan,
19 Mar   11am & 2pm

HOW TO FIND US

Direction: Richmond Rd, Twickenham
Train: St Margaret's or Twickenham
Bus: Tfl 33, 490, H22, R68, R70
Tube: Richmond 1 mile
Ferry: Hammertons Ferry to Ham (10am-6.30pm) weekends and Bank Holidays. Owned by EH and leased to Hammertons – this ferry takes visitors back and forth from Ham House (National Trust) to Marble Hill

Tel: 020 8892 5115

Café (Coach House Café, open all year).
Disabled access (exterior & ground floor only; toilets).
Parking charge.

MAP Page 314 (4E)
OS Map 176, 161: TQ173736

Ranger's House – The Wernher Collection

Greenwich Park – SE10 8QX

Ranger's House is an elegant Georgian villa built in 1723, which became the official residence of the 'Ranger of Greenwich Park'. From 1815 this post was held by Princess Sophia Matilda, niece of George III. It remained an aristocratic and then royal home until 1902. Today it houses the Wernher Collection – an astounding display of medieval and Renaissance works of art, all purchased by the diamond magnate Sir Julius Wernher (1850-1912).

Arranged within the panelled interiors of this graceful mansion, the Wernher Collection presents a glittering spectacle.

Nearly 700 works of art are on display, including early religious paintings and Dutch Old Masters, minute carved Gothic ivories, fine Renaissance bronzes and silver treasures. Together they proclaim the genius of medieval craftsmen, and the unparalleled quality of Renaissance decorative arts.

Entrance is by guided tour only (included in the entrance fee), providing a detailed insight into the history of the Collection.

Please note: No photography in the house.

www.english-heritage.org.uk/rangershouse

☎ Available for corporate and private hire
🔔 Licensed for civil wedding ceremonies

NON-MEMBERS

Adult	£6.50
Concession	£5.90
Child	£3.90

© The Wernher Foundation

OPENING TIMES

1 Apr-30 Jul, Sun-Wed
Entry by guided tours only at 11.30am and 2pm. Tours last around 1½ hours

31 Jul-15 Aug   Closed

16 Aug-30 Sep, Sun-Wed
Entry by guided tours only at 11.30am and 2.00pm. Tours last around 1½ hours

1 Oct-28 Mar Available for group tours – please call for details

The property may close at short notice, please ring in advance for details

Free members' guided tours
12 Nov, 10 Dec, 14 Jan, 11 Feb, 11 Mar   11am & 2pm

HOW TO FIND US

Direction: Ranger's House is on Chesterfield Walk and overlooks the junction of General Wolfe Road and Shooters Hill Road

DLR: Deptford Bridge then bus 53

Train: Blackheath ¾ mile

Bus: TfL 53, 386

River: Greenwich Pier

Tel: 020 8294 2548

🖵☎🔔🚹🚼♿🅿♿ OVP
Toilets (including disabled).

MAP Page 315 (4F)
OS Map 177, 161/162: TQ388769

Wellington Arch Hyde Park – W1J 7JZ

Set in the heart of the capital at Hyde Park Corner, Wellington Arch is one of London's most famous and striking landmarks. It is crowned by the largest bronze sculpture in Europe, depicting the Angel of Peace descending on the 'Quadriga' – or four-horsed chariot – of War. The balconies just below the sculpture offer glorious panoramas over the Royal Parks and the Houses of Parliament, as well as unique views of the Household Cavalry, passing beneath to and from the Changing of the Guard at Horse Guards Parade.

Despite its air of immovably changeless grandeur, both the appearance and the siting of Wellington Arch have in fact altered since it was designed by the architect Decimus Burton and erected in 1828. Intended both as a victory arch proclaiming Wellington's defeat of Napoleon and a grand outer entrance to Buckingham Palace, it was originally aligned with the Hyde Park Screen across the road, with London's busy traffic bustling past it. The original plan to embellish it with sculptures celebrating Napoleon's defeat failed due to lack of funds, but in 1846 a colossal bronze statue of Wellington on horseback was added to the top, sparking furious controversy. By 1883, moreover, the original siting of the Arch was causing serious traffic bottlenecks: so it was dismantled stone by stone and moved some 20 métres eastwards to its current position, the present great bronze sculpture being substituted for the Wellington statue (now at Aldershot) at the same time.

www.english-heritage.org.uk/wellingtonarch

NON-MEMBERS

Adult	£4.00
Concession	£3.60
Child	£2.40
Family	£21.30

Joint ticket with Apsley House

Adult	£8.20
Concession	£7.40
Child	£4.90

OPENING TIMES

1 Apr–1 May	Closed
2 May–28 Mar, Wed–Sun & Bank Hols	10am–5pm
24–26 Dec and 1 Jan	Closed

Last admission ½ hour before closing

The property may close to install new exhibitions. Please call in advance for details

HOW TO FIND US

Direction: Hyde Park Corner, W1J
Train: Victoria ¾ mile
Bus: From surrounding areas
Tube: Hyde Park Corner, adjacent
Tel: 020 7930 2726

MAP Page 314 (4E)
OS Map 176, 161/173: TQ284798

T Available for corporate and private hire

NEW FOR 2012

After extensive refurbishment designed to provide environmentally controlled and secure exhibition spaces, Wellington Arch will re-open in May 2012 with a rolling series of exhibitions in a new purpose-built gallery within the Arch. An exciting programme of exhibitions, talks and debates will highlight the work of English Heritage: they will explore heritage in all its different guises, ranging from displays of archive photography and artefacts to examining the contemporary issues affecting historic buildings and places. There will also be new permanent displays interpreting the history of the Arch.

Please note that during changeovers of exhibitions Wellington Arch may have to temporarily close to the public. Please telephone in advance or visit our website for up-to-date information.

London Statues

An important part of the National Heritage Collection are 47 statues and monuments in Central London, including the Wellington Arch, which you are invited to explore (see p.38).

Cenotaph

Sir Walter Raleigh

Clive of India

Thomas Cubitt

SIR WALTER RALEIGH

Statues provide a fascinating insight into the preoccupations of the period. Many of them are associated with wars and military campaigns, such as the Napoleonic Wars, the Boer War and the two World Wars – including the Cenotaph in Whitehall (pictured opposite). Others represent Royal figures such as Charles I (1633) and Edward VII (1921).

A leaflet giving more information about the intriguing history of 20th-century war memorials in London is available from Customer Services (tel 0870 333 1181).

The Capital's Monuments

Viscount Alanbrooke   Whitehall, SW1

Queen Anne   Queen Anne's Gate, SW1

Belgian War Memorial
Victoria Embankment

Simon Bolivar   Belgrave Square, SW1

Duke of Cambridge   Whitehall, SW1

Colin Campbell   Waterloo Place, SW1

Carabiniers Memorial
Chelsea Embankment, SW3

Edith Cavell   St Martin's Place, WC2

Cenotaph   Whitehall, SW1

King Charles I   Whitehall, SW1

Queen Charlotte   Queen Square, WC1

Clive of India   King Charles St, SW1

Christopher Columbus
Belgrave Square, SW1

Crimea Memorial
Waterloo Place, SW1

Thomas Cubitt
St George's Drive, Pimlico, SW1

Lord Curzon
Carlton House Terrace, SW1

Duke of Devonshire   Whitehall, SW1

Edward VII   Waterloo Place, SW1

General Eisenhower
Grosvenor Square, W1

Sir John Franklin
Waterloo Place, SW1

General de Gaulle
Carlton Gardens, SW1

King George II   Golden Square, W1

King George III   Cockspur St, SW1

General Gordon   Victoria Embankment

Earl Haig   Whitehall, SW1

Sir Arthur Harris
St Clement Danes, WC2

Lord Herbert   Waterloo Place, SW1

King James II
National Gallery, Trafalgar Square, WC2

Duke of Kent   Crescent Gardens
(locked), Portland Place, W1

Baron Lawrence   Waterloo Place, SW1

Machine Gun Corps   Apsley Way, W1

Montgomery
Whitehall, SW1

Lord Napier of Magdala
Queen's Gate, SW7

Marble Arch   W1

Florence Nightingale
Waterloo Place, SW1

Samuel Plimsoll
Victoria Embankment

Lord Portal
Victoria Embankment

Sir Walter Raleigh
Old Royal Naval College,
Greenwich, SE10

Royal Artillery Memorial
Apsley Way, W1

General de San Martin
Belgrave Square, SW1

Captain Scott
Waterloo Place, SW1

Viscount Slim
Whitehall, SW1

Lord Trenchard
Victoria Embankment

George Washington
Trafalgar Square, WC2

Duke of Wellington
Apsley Way, W1

Wellington Arch
and Quadriga
Apsley Way, W1

King William III
St James's Square, SW1

Associated attractions in London

These visitor attractions, all independent of EH, offer discounts to our members. Please call before you visit to confirm details. A valid EH membership card must be produced for each member.

The Albert Memorial
Kensington SW7

A professional Blue Badge guide explains the statues and mosaics of the Albert Memorial, bringing to life this iconic Victorian monument, erected in memory of Queen Victoria's husband.

Tours at 2pm/3pm 1st Sun of month from Mar to Dec.

Tel: 020 7936 2568
www.tourguides.co.uk

£5 discount
tour price

Benjamin Franklin House
London WC2N 5NF

Benjamin Franklin House, the world's only remaining Franklin home, sits in the heart of London. Dr Benjamin Franklin – Founding Father of the Unites States – lived here between 1757 and 1775.

Tel: 020 7925 1405
www.benjaminfranklinhouse.org

2 for 1 entry to the
Historical Experience Show

Churchill War Rooms
London SW1A 2AQ

Visit the Churchill War Rooms, part of Imperial War Museums, to discover the underground headquarters that sheltered Churchill and his wartime government during the Blitz and explore the Churchill Museum.

5 mins from Jewel Tower
Tel: 020 7930 6961
www.iwm.org.uk

2 for 1
adult entry

Craven Cottage (Stadium)
London SW6 6HH

Craven Cottage exudes the character and history befitting London's oldest professional football club. Step through the listed turnstiles of our 19th-century grounds before exploring this truly unique Premier League stadium.

Approx 4 miles from Chiswick House
Tel: 0843 208 1234 (Option 4)
www.fulhamfc.com/visit

2 for 1 entry
Under 5s Free

Danson House
Kent DA6 8HL

The most significant building at risk in London in 1995, one of Sir Robert Taylor's finest villas. Now restored for the nation by English Heritage and open to the public.

10 mins from J2 M25
Tel: 020 8303 6699
www.dansonhouse.org.uk

£2.00 off
adult ticket price

Dulwich Picture Gallery
London SE21 7AD

Dulwich Picture Gallery, England's first public gallery, was founded in 1811. A masterpiece of Regency architecture by Sir John Soane, the view along the gallery is one of the most dazzling visual feasts in London.

Tel: 020 8693 5254
www.dulwichpicturegallery.org.uk

2 for 1 entry (permanent collection)
Children free admission

HMS Belfast
London SE1 2JH

HMS *Belfast* tells the stories of life on board during the Second World War and beyond. Explore the interactive Operations Room, hear veterans' stories, and discover the Gun Turret Experience.

5 mins from Winchester Palace

Tel: 020 7940 6300

www.iwm.org.uk

2 for 1 adult entry   ⊞

Kensal Green Cemetery
Kensal Green W10

First London cemetery, established to cope with the population explosion of the Industrial Revolution. Spectacular Victorian Gothic mausoleums. Tours (2pm Sunday) include visit to catacombs twice a month.

Tel: 07904 495012

www.kensalgreen.co.uk

£4.00 discount tour price   ⊞

London Canal Museum
London N1 9RT

The museum tells the story of London's fascinating canals: the people and their horses and trades. The building is a unique piece of London's heritage – a former ice warehouse where visitors can peer into a giant Victorian ice well.

Winchester Palace 2 miles

Tel: 020 7713 0836

www.canalmuseum.org.uk

2 for 1 entry   ⊞ 👪6

43

London Transport Museum
London WC2E 7BB

Lively galleries depict transport and how it shaped the lives of people living and working in London. Featuring iconic transport posters, the Routemaster bus and the world's first underground steam train.

Close to Chapter House and Wellington Arch

Tel: 020 7565 7298

www.ltmuseum.co.uk

2 for 1 entry   ⊞ 👪3

Strawberry Hill House
London TW1 4ST

Visiting Strawberry Hill is a truly theatrical experience. Magically lit by a unique collection of renaissance glass, its gloomy castle-like hall and grey Gothic staircase lead dramatically to the magnificence of the Gallery.

Near to J1 of the M3

Tel: 020 8744 1241

www.strawberryhillhouse.org.uk

£1 off standard adult ticket   ⊞

Dover Castle

SOUTH EAST

PROPERTIES

South East properties consist of:

64	English Heritage
10	The Churches Conservation Trust
18	Associated Attractions

Remember to check opening times before you visit any of our properties www.english-heritage. org.uk/daysout

Details of local public transport information in England are available from Traveline www.traveline.org.uk or call 0871 200 2233.

Make the most of your membership and keep up to date with upcoming events, the latest news and special offers by subscribing to our e-newsletter. Register online now at **www.english-heritage.org.uk/ newsletter**

BERKSHIRE
Donnington Castle

HAMPSHIRE
Bishop's Waltham Palace
Calshot Castle
Flowerdown Barrows
Fort Brockhurst
Fort Cumberland
The Grange at Northington
Hurst Castle
King James's and Landport Gates
Medieval Merchant's House
Netley Abbey
Portchester Castle
Royal Garrison Church
Silchester Roman City Walls and Amphitheatre
Southwick Priory
Titchfield Abbey
Wolvesey Castle (Old Bishop's Palace)

KENT
Bayham Old Abbey
Deal Castle
Dover Castle
Dymchurch Martello Tower
Eynsford Castle
Faversham Stone Chapel
The Home of Charles Darwin, Down House
Horne's Place Chapel
Kit's Coty House and Little Kit's Coty House
Knights Templar Church
Lullingstone Roman Villa
Maison Dieu
Milton Chantry
Old Soar Manor
Reculver Towers and Roman Fort
Richborough Roman Amphitheatre
Richborough Roman Fort

Rochester Castle
St Augustine's Abbey and Conduit House
St Augustine's Cross
St John's Commandery
St Leonard's Tower
Sutton Valence Castle
Temple Manor
Upnor Castle
Walmer Castle and Gardens
Western Heights

OXFORDSHIRE
Abingdon County Hall Museum
Deddington Castle
Minster Lovell Hall and Dovecote
North Hinksey Conduit House
North Leigh Roman Villa
Rollright Stones
Uffington Castle, White Horse and Dragon Hill
Wayland's Smithy

SURREY
Farnham Castle Keep
Waverley Abbey

EAST SUSSEX
1066 Battle of Hastings, Abbey and Battlefield
Camber Castle
Pevensey Castle

WEST SUSSEX
Boxgrove Priory
Bramber Castle

ISLE OF WIGHT – see page 82
Appuldurcombe House
Carisbrooke Castle
Osborne House
St Catherine's Oratory
Yarmouth Castle

SOUTH EAST

Banbury
Milton Keynes
Buckingham
Oxford
Buckinghamshire
Oxfordshire
High Wycombe
Berkshire
Windsor
Newbury
Reading
Woking
Gillingham
Maidstone
Canterbury
Basingstoke
Guildford
Surrey
Tonbridge
Kent
Ashford
Dover
Folkestone
Hampshire
Crawley
Winchester
West Sussex
East Sussex
Southampton
Lewes
Hastings
Portsmouth
Chichester
Brighton
Cowes
Worthing
Newport
Isle of Wight

HIGHLIGHTS FOR 2012/13 IN THE SOUTH EAST

■ **Dover Castle:** a magnificent day out for all the family, open all year.

■ **Osborne House:** visit the seaside home of Queen Victoria.

■ **1066 Battle of Hastings, Abbey & Battlefield:** scene of the most famous battle in England's history.

BERKSHIRE

Donnington Castle
West Berkshire

The striking, twin-towered, 14th-century gatehouse of this castle, later the focus of a Civil War siege and battle, survives amid impressive earthworks.

OPENING TIMES
Any reasonable time in daylight hours; exterior viewing only

HOW TO FIND US
Direction: 1 mile N of Newbury, off B4494

Train: Newbury 1¼ miles

Bus: Newbury Buses 6, 6A, 107 & 115

🖰 **P** ♿
Disabled access (steep slopes within grounds).

MAP Page 314 (4C)
OS Map 174, 158: SU461692

St Bartholomew's Church, Lower Basildon
Berkshire – RG8 9NH

© James Davies

This striking 700-year-old flint and brick church stands in a pretty churchyard near a beautiful stretch of the Thames. Inside it is simple and serene, with ornate roof timbers and memorials to past parishioners. Jethro Tull is buried here.

Owned and managed by The Churches Conservation Trust.

St Bartholomew's Church, Lower Basildon

OPENING TIMES
Keyholder nearby

HOW TO FIND US
Train: Nearest 🚆 Pangbourne 2 miles

Bus: 132, 133

30 mins from Donnington Castle

MAP Page 314 (4C)
OS Map 175, 159/171: SU612793

St Thomas' Church, East Shefford
Berkshire – RG17 7EF

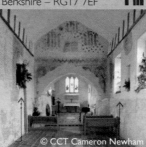
© CCT Cameron Newham

This simple little church stands in an idyllic spot beside a water meadow. Its village has long since vanished, but the spirit of the villagers shines through in the church's simple craftsmanship, glorious medieval wall paintings and fabulous tombs, giving an intriguing glimpse into 15th-century fashion.

Owned and managed by The Churches Conservation Trust.

OPENING TIMES
Open daily during daylight hours

HOW TO FIND US
Train: Nearest 🚆 Kintbury 5 miles

Bus: Route 4

15 mins from Donnington Castle

MAP Page 314 (4B)
OS Map 174, 158: SU391747

HAMPSHIRE

Bishop's Waltham Palace
Hampshire – SO32 1DH

The ruins of a medieval palace (and its later additions) used by the bishops and senior clergy of Winchester as they travelled through their diocese. Winchester was the richest diocese in England, and its properties were grandiose and extravagantly appointed. Much of what can be seen today is the work of William Wykeham, who was bishop from 1367. The ground floor of the farmhouse adapted from the palace's lodging range is occupied by the Bishop's Waltham Town Museum, which exhibits local artefacts.

Other palaces of the bishops of Winchester include Farnham Castle Keep (p.76) and Wolvesey Castle (Old Bishop's Palace) (p.54).

OPENING TIMES
Grounds
1 May-30 Sep, daily   10am-5pm

Farmhouse Museum
1 May-30 Sep, Sat-Sun   2pm-4pm

HOW TO FIND US
Direction: In Bishop's Waltham

Train: Botley 3½ miles

Bus: Brijan bus 7, 8, 17, Stagecoach bus 69, Blue Star F

Tel: 01489 892460

🖰 🖵 ♿ **P** 🅿 🔄 🚻 ⚠
Disabled access (grounds only).

Dogs on leads (restricted areas only).

MAP Page 314 (6C)
OS Map 185, 119: SU552174

Calshot Castle
Hampshire – SO45 1BR

This artillery fort, built by Henry VIII to defend the sea passage to Southampton, later saw service in both World Wars.

Managed by Hampshire County Council.

NON-MEMBERS

Adult	£3.00
Concession	£2.10
Child	£2.10
Family	£7.60

OPENING TIMES

Please check website or call for details

HOW TO FIND US

Direction: On spit, 2 miles SE of Fawley, off B3053

Bus: Solent Blue Line Bluestar 9 & H3 pass within 1 mile

Tel: 02380 892023; when castle is closed, please call 02380 892077

Disabled access (Keep: ground floor only; toilets).

MAP Page 314 (6C)
OS Map 196, OL22/OL29/119: SU489025

Flowerdown Barrows
Hampshire

Flowerdown Barrows

Three Bronze Age burial mounds, once part of a much larger 'barrow cemetery', including two bowl barrows, and the largest and finest disc barrow in Hampshire.

OPENING TIMES

Any reasonable time in daylight hours

HOW TO FIND US

Direction: Off B3049, out of Winchester to Littleton; at crossroads in centre of village

Train: Winchester 2 miles

Bus: Stagecoach in Hampshire 7, 68

MAP Page 314 (5C)
OS Map 185, 132: SU459320

Fort Brockhurst
Hampshire – PO12 4DS

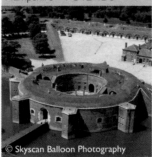

© Skyscan Balloon Photography

One of a number of forts built in the 1850s and 1860s to protect Portsmouth and its vital harbour against a French invasion. Largely unaltered, the parade ground, gun ramps and moated keep can all be viewed.

The fort currently stores a treasure trove of objects from English Heritage's extensive reserve collections. Objects on display have been excavated from sites in the South East and South West. They include stonework, textiles, jewellery and furniture from many periods, as well as rarely-seen treasures on tour from stores in the North and East. The Collections Access Centre offers pre-booked adult and school groups a hands-on experience of English Heritage's rich and varied collections of artefacts, under the guidance of a curator, conservator or trained educator.

Portchester Castle – which acted as a prison during the Napoleonic Wars – is nearby (see p.53).

OPENING TIMES

1 Apr-30 Sep	11am-3pm

on the second Sat of every month

Sun 10 June for 'Gosport's Big Day Out' and 7-9 Sep for Heritage Open Days

HOW TO FIND US

Direction: Off A32, in Gunner's Way, Elson; on N side of Gosport

Train: Fareham 3 miles

Bus: First 82, 83, 85, 86, 87, 87A Fareham – Gosport Ferry (passes Fareham; also Gosport Ferry links with ⊠ Portsmouth & Southsea)

Tel: 02392 581059

Disabled access (grounds and ground floor only).

Dogs on leads (restricted areas only).

MAP Page 314 (6C)
OS Map 196, OL29/119: SU596021

Fort Cumberland
Hampshire – PO4 9LD

Perhaps England's most impressive piece of 18th-century defensive architecture, Fort Cumberland was reconstructed in pentagonal form by the Duke of Richmond between 1785 and 1810, and designed to protect Langstone Harbour. Southsea beach is nearby.

OPENING TIMES
The fort opens for pre-booked group guided tours and Heritage Open Days

Call 02392 378291 for opening details

HOW TO FIND US
Direction: In Portsmouth's Eastney district on the estuary approach, via Henderson Rd off Eastney Rd, or from the Esplanade

Train: Fratton 2 miles

Bus: First 15, 16A ⊠ Portsmouth Harbour – Hayling Ferry

Tel: 02392 378291

⚠️

MAP Page 314 (6C)
OS Map 196, 119/120: SZ683993

The Grange at Northington
Hampshire

Set like a lakeside temple in a landscaped park, the Grange at Northington is the foremost example of the Greek Revival style in England. Created between 1804 and 1809 when William Wilkins encased an earlier house in Classical facades. Most striking is the temple front supported on eight gigantic columns. It provides a stunning backdrop

The Grange at Northington

for the opera evenings which take place here in the summer; call 01962 868600 for details.

🎬 The 1999 film, *Onegin*, with Ralph Fiennes.

OPENING TIMES

Exterior only:	
1 Apr-31 May, daily	10am-6pm
1 Jun-31 Jul, daily	9am-12pm
1 Aug-30 Sep, daily	10am-6pm
1 Oct-28 Mar, daily	10am-4pm
Closes early for opera evenings in June and July	
24-26 Dec and 1 Jan	Closed

HOW TO FIND US
Direction: Located 4 miles N of New Alresford, off B3046 along a farm track – 450 metres (493 yards)

Train: Winchester 8 miles

Bus: Nearest bus service is Stagecoach Hampshire 64 to Itchen Abbas or Mervyns Coaches 95, 96 to Lunways then 3 mile walk

Tel: 01424 775705

🐕 🛡️ 🅿️ 🪑 ♿ ⚠️
Disabled access (with assistance, steep steps to terrace).

MAP Page 314 (5C)
OS Map 185, 132: SU562362

Holy Trinity Church, Privett
Hampshire – GU34 3PE

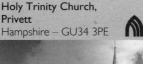

© Christopher Dalton

Holy Trinity Church, Privett

The spire of Holy Trinity is visible for miles around in this idyllic corner of Hampshire. It is extraordinary to find such a lavishly decorated church in a rural location. Magnificent stonework and dazzling stained glass blend beautifully with the colourful marble mosaiced floors.

Owned and managed by The Churches Conservation Trust.

OPENING TIMES
Open daily	10am-3pm

HOW TO FIND US
Train: Nearest ⊠ Petersfield 4¾ miles

Bus: Route 205 is 10-15 minutes walk away

30 mins from Wolvesey Castle

MAP Page 314 (5C)
OS Map 186, 132: SU677270

Hurst Castle
Hampshire – SO41 0TP

One of the most advanced of the artillery fortresses built by Henry VIII: used as a prison for eminent 17th-century captives, including King Charles I, and later strengthened during the 19th and 20th centuries. It commands the narrow entrance to the Solent.

Hurst Castle

Managed by Hurst Castle Services.

NON-MEMBERS

Adult	£4.20
Concession	£3.70
Child	£2.50

OPENING TIMES

1 Apr-30 Sep, daily	10.30am-5.30pm
1 Oct-4 Nov, daily	10.30am-4pm

Occasional opening winter weekends – please ring 01590 642500 to confirm

HOW TO FIND US

Direction: 1½ mile walk on shingle spit from Milford-on-Sea. Best approached by ferry from Keyhaven – call 01590 642500 for ferry details and fares

Train: Lymington Town 6½ miles

Bus: Wilts & Dorset X1 to Milford-On-Sea to within 2½ miles, or 1 mile to ferry

Tel: 01590 642344

Dogs on leads (restricted areas only).

Tearoom/restaurant (Castle Café, not managed by EH. Open Apr-May weekends only, Jun-Sep daily).

Parking (charge payable, at Milford seafront or Keyhaven).

MAP Page 314 (7B)
OS Map 196, OL22/OL29: SZ318897

King James's and Landport Gates, Portsmouth
Hampshire – PO1 2EJ

Two ornamental gateways, once part of Portsmouth's defences, King James's Gate (of 1687) has been moved,

King James's and Landport Gates, Portsmouth

but Landport Gate (1760), once the principal entrance to Portsmouth and possibly based on a design by Nicholas Hawksmoor, remains in its original position.

OPENING TIMES

Any reasonable time in daylight hours; exterior viewing only

HOW TO FIND US

Direction: King James's Gate forms the entrance to United Services Recreation Ground (officers), Burnaby Rd; Landport Gate as above, men's entrance on St George's Road

Train: Portsmouth Harbour ¼ mile

Bus: First services 5, 5A, 6, 6A, 15, 16A and Stagecoach service 700 pass Landport Gate. First services 15, 19 and Stagecoach 23 pass within a short walk of King James's Gate

MAP Page 314 (6C)
OS Map 196, OL29/119
King James's Gate: SZ636999
Landport Gate: SZ634998

Medieval Merchant's House
Hampshire – SO1 0AT

John Fortin, a merchant who traded with Bordeaux, started building this house c. 1290. A residence and place of

Medieval Merchant's House

business, it stood on one of the busiest streets in medieval Southampton. Now restored to its mid-14th-century appearance by the removal of later additions, it is equipped with replica period furnishings. It stands near the medieval town wall, built to defend Southampton against seaborne attacks. Netley Abbey (p.52), Calshot Castle (p.49) and Hurst Castle (p.50) are all within reasonable travelling distance.

NON-MEMBERS

Adult	£4.00
Concession	£3.60
Child	£2.40

OPENING TIMES

1 Apr-30 Sep, Sun only	12pm-5pm

HOW TO FIND US

Direction: 58 French St, ¼ mile S of city centre, just off Castle Way (between High St and Bugle St)

Train: Southampton ¾ mile

Bus: Unilink U1, U6; First 11A, 12A & 16

Tel: 02380 221503

Disabled access (one step).

MAP Page 314 (6B)
OS Map 196, OL22: SU419112

51

Netley Abbey
Hampshire

The most complete surviving Cistercian monastery in southern England, with almost all the walls of its 13th-century church still standing, along with many monastic buildings. After the Dissolution, the buildings were converted into the mansion house of Sir William Paulet. Even in ruins, the abbey continued to be influential, inspiring Romantic writers and poets. A free downloadable audio tour is available from the English Heritage website.

OPENING TIMES

1 Apr–30 Sep, daily	10am–6pm
1 Oct–28 Mar, Sat–Sun	10am–3pm
24–26 Dec and 1 Jan	Closed

HOW TO FIND US

Direction: In Netley; 4 miles SE of Southampton, facing Southampton Water

Train: Netley 1 mile

Bus: First 16

Tel: 02392 378291

Toilets (nearby, across the road near the estuary).

Gravel car park, limited spaces.

MAP Page 314 (6C)
OS Map 196, OL22: SU453090

Portchester Castle
See feature opposite

Royal Garrison Church, Portsmouth
Hampshire – PO1 2NJ

Royal Garrison Church was constructed c. 1212 as part of a hospital complex. Although the nave was badly damaged in a 1941 fire-bomb raid on Portsmouth, the chancel remains roofed and furnished.

Managed by the Friends of the Royal Garrison.

OPENING TIMES

1 Apr–30 Sep,
Mon–Sat 11am–4pm

Contact the keykeeper at other times, tel 02392 378291

HOW TO FIND US

Direction: In Portsmouth; on Grand Parade S of High St

Train: Portsmouth Harbour ¾ mile

Bus: First services 6, 6A, 16A, 19 and Stagecoach 700 pass within a short walk

Tel: 02392 378291

Parking (nearby).

MAP Page 314 (6C)
OS Map 196, OL29/119: SZ633992

Silchester Roman City Walls and Amphitheatre
Hampshire

Originally a tribal centre of the Iron Age Atrebates, Silchester became the large and important Roman town of Calleva Atrebatum. Unlike most Roman towns, it was never re-occupied or built over after its abandonment in the 5th century, so archaeological investigations give an unusually complete picture of its development. The complete circuit of its 3rd-century walls, among the best-preserved Roman town defences in England and 2½ km (1½ miles)

Silchester Roman City Walls and Amphitheatre

long, can still be traced, although none of the buildings within them survive above ground. Outside them are the remains of a Roman amphitheatre, which provided seating for over 4500 spectators. A free downloadable audio tour is available from the English Heritage website.

OPENING TIMES

Any reasonable time in daylight hours

HOW TO FIND US

Direction: On a minor road, 1 mile E of Silchester

Train: Bramley or Mortimer, both 2¾ miles

Bus: Stagecoach Hampshire 14, 15 to Silchester (within ½ mile). Otherwise Stagecoach Jazz2 from Basingstoke to Tadley and then 2½ miles walk

Parking (operated by Hampshire County Council – contact 0118 970 0132).

MAP Page 314 (4C)
OS Map 175, 159: SU639624

Southwick Priory
Hampshire

Remains of a wealthy Augustinian priory, originally founded at Portchester: once a famous place of pilgrimage. Only part of the refectory wall survives.

OPENING TIMES

Any reasonable time in daylight hours

HOW TO FIND US

Direction: Fully accessible through Southwick village, signposted. Please park in car park opposite

Bus: First services 38, 38A, 138 & 139

MAP Page 314 (6C)
OS Map 196, 119: SU629084

Portchester Castle Hampshire – PO16 9QW

Portchester Castle's commanding location has made it a major factor in the Solent's defences for hundreds of years.

The most impressive and best-preserved of the Roman 'Saxon Shore' forts, Portchester Castle was originally built in the late 3rd century. Covering an area of nearly ten acres, it is the only Roman stronghold in northern Europe whose walls still mainly stand to their full 6 metre height, complete with most of their original twenty towers. Subsequently housing a Saxon settlement, the huge waterside fortress became a Norman castle in the 12th century, when a formidable tower-keep was built in one corner.

Portchester Castle was in the front line throughout the Hundred Years War, serving as a staging-post for expeditions to France and repelling cross-Channel raids. Richard II transformed part of the castle into a palace in 1396, and

Henry V used it as an embarkation point for the Agincourt campaign in 1415. Thereafter it saw little action, but was used to house troops in the Civil War, and prisoners of war during the Dutch and Napoleonic Wars and the Anglo-American War of 1812-14.

An exhibition in the keep interprets the history of the castle and Portchester village, and displays finds excavated on site. The inclusive audio tour explains life in the castle over the centuries, from the point of view of some of the people who worked or were incarcerated there.

www.english-heritage.org.uk/portchestercastle

NON-MEMBERS

Adult	£4.90
Concession	£4.40
Child	£2.90
Family	£12.70

OPENING TIMES

1 Apr-30 Sep, daily	10am-6pm
1 Oct-4 Nov, daily	10am-4pm
5 Nov-17 Feb, Sat-Sun	10am-4pm
18-22 Feb, daily	10am-4pm
23 Feb-28 Mar, Sat-Sun	10am-4pm
24-26 Dec and 1 Jan	Closed
Free members' guided tours	
12 Nov, 3 Dec, 16 Jan, 20 Mar	11am & 1pm

HOW TO FIND US

Direction: On the S side of Portchester off A27; Junction 11 on M27

Train: Portchester 1 mile

Bus: First 1A, 5, 5A Fareham – Southsea to within ¼ mile

Tel: 02392 378291

Disabled access (grounds and lower levels only).

Dogs on leads (outer grounds only).

Toilets (facilities are in the car park, operated by Fareham District Council).

MAP Page 314 (6C)
OS Map 196, OL29/119: SU625046

St Mary's Church, Itchen Stoke
Hampshire – SO24 0QU

© CCT

Inspired by the Sainte Chapelle (Paris), this dazzling and colourful Victorian jewel overwhelms the senses. Inside is an exhilarating, kaleidoscopic wonderland of pattern and colour from floor to ceiling, with dazzling stained glass, an unusual floor-tile maze and a richly painted roof.

Owned and managed by The Churches Conservation Trust.

OPENING TIMES
Open daily   10am-4pm

HOW TO FIND US
Train: Nearest 🚆 Winchester 5¼ miles

Bus: Route 67

10 mins from The Grange at Northington

MAP Page 314 (5C)
OS Map 185, 132: SU559323

Titchfield Abbey
Hampshire – PO15 5RA

The ruins of a 13th-century abbey of Premonstratensian canons, later converted into a Tudor mansion. The church was rebuilt as a grand turreted gatehouse. Information panels tell the story of the monastery and its conversion into a mansion. A free downloadable audio tour is available from the English Heritage website.

OPENING TIMES
1 Apr-30 Sep, daily	10am-5pm
1 Oct-28 Mar, daily	10am-4pm
24-26 Dec and 1 Jan	Closed

HOW TO FIND US
Direction: Located ½ mile N of Titchfield, off A27

Train: Fareham 2 miles

Bus: First 26 & 28

Tel: 02392 378291

🐕 P ♿

MAP Page 314 (6C)
OS Map 196, 119: SU542067

Wolvesey Castle (Old Bishop's Palace)
Hampshire

Wolvesey has been an important residence of the wealthy and powerful Bishops of Winchester since Anglo-Saxon times. Standing next to Winchester Cathedral, the extensive surviving ruins of the palace date largely from the 12th-century work of Bishop Henry of Blois. The last great occasion here was on 25 July 1554, when Queen Mary and Philip of Spain held their wedding breakfast in the East Hall. A free downloadable audio tour is available from the English Heritage website.

OPENING TIMES
1 Apr-30 Sep, daily	10am-5pm
1 Oct-31 Mar	Closed

HOW TO FIND US
Direction: ¾ mile SE of Winchester Cathedral, next to the Bishop's Palace; access from College St

Train: Winchester ¾ mile

Bus: From surrounding areas

Tel: 02392 378291

🐕 🖼 ⚠

MAP Page 314 (5C)
OS Map 185, 132: SU484291

All Saints' Church, Waldershare
Kent – CT15 5AT

© CCT Ian Sumner

This pretty church is an ideal resting point for walkers crossing the beautiful North Downs. The south chapel of 1697 contains a touching memorial of life-size marble figures of a husband and wife holding hands. Fantastical monuments, murals and stained glass can be found throughout.

Owned and managed by The Churches Conservation Trust.

OPENING TIMES

Open daily   10.30am-3.30pm

HOW TO FIND US

Train: Nearest ⇥ Shepherdswell 3 miles

Bus: Route 89

10 mins from Dover Castle

MAP Page 315 (5J)
OS Map 179, 138: TR298483

Don't forget to check opening times online before you visit

www.english-heritage.org.uk/daysout/properties

Bayham Old Abbey
Kent – TN3 8BE

The impressive ruins of an abbey of Premonstratensian 'white canons', on the Kent-Sussex border. They include much of the 13th to 15th-century church, the chapter house and a picturesque 14th-century gatehouse. Now set in a landscape designed by Humphry Repton, the famous landscape gardener, who also planned the grounds of Kenwood House in London. Rooms in the 'Georgian Gothick' dower house are also open to visitors.

NON-MEMBERS

Adult	£4.30
Concession	£3.90
Child	£2.60

OPENING TIMES

1 Apr-30 Sep, daily	11am-5pm
1 Oct-28 Mar	Closed

HOW TO FIND US

Direction: 1¾ miles W of Lamberhurst, off B2169

Train: Frant 4 miles then bus

Bus: Countryliner/Autocar 256 (Tunbridge Wells – Wadhurst)

Tel: 01892 890381

 OVP

Disabled access (grounds only).

MAP Page 315 (5G)
OS Map 188, 136: TQ650365

Deal Castle
See feature – Page 60

Dover Castle
See feature – Page 56

Down House – see The Home of Charles Darwin
See feature – Page 62

Dymchurch Martello Tower
Kent – TN29 0NL

One of 103 ingeniously-designed artillery towers built from 1805 at vulnerable points around the south and east coasts to resist threatened Napoleonic invasion. Exterior viewing only.

OPENING TIMES

Viewing by appointment only – please call 01304 211067

HOW TO FIND US

Direction: Access from Dymchurch High Street

Train: Sandling 7 miles; Dymchurch (Romney, Hythe and Dymchurch Railway) adjacent

Bus: Stagecoach in East Kent 'The Wave' services 101 & 102

MAP Page 315 (5H)
OS Map 189, 138: TR102292

Dover Castle Kent – CT16 1HU

'The Key to England' for over nine centuries, the mighty fortress of Dover Castle displays at its core a dazzling evocation of a medieval royal palace. The Secret Wartime Tunnels in the White Cliffs beneath the castle now host an astonishingly realistic presentation of the 'Miracle of Dunkirk', master-minded here in 1940.

Henry II and his successors reared the mighty stone castle, creating here the first 'concentric' fortress in western Europe.

© J Brady

Commanding the shortest sea crossing between England and the continent, Dover Castle boasts a long and immensely eventful history. Its spectacular site atop the famous 'White Cliffs' was probably an Iron Age hill fort, and still houses a Roman lighthouse. The Anglo-Saxon church beside it was probably part of a Saxon fortified settlement, converted soon after 1066 into a Norman earthwork castle. Thereafter Dover Castle was garrisoned uninterruptedly until 1958, a record equalled only by the Tower of London and Windsor Castle. From 1740 its defences were updated in response to every European war involving Britain, and were crucially tested during the darkest days of World War II.

Operation Dynamo: Rescue from Dunkirk

At the beginning of World War II the network of chalk-cut tunnels deep beneath the castle – begun in 1797 to counter the threat of invasion from Napoleonic France – was recommissioned and further enlarged. Housing a hospital,

they crucially also became Vice Admiral Bertram Ramsay's bomb-proof naval headquarters, where a handful of men and women planned the activities of a determined squadron of Royal Navy ships whose task was to keep the enemy out of the Straits of Dover.

There, at 6:57pm on May 26th 1940, a teleprinter spluttered into life. The words of its brief message – 'Operation Dynamo is to commence' – were meaningless to all but a few. One of the few was Vice Admiral Ramsay, and this was the bad news he had been expecting. The British Army and its French and Belgian allies were trapped at Dunkirk, backs to the sea, fighting for their lives in a shrinking pocket of land. The task of rescuing them demanded rapid planning and round-the-clock working to assemble and send a huge improvised fleet of ships, naval and civilian, large and small, to Dunkirk, under attack from air, sea and land. Over 300,000 soldiers were depending on Ramsay, his HQ staff and the sailors in his ships.

Visitors can now make the adventurous journey into the tunnels up to 26 metres beneath the castle, and immerse themselves in the drama of the daring evacuation that followed. Film presentations and displays vividly recreate the outbreak of war in 1939 and the Battle of France in Spring 1940, when allied forces came close to total destruction by the advancing German blitzkrieg. See the pivotal part the Secret Wartime Tunnels played in *Operation Dynamo*. Then, in the very place where it was planned, visitors witness with breathtaking realism the amazing beach rescue operation happening all around them.

They can also take a fascinating guided tour of the (separately accessed) Underground Hospital within the tunnels, and relive the tension as a surgeon battles to save an injured pilot. Find out more about the 'Miracle of Dunkirk', and how it snatched victory from the jaws of defeat, in the *Wartime Tunnels Uncovered* exhibition, featuring the recorded voices of many who actually took part, from rescued soldiers and

Dover Castle continued

Check opening times at www.english-heritage.org.uk

skippers of 'Little Ships' to those who welcomed the battered forces home. A new guidebook to 'Frontline Fortress Dover' is available in the Secret Wartime Tunnels shop, specialising in 1940s books and material.

The Great Tower

Above ground Dover Castle is essentially the greatest medieval fortress in England, created by King Henry II and his Plantagenet successors. At its heart stands the mighty Great Tower, the grandest and among the last of the keeps raised by the kings of England during the 11th and 12th centuries. Built between 1180 and 1185, this symbol of kingly power was also a palace designed for royal ceremony. Here, Henry could welcome and impress distinguished visitors to England – particularly noble pilgrims travelling to the new shrine in Canterbury Cathedral of St Thomas Becket.

The entire interior of Henry's Great Tower palace has been recreated as it might have appeared when newly completed. Visitors begin their tour in the exhibition near the foot of the towering keep, where imaginative interactive displays tell the dramatic story of Henry II and his turbulent brood – *A Family at War*. A man of superhuman energy and violent rages, Henry ruled an empire stretching from the Scottish Borders to the Pyrenees, but proved unable to master his own quarrelsome and treacherous family. Children can help European pilgrims reach Becket's shrine at Canterbury and visitors can 'Ask the Experts' about the recreated rooms, of which a virtual tour is provided for those unable to tour the Great Tower itself.

Ascending the stairs into the Great Tower, visitors meet the first of the many lifelike

projected figures which help to guide them round the six great recreated rooms and several lesser chambers of the palace. Among the most spectacular is the King's Hall, dominated by its canopied throne and decked with wall hangings and recreations of contemporary furniture, all brilliantly coloured. The vibrant colours of the Great Tower's interiors, reflecting medieval reality, are indeed the most striking aspect of the re-creation.

The tour continues via the Royal Chapel to the King's Chamber, focussed on the royal bed. Next come the Guests' Bedchamber and the Guest Hall, shown ready for a feast. The cavernous ground floor is fascinatingly set as the fully-equipped royal Kitchen, Brewery and Bakehouse, while the Armoury displays replicas of the weapons used by Henry's household knights. On selected days, visitors may also encounter costumed live interpreters – including Henry himself – throughout the Great Tower.

A Mighty Fortress

Visitors can then climb to the Great Tower's roof for panoramic views over the castle's immense complex of fortifications, with busy Dover harbour below. Around his impressive keep Henry built a powerful inner curtain wall, and beyond that an outer curtain wall. These three mutually-supporting lines of defence made Dover the very first 'concentric' fortress in western Europe. Its defences were severely tested during the epic sieges of 1216-17, when the castle resisted ten months of attack. Intrepid visitors can still descend into the 'Medieval Tunnels', burrowed beneath the castle during and after the 1216-7 siege.

The cliff-top Admiralty Lookout also played an important role in both World Wars. Inside, a First World War Fire Command Post has been recreated, with displays on the castle's role as a naval signal station.

The Stone Hut, built in 1912 for the Royal Garrison Artillery, is now used as an archaeological store. On the first Friday of every month (or by pre-arranged booking), visitors can view changing exhibitions of treasures from across the region, including artefacts from both World War II and the Cold War.

All this, and very much more, makes Dover Castle well worth a whole day's exploration.

The Other Boleyn Girl, starring Natalie Portman and Scarlett Johanssen; Zeffirelli's *Hamlet*, starring Mel Gibson; and *To Kill a King*, starring Dougray Scott.

www.english-heritage.org.uk/dovercastle

www.facebook.com/EHDoverCastle

Holiday cottages available to let

NON-MEMBERS

Adult	£16.50
Concession	£14.90
Child	£9.90
Family	£42.90

Price includes Secret Wartime Tunnels tour. Additional charges for members and non-members may apply on event days

OPENING TIMES

1 Apr-31 Jul, daily	10am-6pm
1-31 Aug, daily	9.30am-6pm
1-30 Sep, daily	10am-6pm
1 Oct-4 Nov, daily	10am-5pm
5 Nov-17 Feb, Sat-Sun	10am-4pm
18-22 Feb, daily	10am-4pm
23 Feb-28 Mar, Sat-Sun	10am-4pm
24-26 Dec and 1 Jan	Closed

Last admission 1 hour before closing

Free members' guided tours (Hidden Dover – lasts 1 hour)
16 Nov, 7 Dec,
16 Feb, 8 Mar   11am & 1pm

The Great Tower offers pulsed, free-flow self-guided tours. Costumed live interpreters welcome you at the Great Tower on selected days and lifelike hologram characters at all other times. The Secret Wartime Tunnels 'Operation Dynamo' tours are part-guided by site staff, and numbers per tour are limited to 30 people, setting off at approximately 10 minute intervals (tour lasts approximately 50 minutes). Due to the immersive nature of these visits, no independent guiding is allowed in these areas. However, tour leaders of groups of

younger visitors must stay with their parties at all times. Access to the Underground Hospital (separate access from Operation Dynamo) is by guided tour only (limited to 30 people and lasting approximately 20 minutes), which is included in the admission price. At peak times, there may be queues at the popular new tunnel experiences. Please ask site staff upon arrival for the best time to visit the tunnels on that specific day. Groups of 11+ are asked to call the site in advance.

HOW TO FIND US

Direction: E of Dover town centre

Train: Dover Priory 1½ miles

Bus: Stagecoach 15/X & 80

Tel: 01304 211067

Local Tourist Information: Dover 01304 205108

Please refer to the Dover Castle web page or ring the site directly for information on accessibility. Mobility scooters, wheelchair routes and guides are available on site.

Dogs on leads (restricted areas only).

We advise you to wear comfortable shoes.

MAP Page 315 (5J)
OS Map 179, 138: TR325419

Deal Castle Kent – CT14 7BA

Deal Castle is one of the finest Tudor artillery castles in England. It is among the earliest and most elaborate of a chain of coastal forts, which also includes Calshot, Camber, Walmer and Pendennis Castles. Most were built 'with all speed, and without sparing any cost' between 1539 and 1542 by order of King Henry VIII, who feared an invasion by European Catholic powers. Its squat, rounded bastions were designed to deflect incoming cannon balls, and acted as platforms from which to fire increasingly sophisticated artillery pieces. Deal is also equipped for close-quarter defence, with no less than 145 embrasures for firearms. The fort guarded the sheltered anchorage of 'the Downs' – the stretch of water between the shore and the hazardous Goodwin Sands, a graveyard of ships.

The foreign invasion never materialised, but Deal Castle saw hard fighting during the Civil War (1648). Taken by forces from the rebel Royalist fleet, it was twice besieged by Parliamentarians, and finally surrendered after the bloody repulse of a relief attempt.

Today, it is a fascinating castle to explore, with long, dark passages, battlements and a massive basement in which an absorbing exhibition is housed. A pleasant cycle path links Deal and Walmer Castles along the beachfront.

NON-MEMBERS

Adult	£4.90
Concession	£4.40
Child	£2.90
Family	£12.70

OPENING TIMES

1 Apr-30 Sep, daily	10am-6pm
1 Oct-28 Mar, Sat-Sun	10am-4pm
24-26 Dec and 1 Jan	Closed
Free members' guided tours 14 Dec, 18 Feb	11am & 1pm

HOW TO FIND US

Direction: SW of Deal town centre

Train: Deal ½ mile

Bus: Stagecoach East Kent services 13, 13A, 14, 14A, 15, 15A, 80, 82, 82A, Regent Coaches 541*, 542, 544 & Eastonways 593

Tel: 01304 372762

Audio tours (also available in Dutch, French and German).

Disabled access (courtyards and ground floor only, parking available).

MAP Page 315 (5J)
OS Map 179, 150: TR378522

Eynsford Castle
Kent – DA4 0AA

The substantial stone walls of a very early Norman 'enclosure castle', begun c. 1085-7 and unusually little altered by later building works. This rare survival stands in an attractive village setting, not far from Lullingstone Roman Villa (p.65).

OPENING TIMES

1 Apr-30 Sep, daily	10am-6pm
1 Oct-28 Mar, daily	10am-4pm
24-26 Dec and 1 Jan	Closed

HOW TO FIND US

Direction: In Eynsford, off A225

Train: Eynsford 1 mile

Bus: Arriva bus 408, Go-Coach 421, Nu Venture 405 (Wednesdays)

MAP Page 315 (4F)
OS Map 177, 162: TQ542658

Faversham Stone Chapel (Our Lady of Elverton)
Kent

Faversham Stone Chapel (Our Lady of Elverton)

The ruins of the small Anglo-Saxon and medieval chapel of Stone-next-Faversham, incorporating within its fabric the remains of a 4th-century Romano-British pagan mausoleum. It lay close to the probable site of the small Roman town of Durolevum and its Roman cemetery at Ospringe, finds from which can be seen at Maison Dieu (see p.66).

Managed by The Faversham Society.

www.faversham.org/society

OPENING TIMES

Any reasonable time in daylight hours

HOW TO FIND US

Direction: In field immediately North of A2 just West of Ospringe and opposite Faversham Road

Train: Faversham 1½ miles

Bus: Chalkwell 324, Arriva/Chalkwell 333, Chalkwell/Kent Top Travel 335

Tel: 01795 534542

E-mail: ticfaversham@btconnect.com

MAP Page 315 (4H)
OS Map 178, 149: TQ992613

The Home of Charles Darwin, Down House
See feature – Page 62

Horne's Place Chapel
Kent

Horne's Place Chapel

A rare survival of a fine domestic chapel, built for William Horne in 1366 and attached to his timber-framed manor house, which was attacked during the Peasants' Revolt of 1381. The house and chapel are privately owned.

OPENING TIMES

By prior arrangement; please call 01304 211067

HOW TO FIND US

Direction: 1½ miles N of Appledore

Train: Appledore 2½ miles

Bus: Stagecoach East Kent service 11B (one return weekday journey) & Renown service 293 (Mon, Wed, Thu & Fri only)

Parking (nearby).

MAP Page 315 (5H)
OS Map 189, 125: TQ958309

Kit's Coty House and Little Kit's Coty House
Kent

The remains of two megalithic burial chambers, Impressive Kit's Coty has three uprights and a massive capstone; Little Kit's Coty, alias the Countless Stones, is now a jumble of sarsens.

Kit's Coty House and Little Kit's Coty House

OPENING TIMES

Any reasonable time in daylight hours

HOW TO FIND US

Direction: W of A229 2 miles N of Maidstone

Train: Aylesford 2½ miles

Bus: Arriva 101 & 142. Kent Top Temps 150

MAP Page 315 (4G)
OS Map 178/188, 148
Kit Coty's House: TQ745608
Little Kit Coty's House: TQ744604

Knights Templar Church, Dover
Kent

The foundations of a small medieval church, traditionally the site of King John's submission to the Papal Legate in 1213.

OPENING TIMES

Any reasonable time in daylight hours

HOW TO FIND US

Direction: On the Western Heights above Dover

Train: Dover Priory ¾ mile

Bus: Eastonways service 593 from Dover town centre

Tel: 01304 211067

Dogs on leads (restricted areas only).

MAP Page 315 (5J)
OS Map 179, 138: TR313407

Lullingstone Roman Villa
See feature – Page 65

61

The Home of Charles Darwin, Down House Kent – BR6 7JT

A delightful place to visit in itself, Down House is also a site of outstanding international significance. Here the famous naturalist Charles Darwin lived with his family for forty years; here he worked on his revolutionary theories; and here he wrote *On the Origin of Species by Means of Natural Selection* – the book which shook the Victorian world and has influenced our thinking ever since.

Visitors are guided round Darwin's family rooms by a hand-held multimedia tour, narrated by Sir David Attenborough and Andrew Marr. The tour also includes the extensive gardens – Darwin's 'outdoor laboratory' and the place where he made many of his discoveries.

Stop off at the tearoom, situated in Darwin's kitchen area, for a refreshing break before exploring the grounds.

f www.facebook.com/ homeofdarwin

Darwin's work and personality are vividly reflected throughout the house and gardens. The ground floor rooms have been recreated as they appeared when he lived here with his indefatigably supportive wife Emma – a member of the renowned Wedgwood family – and their many children. They include the 'Old Study' where Darwin wrote his most famous books, following a rigid routine despite chronic illness and frequent good-natured interruptions by his children. It still displays his chair, writing desk and many personal items. The family's Drawing Room – with Emma's grand piano – Billiard Room and Dining Room are also on show, likewise mainly furnished with items original to the house.

The video guide includes commentaries by experts, animations, film footage and games for all the family. It is one of many exciting interactive developments at the Home of Charles Darwin introduced to celebrate the 200th anniversary of Darwin's birth and the 150th anniversary of the publication of *On the Origin of Species* in 2009.

'Uncovering Origin' Exhibition

An award-winning exhibition on the house's first floor covers Darwin's life, his scientific work, and the controversy which it provoked. It includes many previously unseen objects, with highlights including manuscript pages from the *On the Origin of Species*; Darwin's hat, microscope and notebooks; and a copy of *Das Kapital* inscribed to him by Karl Marx.

Beginning with an introduction to Darwin, his place in Victorian science, and the impact of his theories, the displays continue with his famous five-year voyage aboard the *Beagle* in 1831-6, including a full-scale recreation of his ship's cabin. The notebooks and journals compiled on this round-the-world voyage have been digitised and annotated, allowing visitors to explore them page by page. Further displays highlight the *On the Origin of Species*, a book which sold out its first edition immediately and consolidated Darwin's international recognition and notoriety. They also examine how his theories were publicised and defended, principally via letter writing. Visitors can explore some of his key ideas (including

his investigations into the expression of emotions in humans and animals) through hands-on interactives and installations. The Darwin children's schoolroom celebrates family life at Down House.

There is also an education room, available for family learning at weekends, and a resources room for those interested in delving deeper.

Experiments in the Gardens

By no means the stereotypically stern Victorian father, Darwin involved his children in his practical experiments in the extensive grounds of Down House. Visitors too can now follow these via the video guide, beginning with Darwin's 'weed garden' illustrating the struggle for existence in nature.

The sundial amid pretty flowerbeds highlights Emma Darwin's role as a gardener; a surviving mulberry tree recalls family traditions; and a 'lawn experiment' investigates proliferation of plant species. Further afield is the 'worm stone', which Darwin used to measure undermining by earthworms.

The nearby hot-house features some of Darwin's most fascinating experiments, involving carnivorous plants,

exotic orchids and climbing species. The curiously-shaped tennis court evokes his family and social life, and in the summer there are working beehives in the laboratory. After a tour of the extensive kitchen gardens, visitors finally reach what is for many a place of pilgrimage: the wooded Sandwalk, Darwin's famous 'thinking path', which he paced five times a day while working out his theories.

Virtual Access

Gain virtual access to Darwin's world through the Home of Charles Darwin pages on the English Heritage website. Features include interactive digital highlights from one of the rarest Darwin manuscript collections in the world, including his *Beagle* notebooks and diary, plus a virtual tour of parts of the house and grounds.

No photography is allowed inside the house.

Unfortunately picnics are not allowed in the grounds, as they are part of a 'Site of Importance for Nature Conservation', nurturing many important protected species, including fungi.

www.english-heritage.org.uk/darwin

NON-MEMBERS

Adult	£9.90
Concession	£8.90
Child	£5.90
Family	£25.70

OPENING TIMES

1 Apr–30 Jun, Wed–Sun & Bank Hols	11am–5pm
1 Jul–31 Aug, daily	11am–5pm
1 Sep–4 Nov, Wed–Sun	11am–5pm
5 Nov–17 Feb, Sat–Sun	10am–4pm
18–22 Feb, Wed–Fri	10am–4pm
23 Feb–28 Mar, Sat–Sun	10am–4pm
24–26 Dec and 1 Jan	Closed

Please note: on open days, gardens can be accessed from 11am in the summer and 10am in the winter

Free members' guided tours
15 Nov, 7 Mar   11.30am & 2pm

HOW TO FIND US

Direction: Luxted Rd, Downe; off A21 or A233

Train: Orpington 3¾ miles Bromley South 6 miles

Bus: TfL bus R8 from Orpington passes; TfL bus 146 from Bromley North & South terminates in Downe village ½ mile from property

Tel: 01689 859119

Audio tour is the multimedia tour.
Parking (plus space for one coach).

MAP Page 315 (4F)
OS Map 177/187,147: TQ431611

Lullingstone Roman Villa

Kent – DA4 0JA

Among the most outstanding Roman villa survivals in Britain, Lullingstone Roman Villa has been vividly re-displayed, providing a unique – and all-weather – opportunity to trace Roman domestic life over three centuries.

Set in the attractive surroundings of the Darent Valley, the villa was begun in about AD 100, and developed to suit the tastes and beliefs of successive wealthy owners. These may have included the family of Pertinax, Governor of Britain and later Roman Emperor for just 87 days in AD 193. Additions included a heated bath-suite and a remarkable underground pagan 'cult-room', including a rare painting of three water-nymphs, by far the oldest wall-painting in English Heritage care.

The villa reached its peak of luxury in the mid-4th century, when a big new dining room was added. This still displays spectacular mosaics, including

Europa and the Bull and *Bellerophon Killing the Chimera*. By now Christians, the owners also created a 'house-church' above the pagan cult-room: the wall-paintings discovered here are among the earliest surviving evidence for Christianity in Britain. Pagan worship may, however, have continued, suggesting a relaxed relationship between the old and new faiths.

All this is appealingly interpreted in the galleries overlooking the fully excavated remains. These display Lullingstone Roman Villa's fascinating and recently-returned collection of Roman artefacts, enlivened by paintings by the award-winning children's illustrator, Jane Ray. Children and other visitors can also play Roman board games, handle original building materials and try on Roman costumes. A specially-commissioned film and light show brings the villa to life, lighting up areas of the remains as the film reveals how they were once used.

NON-MEMBERS

Adult	£6.00
Concession	£5.40
Child	£3.60
Family	£15.60

OPENING TIMES

1 Apr-30 Sep, daily	10am-6pm
1 Oct-4 Nov, daily	10am-4pm
5 Nov-17 Feb, Sat-Sun	10am-4pm
18-22 Feb, daily	10am-4pm
23 Feb-28 Mar, Sat-Sun	10am-4pm
24-26 Dec and 1 Jan	Closed
Free members' guided tours	
16 Nov, 17 Feb	11am & 1pm

HOW TO FIND US

Direction: ½ mile SW of Eynsford; off A225; off junction 3 of M25

Bus: Arriva Bus 408, Go-Coach 421, Nu Venture 405 (Wed) to Eynsford Village then 1 mile walk

Train: Eynsford 2 miles

Tel: 01322 863467

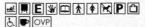

Parking charge £2.50 to non-members.

MAP Page 315 (4F)
OS Map 177/188, 147/162: TQ530651

Check opening times at www.english-heritage.org.uk

66

Maison Dieu
Kent – ME13 8TS

This 13th and 16th-century flint and timber-framed building is virtually all that survives of a much larger complex. It included a 'hospital' for the overnight lodging of pilgrims to Canterbury; a royal suite where many crowned heads stayed on their way to or from the continent; and a school. In layout and appearance it was much like a small monastery. The present building now known as the Maison Dieu is thought to have been a chantry-priest's house. It houses a museum focussing on the Maison Dieu foundation itself and its immediate neighbourhood, and on the extensive finds made during excavations at the main complex and an important Roman cemetery nearby.

Managed by The Faversham Society.

www.faversham.org/society

NON-MEMBERS

Adult	£2.00
Concession	£1.00

OPENING TIMES

6 Apr-4 Nov, Sat-Sun, & Bank Hols 2pm-5pm

Group visits at other times by appointment

HOW TO FIND US

Direction: On main A2 on W corner of Water Lane in village of Ospringe. Public car park 300yds W

Train: Faversham ¾ mile

Bus: Chalkwell 324, Arriva/Chalkwell 333, Chalkwell/Kent Top Travel 335

Tel: 01795 534542

E-mail: ticfaversham@btconnect.com

MAP Page 315 (4H)
OS Map 178, 149: TR003609

Milton Chantry
Kent – DA12 2BH

Mainly encased in brick but still retaining its 14th-century timber roof, this was in turn part of a hospital, a chantry chapel, a public house and a Georgian barracks before its basement became a World War II gas decontamination chamber. The building is within Gravesham's Heritage Quarter and currently exhibits a fascinating insight into the borough's heritage.

Managed by Gravesham Borough Council.

OPENING TIMES

1 Apr-30 Sep, Sat-Sun & Bank Hols 12pm-5pm

Admission outside these times by appointment

HOW TO FIND US

Direction: In New Tavern Fort Gardens; E of central Gravesend, off A226

Train: Gravesend ¾ mile

Bus: Arriva, Red Route and Nu Venture services pass within a short distance

Tel: 01474 321520

Audio tour (new for 2012)

MAP Page 315 (4G)
OS Map 177/178, 162/163: TQ653743

Old Soar Manor
Kent – TN15 0QX

A small but complete portion of a stone manor house built c. 1290. The first floor 'solar' private chamber, with attendant chapel and garderobe, stands over a vaulted undercroft.

Managed by the National Trust on behalf of English Heritage.

OPENING TIMES

1 Apr-30 Sep,
Sat-Thu 10am-6pm

Old Soar Manor

HOW TO FIND US

Direction: 1 mile E of Plaxtol

Train: Borough Green and Wrotham 2½ miles

Bus: Autocar 222 ⊠ Tonbridge – ⊠ Borough Green; New Enterprise 404 from ⊠ Sevenoaks. On both, alight at the E end of Plaxtol, then ¾ mile by footpath

Tel: 01732 810378

Parking (limited).

MAP Page 315 (5G)
OS Map 188, 147/148: TQ619541

Reculver Towers and Roman Fort
Kent – CT6 6SS

An imposing landmark, the twin 12th-century towers of the ruined church stand amid the remains of an important Roman 'Saxon Shore' fort and a Saxon monastery. Richborough Roman Fort is within easy travelling distance.

OPENING TIMES

Any reasonable time in daylight hours; external viewing only

HOW TO FIND US

Direction: At Reculver; 3 miles E of Herne Bay

Train: Herne Bay 4 miles

Bus: Stagecoach in East Kent 7, 7A and Kent Top Temps 36

Tel: 01227 740676

Disabled access (grounds only – long slope up from car park).
Please note: parking (pay and display). Not EH.

MAP Page 315 (4J)
OS Map 179, 150: TR228693

Richborough Roman Fort and Amphitheatre

Kent – CT13 9JW

Evocatively sited amid the East Kent marshes, Richborough Roman Fort is the most symbolically important of all Roman sites in Britain, witnessing both the beginning and almost the end of Roman rule here. Now landlocked, in AD 43 it overlooked a sheltered channel where the invading Roman forces first came ashore. The line of the Roman foreshore, now two miles inland from the sea, was discovered in 2008 by English Heritage archaeologists digging just outside the fort wall.

The landing was commemorated by a mighty triumphal arch, whose foundations still survive: the arch also provided an impressive gateway for arrivals at what became the port of 'Rutupiae', the province's main point of entry.

By the mid-3rd century, however, Roman Britain was threatened by sea-borne raiders. A fort was therefore hastily created within the port. At first defended by the triple ditches still visible, but soon after by stone walls, this became one of the most important of the 'Saxon Shore' forts. It was also among the last to be regularly occupied: there was still a large Roman population here in the early 5th century.

You can choose to reach the fort as the Romans would have done, by boat. Boats sail from Sandwich, but not every day: please contact the site for more information.

NON-MEMBERS

Adult	£4.90
Concession	£4.40
Child	£2.90
Family	£12.70

OPENING TIMES

Fort:

1 Apr-30 Sep, daily	10am-6pm
1 Oct-28 Mar, Sat-Sun	10am-4pm
24-26 Dec and 1 Jan	Closed

Amphitheatre: Any reasonable time in daylight hours, access across grazed land from footpath; please call 01304 612013 for details

HOW TO FIND US

Direction: At the A256/A257 roundabout, take the road for Sandwich and then turn left at the fire station

Train: Sandwich 2 miles

Bus: Stagecoach East Kent 87, 88 then walk using Stour Valley Walk/ Saxon Shore Way

Tel: 01304 612013

Dogs on leads (restricted areas only).

MAP Page 315 (4J) OS Map 179, 150
Fort: TR324602
Amphitheatre: TR321598

Rochester Castle
Kent – ME1 1SW

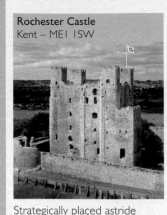

Strategically placed astride the London Road, guarding an important crossing of the River Medway, this imposing fortress has a complex history of destruction and rebuilding. Its mighty Norman tower-keep of Kentish ragstone was built c. 1127 by William of Corbeil, Archbishop of Canterbury, with the encouragement of Henry I. Consisting of three floors above a basement, it still stands 113 feet high. Attached is a tall protruding forebuilding, with its own set of defences to pass through before the keep itself could be entered at first floor level.

In 1215, garrisoned by rebel barons, the castle endured an epic siege by King John. Having first undermined the outer wall, John used the fat of 40 pigs to fire a mine under the keep, bringing its southern corner crashing down. Even then the defenders held out within the building, until they were eventually starved out after a resistance of nearly two months.

Rebuilt under Henry III and Edward I, the castle remained a viable fortress in the 15th century, but a century later it was decaying. Today it stands

Rochester Castle

as a proud reminder of the history of Rochester, along with the nearby cathedral and Dickensian cobbled streets.

Managed by Medway Council.
www.medway.gov.uk

NON-MEMBERS

Adult	£5.65
Concession	£3.60
Child	£3.60
Family	£15.00

OPENING TIMES

1 Apr-30 Sep, daily	10am-6pm
1 Oct-31 Mar, daily	10am-4pm
Last admission 45 mins before closing	
24-26 Dec and 1 Jan	Closed

HOW TO FIND US

Direction: By Rochester Bridge (A2); junction 1 of M2 and junction 2 of M25

Train: Rochester ½ mile

Bus: From surrounding areas

Tel: 01634 335882

Audio tours (small charge).
Toilets (in castle grounds).

MAP Page 315 (4G)
OS Map 178, 148/163: TQ741686

St Augustine's Abbey
Kent – CT1 1TF

This great abbey, marking the rebirth of Christianity in southern England, was founded shortly after AD 597 by St Augustine. Originally created as a burial place for

the Anglo-Saxon kings of Kent, it is part of the Canterbury World Heritage Site, along with the cathedral and St Martin's Church.

The impressive and historically important abbey is situated outside the city walls, but should not be missed by visitors. You can also enjoy the museum and free audio tour.

NON-MEMBERS

Adult	£4.90
Concession	£4.40
Child	£2.90
Family	£12.70

OPENING TIMES

1 Apr-30 Jun, Wed-Sun	10am-5pm
1 Jul-31 Aug, daily	10am-6pm
1 Sep-4 Nov, Sat-Sun	10am-5pm
5 Nov-28 Mar, Sat-Sun	10am-4pm
24-26 Dec and 1 Jan	Closed
Free members' guided tours	
9 Nov, 11 Feb	11am & 1pm

HOW TO FIND US

Direction: In Canterbury, ¼ mile E of Cathedral Close

Train: Canterbury East and West, both ¾ mile

Bus: From surrounding areas

Tel: 01227 767345

Local Tourist Information:
Canterbury 01227 766567

Audio tours (interactive).
Disabled access (all site can be viewed, but some steps).
Parking (nearby).

MAP Page 315 (4J)
OS Map 179, 150: TR155578

St Augustine's Abbey Conduit House
Kent

The Conduit House is part of the monastic waterworks which supplied nearby St Augustine's Abbey.

St Augustine's Abbey Conduit House

OPENING TIMES

Any reasonable time in daylight hours; exterior viewing only

HOW TO FIND US

Direction: In King's Park. Approx. 5-10 min walk from St Augustine's Abbey. Please call or ask at the abbey for directions

Train: Canterbury East or West, both 1½ miles

MAP Page 315 (4J)
OS Map 179, 150: TR159580

St Augustine's Cross
Kent

This 19th-century cross in Saxon style marks what is traditionally believed to be the site of St Augustine's landing on the shores of England in AD 597. Accompanied by 30 followers, Augustine is said to have held a mass here before moving on.

OPENING TIMES

Any reasonable time in daylight hours

HOW TO FIND US

Direction: 2 miles E of Minster off B29048

Train: Minster 2 miles

Bus: Eastonways 42 from Ramsgate

MAP Page 315 (4J)
OS Map 179, 150: TR340642

St James' Church, Cooling
Kent – ME3 8DG

© CCT

Charles Dickens used the churchyard of St James' as his inspiration for the opening chapter of *Great Expectations*. Surrounded by marshes, the site can look desolate, but inside the church is light and spacious. Its vestry walls are lined with thousands of cockle shells, the emblem of St James.

Owned and managed by The Churches Conservation Trust.

OPENING TIMES

Open daily   10am-4pm

HOW TO FIND US

Train: Nearest ⬛ Higham 3¼ miles

Bus: No bus routes nearby

20 mins from Rochester Castle, 40 mins from Eltham Palace and Gardens; 45 mins from The Home of Charles Darwin

MAP Page 315 (4G)
OS Map 178, 163: TQ756759

St John's Commandery
Kent

The flint-walled 13th-century chapel and hall of a 'Commandery' of Knights Hospitallers, later converted into a farmhouse. It has a remarkable medieval crown-post roof and 16th-century ceilings with moulded beams.

OPENING TIMES

Any reasonable time in daylight hours for exterior viewing. Internal viewing by appointment only; please call 01304 211067

St John's Commandery

HOW TO FIND US

Direction: 2 miles NE of Densole, off A260

Train: Kearsney 4 miles

Bus: Stagecoach in East Kent 16/A ⬛ Folkestone Central – Canterbury, to within 1 mile

MAP Page 315 (5J)
OS Map 179/189, 138: TR232440

St Leonard's Tower
Kent

An early and well-preserved example of a small free-standing Norman tower keep, surviving almost to its original height. It was probably built c. 1080 by Gundulf, Bishop of Rochester, and takes its name from a chapel of St Leonard which once stood nearby.

Managed by West Malling Parish Council.

OPENING TIMES

Any reasonable time in daylight hours for exterior viewing. Internal viewing by appointment only; please call 01732 870872

HOW TO FIND US

Direction: Nr West Malling, on unclassified road W of A228

Train: West Malling 1 mile

Bus: New Venture 123 & 406, Arriva 72 & 77, 149, 151, New Venture/Go-Coach 58, 70

Disabled access (grounds only).

MAP Page 315 (4G)
OS Map 178/188, 148: TQ676571

St Mary's Church, Higham
Kent – ME3 7LS

© CCT Neil Rushton

This remote church stands in the middle of orchards, on the edge of the Thames marshes. It has a great charm and eccentricity, with striped walls of ragstone and flint, and a near-symmetrical arrangement of two naves and two chancels.

Owned and managed by The Churches Conservation Trust.

OPENING TIMES
Open daily   9am-6pm

HOW TO FIND US
Train: Nearest ⊠ Higham 1 mile

Bus: Routes 417/418

15 mins from Upnor Castle, 40 mins from Eltham Palace and Gardens, 40 mins from The Home of Charles Darwin

MAP Page 315 (4G)
OS Map 178, 163: TQ716742

St Mary's Church, Sandwich
Kent – CT13 9EU

© CCT

Immense, barn-like St Mary's occupies what may be the oldest church site in Sandwich. During its rich history, it has twice survived town sackings by the French in the 13th and 15th centuries; an earthquake in the 16th century; and the collapse of its tower in the 17th century.

Owned and managed by The Churches Conservation Trust.

OPENING TIMES
Open daily   10am-4pm
Occasionally closed for events

HOW TO FIND US
Train: Nearest ⊠ Sandwich ½ mile

Bus: Route 14

15 mins from Deal Castle, 25 mins from Dover Castle

MAP Page 315 (4J)
OS Map 179, 150: TR329584

St Peter's Church, Sandwich
Kent – CT13 9DA

© CCT

This spacious 800-year-old Cinque Port church is a local landmark. The handsome tower has a distinctive onion dome built by Flemish refugees, and the atmospheric crypt was once a charnel house where bones from the graveyard were stored.

Owned and managed by The Churches Conservation Trust.

OPENING TIMES
Open daily but occasionally closed at short notice for events; please telephone 01304 621554 in advance of your visit

HOW TO FIND US
Train: Nearest ⊠ Sandwich ¼ mile

Bus: Routes 13, 13a, 14, 14a

5 mins from Richborough Roman Fort and Ampitheatre, 25 mins from Dover Castle

MAP Page 315 (4J)
OS Map 179, 150: TR331580

Sutton Valence Castle
Kent

The ruins of a small 12th-century Norman keep, with panoramic views over the Weald.

OPENING TIMES
Any reasonable time in daylight hours

HOW TO FIND US
Direction: 5 miles SE of Maidstone; in Sutton Valence village, on A274

Train: Headcorn 4 miles, Hollingbourne 5 miles

Bus: Arriva 12 Maidstone – Tenterden (passes ⬚ Headcorn)

MAP Page 315 (5G)
OS Map 188, 137: TQ815491

Temple Manor
Kent

Part of a manor house of the Knights Templar, built in about 1240, with a fine first floor hall displaying traces of wall paintings.

Managed by Medway Council.
www.medway.gov.uk

OPENING TIMES
1 Apr-4 Nov, Sat-Sun	11am-4pm
5 Nov-28 Mar	Closed

For group visits please call 01634 335882

HOW TO FIND US
Direction: Located in Strood (Rochester), off A228

Train: Strood ¾ mile

Temple Manor
Bus: Arriva 140, 141 and Arriva and Nu Venture 151 from ⬚ Chatham, or Arriva 700, 701, 711 from ⬚ Rochester then short walk

Disabled access (grounds only).

MAP Page 315 (4G)
OS Map 178, 148/163: TQ733685

Upnor Castle
Kent – ME2 4XG

Set in tranquil grounds adjoining a riverside village, this rare example of an Elizabethan artillery fort was begun in 1559 and strengthened in 1599-1601 to protect warships moored at Chatham dockyards (p.92). Despite a brave attempt, it entirely failed to do so in 1667, when the Dutch sailed past it to burn or capture the English fleet at anchor.

Managed by Medway Council.
www.medway.gov.uk

NON-MEMBERS
Adult	£5.65
Concession	£3.60
Child	£3.60
Family	£15.00

Members also get discounted entry to Chatham History Dockyard (p.92)

OPENING TIMES
1 Apr-30 Sep, daily	10am-6pm
1 Oct-4 Nov, daily	10am-4pm
5 Nov-28 Mar	Closed

Last admission 45 mins before closing

May close early on Fri and Sat for weddings. Please call in advance to check

HOW TO FIND US
Direction: At Upnor, on unclassified road off A228

Upnor Castle
Train: Strood 2 miles

Bus: Arriva service 197 from Chatham

Tel: 01634 718742 or 01634 338106 when castle is closed

Audio guide (small charge).

Disabled access (grounds only).

Parking (at a slight distance from castle – park before village).

MAP Page 315 (4G)
OS Map 178, 163: TQ759706

Walmer Castle and Gardens
See feature – Page 72

Western Heights, Dover
Kent

A huge fortification constructed during the Napoleonic Wars and completed in the 1860s, designed to protect Dover from French invasion.

OPENING TIMES
Any reasonable time in daylight hours

Free to visit the outside and moat. Drop Redoubt fortress open on special occasions and annual open weekend 14-15 Jul, visit www.doverwesternheights.org

HOW TO FIND US
Direction: Above Dover town on W side of harbour

Train: Dover Priory ¾ mile

Bus: Eastonways 593 from Dover town centre

Tel: 01304 211067

MAP Page 315 (5J)
OS Map 179, 138: TR312408

Walmer Castle and Gardens

Kent – CT14 7LJ

Originally built during the reign of Henry VIII as part of a chain of coastal artillery defences against Catholic attack from Europe, Walmer Castle has evolved over time into an elegant residence.

The Dining Room

Duke of Wellington Bust

Walmer Castle has two holiday cottages, offering great views over the traditional kitchen garden to the castle beyond, and only a few minutes walk from a secluded expanse of shingle beach and the sea.

Queen Mother's Garden

Greenhouse interior

wild flowers and insects. These wild garden areas are also a great place to spot birds.

Home-made lunches and teas are available at the Lord Warden's Tearoom and there is a well-stocked gift shop. An audio tour is available and plants are on sale.

⌂ Holiday cottages available to let

www.english-heritage.org.uk/walmercastle

NON-MEMBERS

Adult	£7.50
Concession	£6.80
Child	£4.50
Family	£19.50

OPENING TIMES

1 Apr-30 Sep, daily	10am-6pm
1 Oct-4 Nov, Wed-Sun	10am-4pm
5 Nov-28 Feb	Closed
1-28 Mar, Sat-Sun	10am-4pm

Closed 6-8 July when Lord Warden in residence

Free members' guided tours
23 Nov, 15 Feb   11am & 1pm

HOW TO FIND US

Direction: On coast S of Walmer, on A258; Junction 13 of M20 or from M2 to Deal

Train: Walmer 1 mile

Bus: Stagecoach East Kent service 82/82A

Tel: 01304 364288

Local Tourist Information:
Deal 01304 369576 and Dover 01304 205108

Audio tours (also in Dutch, French and German).

Disabled access (courtyard and garden only; parking available).

Parking (near approach to castle).

MAP Page 315 (5J)
OS Map 179, 138: TR378501

Walmer Castle is the official residence of the Lord Warden of the Cinque Ports. Once an important military command, supervising the five ('Cinque') south-eastern ports which provided ships for medieval England's defence, the Lord Wardenship was later granted as an honorary distinction. It is easy to imagine why the Duke of Wellington, who held the post for 23 years, enjoyed his time here so much.

Wellington's spirit lives on at Walmer Castle, where the armchair in which he died in 1852 can still be seen. His campaign bed also remains on display as a testament to his spartan tastes, along with a pair of original 'Wellington boots' and many personal effects in the fascinating on-site Wellington museum.

Successive Lords Warden have left their mark on Walmer Castle. Thus Lady Hester Stanhope created new landscaping as a surprise for her uncle, Lord Warden William Pitt: while Lord Warden W.H. Smith – member of the famous stationer's family – saved many of the historic and valuable furnishings now on display.

Recent Lords Warden have been provided with private apartments above the gatehouse, and both Sir Robert Menzies (former Australian Prime Minister) and Her Majesty Queen Elizabeth the Queen Mother made regular visits to the castle, as does the current title holder, Admiral the Lord Boyce. Some of the rooms used by the Queen Mother are open to visitors, as is her magnificent garden, given to Her Majesty on her 95th birthday.

The beautiful gardens also include the Broad Walk, with formal borders framed by the famous Cloud Yew Hedge; a commemorative lawn; woodland walk; croquet lawn and a working kitchen garden. The gardens include areas carefully managed to encourage

OXFORDSHIRE

Abingdon County Hall Museum
Oxfordshire – OX14 3HG

This splendid 17th-century Baroque building housed a courtroom for assizes, raised on arches over a market space. It now houses the Abingdon Museum.

Managed by Abingdon Town Council, maintained by English Heritage.

www.abingdonmuseum.org.uk

NON-MEMBERS
Free admission but small charge for roof entry
Adult	£2.00
Child	50p

OPENING TIMES
Closed for renovation until summer 2012. Call for details	
Open thereafter, Tue-Sun & Bank Hols	10am-4pm
25 Dec-1 Jan & Good Friday	Closed
Roof open Sat-Sun, Apr-Sep	

HOW TO FIND US
Direction: In Abingdon, 7 miles south of Oxford; in Market Place

Train: Radley 2½ miles

Bus: Oxford Bus Co X2, X3, 4, X13, 35, Stagecoach 31, 34, Thames Travel 32, 32B, 32C, RH Transport X15, 32A (Sun only), Whites Coaches 43, 97; Heyfordian 40, 41, 42, 44, 114 & 116

Tel: 01235 523703

MAP Page 314 (3C)
OS Map 164, 170: SU498971

Deddington Castle
Oxfordshire

These extensive earthworks are the remains of an 11th-century motte and bailey castle, possibly associated with Odo, bishop of Bayeux and half-brother of William the Conqueror.

Managed by Deddington Parish Council.

OPENING TIMES
Any reasonable time in daylight hours

HOW TO FIND US
Direction: S of B4031 on E side of Deddington; 17 miles N of Oxford

Train: King's Sutton 5 miles

Bus: Stagecoach in Oxfordshire S4 to within ½ mile; Heyfordian 90 & 90A

MAP Page 314 (2C)
OS Map 151, 191: SP472316

Minster Lovell Hall and Dovecote
Oxfordshire

The extensive and picturesque ruins of a 15th-century riverside manor house, including a fine hall, south-west tower and complete nearby dovecote. The home of Richard III's henchman Lord Lovell.

Minster Lovell Hall and Dovecote

OPENING TIMES
1 Apr-30 Sep, daily	10am-5pm
1 Oct-28 Mar, daily	10am-4pm
24-26 Dec and 1 Jan	Closed

HOW TO FIND US
Direction: Adjacent to Minster Lovell church; 3 miles W of Witney, off A40

Train: Charlbury 7 miles

Bus: Stagecoach in Oxford S2, 233. Bakers 6. Swanbrook 853. Also Villager Community Bus. Then short walk

MAP Page 314 (2B)
OS Map 164, 180: SP325113

North Hinksey Conduit House
Oxfordshire

Roofed conduit for Oxford's first water mains, constructed during the early 17th century.

OPENING TIMES
Exterior viewing only 1 Apr-30 Sep, Thu-Sun & Bank Hols	10am-4pm

HOW TO FIND US
Direction: In North Hinksey off A34; 1½ miles W of Oxford. Located off track leading from Harcourt Hill; use the footpath from Ferry Hinksey Lane (near railway station)

Train: Oxford 1½ mile

Bus: Heyfordian service 44. Also Stagecoach Brookes Bus service U1 passes within ¾ mile

MAP Page 314 (3C)
OS Map 164, 180: SP495050

North Leigh Roman Villa
Oxfordshire

The remains of a large, well-built Roman courtyard villa. The most important feature is a nearly complete mosaic tile floor, patterned in reds and browns.

OPENING TIMES
Grounds – any reasonable time in daylight hours. There is a viewing window for the mosaic tile floor

HOW TO FIND US
Direction: 2 miles N of North Leigh; 10 miles W of Oxford, off A4095

Train: Hanborough 3½ miles

Bus: Stagecoach in Oxford 11 & 242 to within 2 miles

Pedestrian access only from main road – 550 metres (600 yards).

Parking (lay-by, not in access lane).

MAP Page 314 (2B)
OS Map 164, 180: SP397154

Rollright Stones
Oxfordshire

Traditionally a monarch and his courtiers petrified by a witch, the Rollright Stones consist of three groups: the King's Men stone circle; the Whispering Knights burial chamber; and the single King Stone. These funerary and ceremonial monuments span nearly 2000 years of Neolithic and Bronze Age development.

Rollright Stones

Managed and owned by the Rollright Trust. Refreshments, toilet, guidebook and postcards available at Wyatts Farm Shop: c. 1 mile east towards Great Rollright.

ADMISSION
Adult	£1.00
Child (over 7 years)	50p

Admission prices relate to members as well as non-members

OPENING TIMES
Entry between sunrise and sunset all year by permission of the Rollright Trust

HOW TO FIND US
Direction: Off unclassified road between A44 and A3400; 3 miles NW of Chipping Norton, near villages of Little Rollright and Long Compton

Train: Moreton-in-Marsh 6½ miles

Bus: Stagecoach 50 (Chipping Norton – Stratford Upon Avon) passes within ½ mile

Contact: sitemanager@rollright stones.co.uk

Parking (in lay-by).

MAP Page 314 (2B)
OS Map 151, OL45/191: SP297309

Uffington Castle, White Horse and Dragon Hill
Oxfordshire

These atmospheric sites lie along the Ridgeway. Uffington 'Castle' is a large Iron Age hillfort, Dragon Hill a natural mound associated in legend with St George. The famous and enigmatic White Horse is the oldest chalk-cut hill figure in Britain, and is believed to be more than 3000 years old.

Managed by the National Trust on behalf of English Heritage.

OPENING TIMES
Any reasonable time in daylight hours

Uffington Castle, White Horse and Dragon Hill

HOW TO FIND US
Direction: S of B4507, 7 miles W of Wantage

Bus: RH Transport 67 to Kingston Lisle, then approx 1 mile walk. X47 (Saturdays only) passes closer to the site

Parking (pay and display). Free to EH members.

MAP Page 314 (3B)
OS Map 174, 170: SU301866

Wayland's Smithy
Oxfordshire

A fine and atmospheric Neolithic chambered long barrow 2km (1¼ miles) along the Ridgeway from the Uffington White Horse: it was once believed to be the habitation of the Saxon smith-god Wayland.

Managed by the National Trust on behalf of English Heritage.

OPENING TIMES
Any reasonable time in daylight hours

HOW TO FIND US
Direction: On the Ridgeway; ¾ mile NE of B4000, Ashbury – Lambourn Road

Bus: Thamesdown Transport service 47 then a short walk along the Ridgeway path; X47 (Saturdays only)

Parking (may be a charge).

MAP Page 314 (3B)
OS Map 174, 170: SU281854

SURREY

Farnham Castle Keep
Surrey – GU9 0JA

The impressive motte and shell keep of a castle founded in 1138 by Bishop Henry of Blois. Long a residence of the wealthy bishops of Winchester, the accommodation in the keep was updated in the 1520s. The keep was abandoned after Civil War service, but much-altered parts of the medieval bishops' residence remain in use in private hands. A viewing platform and stairway now reveal the buried remains of an earlier tower.

Managed by Farnham Castle.

OPENING TIMES

1 Apr-23 Dec, Mon-Fri 9am-5pm (or dusk, whichever is earlier)
Sat-Sun & Bank Hols 10am-4pm

24 Dec-31 Jan Closed

1 Feb-31 Mar, Mon-Fri 9am-5pm (or dusk, whichever is earlier)
Sat-Sun & Bank Hols 10am-4pm

Last admission 30 minutes before closing time

HOW TO FIND US

Direction: ½ mile N of Farnham town centre, on A287

Train: Farnham ¾ mile

Bus: Stagecoach Service 71 passes the castle, but other Stagecoach services stop nearby

Tel: 01252 713393

MAP Page 314 (5D)
OS Map 186, 145: SU837473

Waverley Abbey
Surrey

Ruins of the church and monastic buildings of the first Cistercian abbey in England, founded in 1128. A free downloadable audio tour is available from the English Heritage website.

Elizabeth.

OPENING TIMES

Any reasonable time in daylight hours

HOW TO FIND US

Direction: 2 miles SE of Farnham, off B3001; off Junction 10 of M25

Train: Farnham 2 miles

Bus: Stagecoach in Hants & Surrey 46 Guildford – Aldershot (passing ≋ Farnham)

Parking (limited).

MAP Page 314 (5D)
OS Map 186, 145: SU868453

SUSSEX (EAST)

1066 Battle of Hastings, Abbey and Battlefield
See feature – Page 78

Camber Castle
East Sussex

The ruins of an unusually unaltered artillery fort, built by Henry VIII to guard the port of Rye. There are limited opening times, but regular guided walks around Rye Harbour Nature Reserve include the castle.

Contact the Reserve Manager for further details.

Managed by Rye Harbour Nature Reserve.

www.wildrye.info/reserve/cambercastle

NON-MEMBERS

Adults	£3.00
Concessions	£1.50
Children	Free
when accompanied by an adult	

OPENING TIMES

Jul-Sep open on the first Sat of the month at 2pm for guided tours. Regular guided walks around the Rye Harbour Nature Reserve include the castle

Please check website or visit www.wildrye.info/dates

HOW TO FIND US

Direction: 1 mile walk across fields, off the A259; 1 mile S of Rye, off Harbour Road. No vehicle access. Follow the public footpath from Brede Lock

Train: Rye 1¼ miles

Bus: From surrounding areas to Winchelsea or Rye, then 1½ mile walk; or Coastal Coaches 344 Hastings – Northiam then ¾ mile walk

Tel: 01797 223862

MAP Page 315 (6H)
OS Map 189, 125: TQ922185

Pevensey Castle East Sussex – BN24 5LE

St Peter's Church, Preston Park
East Sussex – BN1 6SD

© CCT

With a history stretching back over 16 centuries, Pevensey Castle chronicles more graphically than any other fortress the story of Britain's south coast defences.

Beginning in the late 3rd century as one of the last and strongest of the Roman 'Saxon Shore' forts – two-thirds of whose towered walls still stand – Pevensey was the landing place of William the Conqueror's army in 1066.

During the century after the Conquest a full-scale Norman castle, with a great square keep and a powerful gatehouse, was built within one corner of the fort. In the 1250s the towered bailey wall was constructed, and soon put to the test during the great siege of 1264. Later still the castle was strengthened to face the threat of the Spanish Armada in 1588. This was not Pevensey's last military service: during World War II, pillboxes and machine-gun posts were cunningly camouflaged among its ancient walls.

An exhibition with artefacts found on-site and an audio tour tell the story of the castle.

NON-MEMBERS

Adult	£4.90
Concession	£4.40
Child	£2.90
Family	£12.70

OPENING TIMES

1 Apr-30 Sep, daily	10am-6pm
1 Oct-4 Nov, daily	10am-4pm
5 Nov-28 Mar, Sat-Sun	10am-4pm
24-26 Dec and 1 Jan	Closed

HOW TO FIND US

Direction: In Pevensey off A259

Train: Pevensey & Westham or Pevensey Bay, both ½ mile

Bus: Stagecoach 55 or 99, Westham & Pevensey Community Transport 46

Tel: 01323 762604

⚠ OVP

Dogs on leads (restricted areas only).

Parking (charge payable). Car park managed by Pevensey Town Trust.

Toilets (nearby).

MAP Page 315 (6G)
OS Map 199, 123/124: TQ645048

This simple, 800 year old church stands in the beautiful landscaped park of Preston Manor. The church nearly lost its greatest treasures – its magnificent 14th century wall paintings – in a fire in 1906; but today the interior glows with a gorgeous mix of pattern and colour.

Owned and managed by The Churches Conservation Trust.

OPENING TIMES

Open daily	11am-3pm
Sometimes longer in the summer	

HOW TO FIND US

Train: Nearest 🚆 Preston Park less than ½ mile

Bus: Routes 5/5a

20 mins from Bramber Castle

MAP Page 315 (6F)
OS Map 198, 122: TQ304064

Check opening times at www.english-heritage.org.uk

1066 Battle of Hastings, Abbey and Battlefield

East Sussex – TN33 0AD

Perhaps the most famous date in English history – 1066 is the year the Normans defeated the English at the Battle of Hastings. William the Conqueror founded 'Battle' Abbey as penance for the bloodshed and as a memorial to the dead. Here, on the site of its high altar, you can stand on the spot where King Harold of England is said to have fallen.

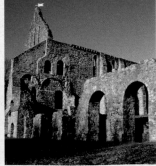

Check opening times at www.english-heritage.org.uk

Don't miss the spectacular re-enactment of the Battle of Hastings, which takes place on 13 and 14 October.

An imaginative exhibition, *1066: The Battle for England*, brings the background and impact of this renowned conflict vividly to life. Up-to-date technology and interactive displays draw a striking picture, from both English and Norman viewpoints, of the years which led up to the conflict. They also illustrate how this pivotal battle shaped English history. Listening points, graphic presentations, handsome exhibits and touch-screen displays explore how life was for the opposing sides. Central to the exhibition is a short film, narrated by Dr David Starkey, which dramatically recounts the events preceding the bloody struggle, culminating on 14 October 1066 when 'the fields were covered in corpses, and all around the only colour to meet the gaze was blood-red'. [*The Chronicle of Battle Abbey*].

The audio tour vividly describes and re-creates the sounds of the battle on the very site where it took place. From their ridge-top 'shield wall' the English watched the Normans advancing towards them. Early in the battle, part of the Norman army panicked and retreated, but William rallied his soldiers and successfully counterattacked. Several 'pretended retreats' followed, in which the English were lured into breaking ranks in pursuit, only to be cut down. After some ten hours of fighting, the Normans launched an assault which finally broke the fatally weakened English shield wall. At this stage King Harold was killed, perhaps struck in the eye by an arrow as depicted in the famous Bayeux Tapestry. By nightfall the Norman victory was complete. The audio tour uses 'interviews' with soldiers, monks and key figures of the time to retell the story of this fateful event, and there also is a version especially created for children.

Battle Abbey enjoyed great wealth and special privileges as the symbol of Norman triumph. Though little of its original Norman structure survives, you can still see many later monastic buildings, including the dormitory range with its fine vaulted novices' chamber. The west range,

Check opening times at www.english-heritage.org.uk

1066 Battle of Hastings, Abbey and Battlefield   continued

From Battle you can take the 1066 Walk to Pevensey Castle (one of Britain's oldest strongholds) where William first landed before moving to Hastings (see p.77).

incorporating the abbots' Great Hall, was converted into a mansion after Henry VIII's Dissolution of the Monasteries, and is now a school. Best preserved and most impressive of all is the Great Gatehouse, rebuilt in about 1338 and among the finest surviving monastic entrances in Britain. The battlefield – later part of the abbey's Great Park – and abbey were purchased for the nation in 1976.

Visit the Abbey Museum, which explores the history of the abbey and includes artefacts found on-site during excavations. Children will also enjoy the Discovery Centre which is open every weekend and throughout the school holidays. Look out, too, for our programme of family-friendly events, including the annual Battle of Hastings re-enactment, 13 & 14 October, Halloween ghost tours and daily children's activities in August.

Take a break in the stylish café, serving light lunches and all-day refreshments. Contemporary in design, it has both indoor and outdoor seating and wonderful views of the historic gatehouse.

Following your visit, why not spend a pleasant afternoon in Battle town: it has a Town Trail, museum, and interesting shops, and hosts events and farmers' markets. From Battle you can take the '1066 Walk' to Pevensey Castle (one of Britain's oldest strongholds) where William first landed before moving to Hastings.

www.english-heritage.org.uk/
1066

⌂ Holiday cottage available to let

NON-MEMBERS

Adult	£7.50
Concession	£6.80
Child	£4.50
Family	£19.50

OPENING TIMES

1 Apr-30 Sep, daily	10am-6pm
1 Oct-4 Nov, daily	10am-4pm
5 Nov-17 Feb, Sat-Sun	10am-4pm
18-22 Feb, daily	10am-4pm
23 Feb-28 Mar, Sat-Sun	10am-4pm
24-26 Dec and 1 Jan	Closed

Free members' guided tours
23 Nov, 8 Feb, 15 Mar 11am & 1pm

HOW TO FIND US

Direction: In Battle, at south end of High St. Take the A2100 off the A21

Train: Battle ½ mile

Bus: Renown Coaches 95, Countryliner 304 & 355, Battle Community Transport B71, B73, B75, B79, B80 & B8

Tel: 01424 775705/776787 (shop)

Local Tourist Information:
Battle and Bexhill Tourist information 01424 776789/776790

Audio tours (suitable for families, the visually impaired and for those in wheelchairs or with learning difficulties. Also available in Dutch, French, German, Japanese and Spanish; braille guides in English only). Audio tours are complimentary but will not be issued on special events days.

Café – winter opening may be limited. Please call for details.

Disabled access (grounds and visitor centre).

Dogs on leads (restricted areas only).

Parking (charge payable for members and non-members).

MAP Page 315 (6G)
OS Map 199, 124: TQ749157

Boxgrove Priory West Sussex

Bramber Castle
West Sussex

81

The remains of a Norman motte-and-bailey castle on the banks of the River Adur, founded by William de Braose c. 1073. The earthworks are dominated by a towering wall of the keep-gatehouse.

OPENING TIMES
Any reasonable time in daylight hours

HOW TO FIND US
Direction: On W side of Bramber village, off A283

Train: Shoreham-by-Sea 4½ miles

Bus: Brighton & Hove 2, 20 & Compass Bus 100 & 106

Parking (limited).

MAP Page 314 (6E)
OS Map 198, 122: TQ185107

In a beautiful setting at the foot of the South Downs, the small Benedictine priory of Boxgrove was founded in about 1117 – originally for just three monks – by Robert de la Haye, as a 'cell' or dependency of Lessay Abbey in Normandy. Like most such 'alien priories', it was 'nationalised' at the outset of the Hundred Years War in 1339, becoming independent of its French mother-house.

The principal survivor of the monastic buildings is the two-storey lodging house for guests and travellers, roofless but standing to full height at the gable ends. One arcaded wall of the chapter house also remains, attached to the north transept of the priory church. This lovely building (not in the guardianship of English Heritage) became Boxgrove's parish church at the Dissolution of the Monasteries.

Though much of its west end was demolished in the 18th century, the church's splendid 12th century chancel, central tower and unusual transepts still survive complete, along with the Early Tudor de la Warr chantry chapel with its fine Renaissance carvings. There is a model of the monastic buildings in the church.

Nearby, in Boxgrove gravel pit, archaeological excavation (funded by English Heritage) has produced much the oldest human remains yet discovered in England: a shinbone and two teeth dating from around 500,000 years ago.

OPENING TIMES
Priory open for viewing at any reasonable time (daylight hours)

HOW TO FIND US
Direction: N of Boxgrove; 4 miles E of Chichester, on minor road off A27

Train: Chichester 4 miles

Bus: Stagecoach in the South Downs 55 from ≷ Chichester and Compass Bus 99

MAP Page 314 (6D)
OS Map 197, 121: SU908076

Check opening times at www.english-heritage.org.uk

The Isle of Wight

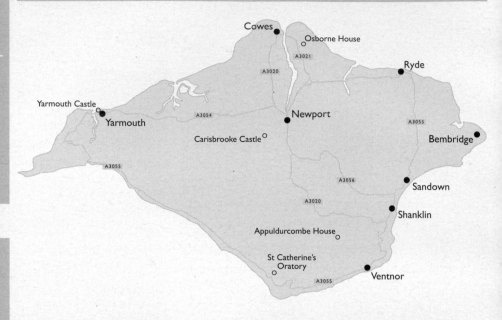

Appuldurcombe House
Isle of Wight – PO38 3EW

The shell of Appuldurcombe, once the grandest house on the Isle of Wight and still an important example of English Baroque architecture, standing in 'Capability' Brown-designed grounds. The 1701 east wing has been re-roofed.

Appuldurcombe House

An exhibition of photographs and prints depicts the house and its history. You can also visit the Freemantle Gate (part of the 1770s neo-Classical addition to the estate) on the nearby public footpath, and the adjacent Falconry Centre (not under the care of English Heritage – extra charge applies).

Managed by Mr and Mrs Owen.

NON-MEMBERS

Adult	£4.00
Concession	£3.50
Child	£3.00
Family	£13.00

OPENING TIMES

1 Apr-21 Oct, Sun-Fri	10am-4pm
22 Oct-27 Mar	Closed

Last entry 1 hour before closing

Appuldurcombe House

HOW TO FIND US

Direction: Wroxall ½ mile, off B3327

Train: Shanklin 3½ miles then bus

Bus: Southern Vectis 2 & 3

Ferry: Ryde 11 miles (Wightlink 0870 582 7744; Hovercraft 01983 811000); West Cowes 12 miles, East Cowes 12 miles (both Red Funnel – 0844 844 9988)

Tel: 01983 852484

MAP Page 314 (7C)
OS Map 196, OL29: SZ543800

Carisbrooke Castle
See feature opposite

Carisbrooke Castle Isle of Wight – PO30 1XY

A fascinatingly varied site to visit, Carisbrooke Castle has been the key to the Isle of Wight's security for more than nine centuries. This great hilltop-crowning fortress has a keep to climb for panoramic views, a colourful history, and of course the famous Carisbrooke donkeys.

After the Spanish Armada passed alarmingly close in 1588, Carisbrooke was updated as an artillery fortification by surrounding it with 'bastioned' outer earthworks, still impressively visible.

Carisbrooke Castle continued

Princess Beatrice Garden

Staircase in Great Hall

There has been a fortress here since Saxon times, but the present castle was begun in c. 1100, when the Isle of Wight was granted to the de Redvers family. They raised the great stone shell-keep on its towering mound and after 1262 the formidable Countess Isabella de Redvers extensively rebuilt the whole stronghold. Following the addition of its double-towered 14th-century gatehouse, Carisbrooke Castle experienced its only siege in 1377, beating off a French raiding force. After the Spanish Armada passed alarmingly close in 1588, the castle was updated as an artillery fortification by surrounding it with 'bastioned' outer earthworks, still impressively visible.

Most famous among the castle's extensive cast of past residents was Charles I, imprisoned here in 1647-8 after his defeat in the Civil War. At first comfortably accommodated in the Constable's Lodging, he later became a closely guarded captive: an attempt to escape was foiled only when he became wedged in the window bars.

Much later, Princess Beatrice, Queen Victoria's youngest daughter and Governor of the Isle of Wight between 1896-1944, made Carisbrooke Castle her summer home. Princess Beatrice also commissioned the altar painting in the tranquil castle chapel in memory of a son killed in action in 1914. The Edwardian-style Princess Beatrice garden, designed by TV and radio gardening presenter Chris Beardshaw, was inspired by the Princess, and includes a fountain and plantings in the rich colours of the royal arms. We are grateful to the late Mrs Dorothy Frazer, whose generous bequest and devotion to the island has made the creation of this garden possible.

Interior of the Chapel

The secluded location of the holiday cottage within the castle walls and the romance of its unique history make this the ideal hideaway for a peaceful break. Enjoy the grounds of the castle in private once the gates close to the public.

85

The castle's most beloved modern residents are undoubtedly the renowned Carisbrooke donkeys. These happy, hard-working animals still operate the tread wheel in the Elizabethan wheelhouse, which raises water 49 metres (161 feet) from the castle well. They give daily demonstrations, and their story is told in a film hosted by Jupiter the cartoon donkey, voiced by locally-raised comedian Phill Jupitus.

The on-site Carisbrooke Museum (managed by the Carisbrooke Museum Trust) provides more historical information about the castle, as well as Charles I memorabilia.

An extensive presentation – including film, hands-on weapons and family interactives and a virtual tour – highlights Carisbrooke Castle's long and often tumultuous history.

www.english-heritage.org.uk/carisbrookecastle

 Holiday cottage available to let

NON-MEMBERS

Adult	£7.50
Concession	£6.80
Child	£4.50
Family	£19.50

OPENING TIMES

1 Apr-30 Sep, daily	10am-5pm
1 Oct-4 Nov, daily	10am-4pm
5 Nov-17 Feb, Sat-Sun	10am-4pm
18-22 Feb, daily	10am-4pm
23 Feb-28 Mar, Sat-Sun	10am-4pm
24-26 Dec and 1 Jan	Closed

HOW TO FIND US

Direction: 1¼ miles SW of Newport. Follow signs to Carisbrooke village, then castle

Bus: Southern Vectis 6, 7, 12, 38 & 39 pass nearby to within ¼ mile

Ferry: West Cowes 5 miles, East Cowes 6 miles (Red Funnel – 0844 844 9988); Fishbourne 6 miles, Ryde 8 miles, Yarmouth 9 miles (Wightlink 0871 376 1000; Hovercraft Ryde 01983 811000)

Tel: 01983 522107

Local Tourist Information: 01983 813813

Disabled access (grounds and lower levels only).

Tearoom (open Apr-Oct).

MAP Page 314 (7C)
OS Map 196, OL29: SZ486878

Osborne House Isle of Wight – PO32 6JX

After her marriage to Prince Albert in 1840, Queen Victoria felt the need for a family residence in the country. To use her words, 'a place of one's own – quiet and retired'.

'It is impossible to imagine a prettier spot,' wrote the Queen after a visit to Osborne House.

The Drawing Room

Marble sculptures, commissioned by Victoria and Albert, line the classically designed Grand Corridor of the house.

Queen Victoria knew and liked the Isle of Wight after visiting as a child, and she and the Prince Consort were both determined to buy a property there.

'It is impossible to imagine a prettier spot,' wrote the Queen after a visit to Osborne House. In 1845 the royal couple purchased the property with an estate of 342 acres, plus the adjacent Barton Manor to house equerries and grooms and to serve as the home farm.

Before the deeds had even changed hands, master builder Thomas Cubitt had been approached – firstly to build a pavilion to house private apartments and then to demolish the old house and add further wings for the royal household. Once all the work was complete, an exquisite pair of Italianate towers dominated the landscape and looked out over passing ships in the nearby Solent.

The interiors of Osborne House abound with opulence in both architectural design and decoration. Marble sculptures, commissioned by Victoria and Albert, line the classically designed Grand Corridor of the house and recall the royal couple's love of the arts. Portraits and frescos adorn the walls, serving as a reminder of the family's links to the crowned heads of Europe, and of the unrivalled supremacy of the British Empire. Family photographs on the desks of Queen Victoria and Prince Albert offer a further insight into the way they lived.

Queen Victoria's role as Empress of India is celebrated in the richly decorated Durbar Room. Constructed from 1890-91, the room served as an elaborate banqueting hall and every surface, from floor to ceiling, is ornately embellished.

The walls are decorated with symbols from India, including Ganesh – the elephant god of good fortune – and the deeply coffered ceiling is composed of fibrous plaster. The completion of the room coincided with the introduction of electricity, so the Indian-influenced lamp stands were designed to take full advantage of this emerging technology.

NEW FOR 2012

From late July visitors will for the first time be able to see the private beach where Queen Victoria and her guests came ashore, and where she first experienced sea bathing. You can see the Queen's bathing machine, and the beach alcove where she used to sit and read or sketch. Exhibition panels explain how important the beach was to Victoria and her family, and how important it is today as a wildlife habitat. You can hire a deckchair and sit by the shore, or enjoy refreshments from the restored 1940s beach pavilion. Regular summer events will include Victorian games and Punch and Judy shows.

The early 1900s holiday cottage brims with period character and once served as a cricket pavilion. Enjoy tranquil views and explore the grounds in private after the gates close to the public.

Swiss Cottage sitting room

The Grand Corridor

Prince Albert worked with Cubitt on the Italianate designs for the terraced formal gardens which complement the house. Visitors can now enjoy the Walled Garden much as Victoria and Albert did, since English Heritage restored it as part of the Contemporary Heritage Gardens Scheme.

Prince Albert was responsible for the layout of the Palm Terrace overlooking the Solent – the view is said to have reminded him of the Bay of Naples – and for the introduction of many fine trees onto the estate. The original palm was a gift to the royal couple from King Ferdinand of Portugal, and was one of the first ever to be planted in this country. It died in 2003 and the current tree – its direct descendent – was planted in 2004 by Queen Elizabeth II. The remainder of the Palm Terrace is planted to recreate its Victorian appearance. It includes beds featuring camellias and pampas grass and a pergola with wisteria and climbing roses for summer colour, and vines producing small grapes in the autumn.

Visitors should not miss the Swiss Cottage and its surrounding gardens. This charming chalet in miniature was built and furnished as an educational tool, where the royal children could learn domestic skills. The surrounding grounds also contain a museum, housing fascinating artefacts collected by the royal children and given to Queen Victoria, as well as a child-size fort and barracks, and the vegetable gardens where the royal children grew their own produce. A beautiful wild flower meadow is nearby, and rare red squirrels can sometimes be seen throughout the gardens. There is a courtesy minibus, with wheelchair access, to the Swiss Cottage.

Queen Victoria loved to stroll through the gardens, and the primroses in the woods were her particular favourites. Most of the gardens are accessible on tarmac and compacted gravel paths.

The exhibition in the Petty Officers Quarters is the best place to start any visit. It covers various aspects of the sumptuously furnished house

On Saturday 17 and Sunday 18 November, Osborne House opens the festive season with its popular annual Victorian Christmas event. The ground floor of the house, dressed festively for the season, remains open for guided tours Wednesday to Sunday until Sunday 6 January. Find out how the Victorian Royal Family celebrated Christmas with these fascinating tours led by our expert guides.

and magnificent grounds, as well as the lives and personalities of the Victorian royal family and the servants who cared for them. A children's play area and picnic tables are located off the visitors' car park.

Visitors can choose to bring a picnic to enjoy in the glorious grounds, or enjoy a light lunch in the stylish café which is located near the shop in the visitor reception building. You can also enjoy a waiter-served gourmet lunch or afternoon tea in the sumptuous Terrace Restaurant which forms part of the house and offers wonderful views across the Terrace Gardens towards the Solent. Please note, non-members will need to purchase an admission ticket to the house to gain access to the restaurant.

Visit www.english-heritage.org. uk/osborne for details.

⊤ Available for corporate and private hire

⌂ Holiday cottage available to let

NON-MEMBERS

House and Grounds*

Adult	£13.00
Concession	£11.70
Child	£7.80
Family	£33.80

* A lower price applies prior to private beach opening

Ground only ticket when house is closed

Adult	£5.00
Concession	£4.50
Child	£3.00
Family	£13.00

OPENING TIMES

House and Grounds

1 Apr–30 Sep, daily (house closes 5pm)	10am–6pm
1 Oct–4 Nov, daily	10am–4pm
25 Feb–28 Mar, Sat–Sun	10am–4pm
24–26 Dec and 1 Jan	Closed

Christmas opening

17–18 Nov (Victorian Christmas event)	10am–5pm

Ground floor of house open for self-guided visits

Christmas guided tours
Pre-booked guided tours of selected ground floor rooms with Victorian Christmas decorations. Last tour starts 2.30pm

21 Nov–6 Jan, Wed–Sun	10am–4pm

Grounds only

10–11 Nov	10am–4pm
7 Jan–15 Feb, Sat–Sun	10am–4pm

House guided tours and grounds
Pre-booked guided tours of selected ground floor rooms

Last tour starts 2.30pm

16–24 Feb, daily	10am–4pm

HOW TO FIND US

Direction: 1 mile SE of East Cowes

Train: Ryde Espalande 7 miles, Wootton (IoW Steam Railway) 3 miles

Bus: Southern Vectis services 4 and 5

Ferry: East Cowes 1½ miles (Red Funnel. Tel: 0844 844 9988); Fishbourne 4 miles; Ryde 7 miles (Wightlink. Tel: 0871 376 1000)

Tel: 01983 200022

Local Tourist Information: Cowes and Newport 01983 813818

Baby carriers are available at the house entrance as pushchairs are not permitted.

Disabled access – access for wheelchairs to the first floor is by an existing lift. Manual wheelchairs are available to borrow on a first come, first served basis. Mobility scooters are not permitted inside the house, but they can be used in the gardens.

MAP Page 314 (7C)
OS Map 196, OL29: SZ516948

St Catherine's Oratory
Isle of Wight

The tall, medieval, octagonal tower, allegedly a lighthouse, was built here in 1328 as penance for stealing church property from a wrecked ship. Affectionately known as the Pepperpot, it stands on one of the highest parts of the Isle of Wight. It is part of the Tennyson Heritage Coast, a series of linked cliff-top monuments. A later lighthouse can be seen nearby.

Managed by the National Trust on behalf of English Heritage.

OPENING TIMES
Any reasonable time in daylight hours

HOW TO FIND US
Direction: E of Blackgang roundabout, off A3055

Train: Shanklin 9 miles

Bus: Southern Vectis service 6 or Island Coaster (Summer) to Blackgang Chine and then ½ mile walk

Ferry: West Cowes 14 miles, East Cowes 14 miles (both Red Funnel – 0844 844 9988); Yarmouth 15 miles (Wightlink – 0870 582 7744)

🍴 🅿

MAP Page 314 (7C)
OS Map 196, OL29: SZ494773

Osborne House
See feature – Page 86

Yarmouth Castle Isle of Wight – PO41 0PB

Built to protect strategic Yarmouth harbour and (in conjunction with Hurst Castle on the mainland) to defend the western end of the Solent against invasion fleets, this last and most sophisticated addition to Henry VIII's chain of coastal forts was completed after his death in 1547. Unlike Henry's earlier circular forts – such as Deal, Portland and Pendennis Castles – Yarmouth Castle is a square blockhouse, with a battery to the front and the first new-style 'arrowhead' bastion built in England protecting its most exposed angle. In the 1560s the castle's central square was filled in to provide a solid gun platform.

Displays inside the castle include atmospheric recreations of how the rooms were used in the 16th century, and an exhibition about the many wrecks which occurred in 'Yarmouth Roads', the treacherous stretch of sea which the castle overlooks. Also a magnificent picnic site, with views over the Solent.

NON-MEMBERS
Adult	£4.00
Concession	£3.60
Child	£2.40

OPENING TIMES
1 Apr-30 Sep, Sun-Thu	11am-4pm
1 Oct-28 Mar, Sat-Sun	11am-4pm
24-26 Dec and 1 Jan	Closed

HOW TO FIND US
Direction: In Yarmouth, adjacent to car ferry terminal

Bus: Southern Vectis 7 & Needles Tour & Island Coaster (summer only)

Ferry: Wightlink – 0871 376 1000 (Lymington – Yarmouth)

Tel: 01983 760678

🍴 🏛 🅿 📷 ♿ ⚠ OVP

Disabled access (ground floor only).

Parking (coaches and cars 200 metres (220 yards). Charges payable).

MAP Page 314 (7B)
OS Map 196, OL29: SZ354898

Associated attractions in the South East

These visitor attractions, all independent of EH, offer discounts to our members. Please call before you visit to confirm details. A valid EH membership card must be produced for each member.

Anne of Cleves House
Lewes East Sussex BN7 1JA

15th-century timber framed Wealden hall-house, given to Anne as part of her divorce settlement from Henry VIII. Houses displays of period furnishings, Lewes history and Bonfire festivities, Tom Paine, and the Wealden iron industry. Enclosed garden.

Tel: 01273 474610

www.sussexpast.co.uk/anneofcleves

50% discount on entry ⊞

Arundel Castle
West Sussex BN18 9AB

Ancient Castle and Stately Home of The Duke of Norfolk with outstanding gardens, including the new Collector Earl's Garden based on early 17th century classical designs.

Tel: 01903 882173

www.arundelcastle.org

Discounted Castle & Gardens Gold Plus ticket ⊞ ⫞⫞⫞3

Dover Museum and Bronze Age Boat Gallery
Kent CT16 1PB

This modern interactive museum tells the story of Dover's rich history, and displays the world's oldest prehistoric seagoing boat, discovered nearby.

Managed by Dover District Council.

Close to Dover Castle
Tel: 01304 201066

www.dovermuseum.co.uk

50% discount on entry ⊞

Fishbourne Roman Palace
West Sussex PO19 3QR

The remains of a palatial Roman building of the 1st century AD. View unique Roman mosaics and replanted Roman garden. Tours of the palace site or behind the scenes, when artefact handling is possible. Café, picnic area, free parking.

Tel: 01243 785859

www.sussexpast.co.uk/fishbourne

50% discount on entry ⊞

Fort Amherst
Chatham, Kent ME4 4UB

Fort Amherst is a fine example of a Napoleonic fortress. Restored areas open to the public include the 2500ft underground tunnel system, gun batteries, and WWII civil defence display.

8 mins from Rochester Castle
Tel: 01634 847747

www.fortamherst.com

20% discount on entry ⊞ ⫞⫞⫞6

Goodwood House
West Sussex PO18 0PX

The family seat of the Dukes of Richmond and Gordon, set in the heart of the Sussex Downs, houses astonishing treasures, including celebrated paintings by George Stubbs and Canaletto.

5 miles from Boxgrove Priory
Tel: 01243 755040

www.goodwood.com

50% discount on entry ⊞

⊞ EH Members   OVP OVP Holders   ⫞⫞⫞? Discounted Child Places Included

Associated attractions in the South East continued

The Historic Dockyard Chatham
Kent ME4 4TZ

This unique, award-winning maritime heritage destination has a remarkable range of museum galleries, iconic buildings and historic warships to explore, together with a diverse programme of events, family activities and outstanding temporary exhibitions.

15 mins from J1 and J4 of M2

Tel: 01634 823800

www.thedockyard.co.uk

15% discount on entry
(Not valid on event days)

Leeds Castle
Kent ME17 1PL

Set in 500 acres of beautiful parkland, there's a lot to discover at Leeds Castle. Attractions include the gardens, maze and grotto, Knights' Realm playground, dog collar museum and bird shows.

2 miles from J8 of M20

Tel: 01622 765400

www.leeds-castle.com

10% discount on entry
(Not valid on event days)   6

Lewes Castle & Barbican House Museum
Lewes East Sussex BN7 1YE

This imposing Norman castle offers magnificent views across the town of Lewes and surrounding downland. The adjacent Barbican House holds an extensive collection of local history and archaeological artefacts.

Tel: 01273 486290

www.sussexpast.co.uk/lewescastle

50% discount
on entry

Lullingstone Castle and The World Garden
Kent DA4 0JA

Lullingstone Castle is one of England's oldest family estates. Home to the amazing World Garden, containing nearly 8000 different plant species from across the globe, planted to show their countries of origin.

300 metres from Lullingstone Roman Villa

Tel: 01322 862114

www.lullingstonecastle.co.uk

2 for 1
entry   OVP 6

Marlipins Museum
West Sussex BN43 5DA

Once a medieval customs house, Marlipins now holds artefacts from the Shoreham area and its maritime past, plus a collection of local archaeological material. The upstairs gallery has displays on the local silent film industry and transport, plus changing exhibitions. Full disabled access.

Tel: 01273 462994

www.sussexpast.co.uk/marlipins

50% discount
on entry

Michelham Priory
East Sussex BN27 3QS

Enter through the 14th-century gatehouse and explore the Tudor mansion which evolved from the former Augustinian Priory. Set on a tranquil island encircled by England's longest water-filled medieval moat. Extensive gardens, artefacts and dramatic Elizabethan Great Barn.

Tel: 01323 844224

www.sussexpast.co.uk/michelham

50% discount
on entry

⊞ EH Members	OVP OVP Holders	👪? Discounted Child Places Included

Newport Roman Villa
Isle of Wight PO30 1HA

Discover this Romano-British farmhouse with its fine bath suite, in suburban Newport. Hands-on activities; mosaic making and weaving, herb garden and museum display. Open 2 April-3 November

5 mins from Carisbrooke Castle

Tel: 01983 529720

www.iwight.com/museums

40% discount on entry ⊞ OVP 👪 6

Penshurst Place & Gardens
Kent TN11 8DG

Ancestral home of Viscount De L'Isle, set in the Weald of Kent, with a stunning medieval Baron's Hall and Tudor gardens. The Staterooms contain fine furniture, tapestries, porcelain and portraits.

15 mins from Hildenborough J of A21

Tel: 01892 870307

www.penshurstplace.com

Free admission to house if grounds ticket purchased ⊞

The Priest House
West Sussex RH19 4PP

Standing in the beautiful surroundings of a traditional and fragrant cottage herb garden on the edge of Ashdown Forest, the Priest House is an early 15th-century timber-framed hall-house with a dramatic roof of Horsham stone.

Tel: 01342 810479

www.sussexpast.co.uk/priesthouse

50% discount on entry ⊞

The Royal Pavilion
Brighton and Hove BN1 1EE

Discover Brighton's extravagant pleasure palace, with its remarkable Indian architecture and contrasting oriental interiors. This magnificent palace is where the Prince Regent, later King George IV, entertained his many esteemed guests.

Tel: 03000 290900

www.brighton-hove-pavilion.org.uk

20% discount on adult ticket ⊞
(Not valid on concessions) 👪 2

Rycote Chapel
Oxfordshire OX9 2PE

This 15th-century chapel has original furniture, including exquisitely carved and painted woodwork. Owned by Mr and Mrs Bernard Taylor. Managed by the Rycote Buildings Charitable Foundation.

1 Apr-30 Sep, Fri-Sun 2pm-6pm Groups by appointment only. No coaches.

3 miles SW of Thame off A329

Tel: 01844 210210

£2.50 entry (subject to change) ⊞

Westenhanger Castle and Mediaeval Barns
Kent CT21 4HX

14th-century castle with towers, dovecote and 16th-century outbuildings. The recently restored great barn was built by Thomas 'Customer' Smythe.

Open Tue only mid Apr-mid Sep (by appointment)

8 miles from Dover Castle

Tel: 01227 738451

www.kentcastle.co.uk

20% discount on entry ⊞

Pendennis Castle

SOUTH WEST

PROPERTIES

South West properties consist of:

96	English Heritage
10	The Churches Conservation Trust
17	Associated Attractions

Remember to check opening times before you visit any of our properties www.english-heritage. org.uk/daysout

Details of local public transport information in England are available from Traveline www.traveline.org.uk or call 0871 200 2233.

BRISTOL & BATH
Sir Bevil Grenville's Monument
Stanton Drew Circles and Cove
Stoney Littleton Long Barrow
Temple Church

CORNWALL
Ballowall Barrow
Carn Euny Ancient Village
Chysauster Ancient Village
Dupath Well
Halliggye Fogou
Hurlers Stone Circles
King Doniert's Stone
Launceston Castle
Pendennis Castle
Penhallam Manor
Restormel Castle
St Breock Downs Monolith
St Catherine's Castle
St Mawes Castle
Tintagel Castle
Tregiffian Burial Chamber
Trethevy Quoit

DEVON
Bayard's Cove Fort
Berry Pomeroy Castle
Blackbury Camp
Dartmouth Castle
Grimspound
Hound Tor Deserted Medieval Village
Kirkham House
Lydford Castle and Saxon Town
Merrivale Prehistoric Settlement
Okehampton Castle
Royal Citadel (Plymouth)
Totnes Castle
Upper Plym Valley

DORSET
Abbotsbury Abbey Remains
Christchurch Castle and Norman House
Fiddleford Manor
Jordan Hill Roman Temple
Kingston Russell Stone Circle
Knowlton Church and Earthworks
Maiden Castle
The Nine Stones
Portland Castle
St Catherine's Chapel
Sherborne Old Castle
Winterbourne Poor Lot Barrows

GLOUCESTERSHIRE
Belas Knap Long Barrow
Blackfriars
Cirencester Amphitheatre
Great Witcombe Roman Villa
Greyfriars
Hailes Abbey
Kingswood Abbey Gatehouse
Notgrove Long Barrow
Nympsfield Long Barrow
Odda's Chapel
Offa's Dyke
Over Bridge
St Briavels Castle
St Mary's Church
Uley Long Barrow (Hetty Pegler's Tump)
Windmill Tump Long Barrow

SOMERSET
Butter Cross
Cleeve Abbey
Farleigh Hungerford Castle
Gallox Bridge
Glastonbury Tribunal
Meare Fish House
Muchelney Abbey
Nunney Castle
Yarn Market

WILTSHIRE
Alexander Keiller Museum
Avebury
Bradford-on-Avon Tithe Barn
Bratton Camp and White Horse
Chisbury Chapel
Hatfield Earthworks
Ludgershall Castle and Cross
Netheravon Dovecote
Old Sarum
Old Wardour Castle
The Sanctuary
Silbury Hill
Stonehenge
West Kennet Avenue
West Kennet Long Barrow
Windmill Hill
Woodhenge

ISLES OF SCILLY
Bant's Carn Burial Chamber and Halangy Down Ancient Village
Cromwell's Castle
Garrison Walls
Harry's Walls
Innisidgen Lower and Upper Burial Chambers
King Charles's Castle
Old Blockhouse
Porth Hellick Down Burial Chamber

SOUTH WEST

Cheltenham
Gloucester
Gloucestershire
Cirencester
Swindon
South Gloucestershire
Bristol
Bath & North East Somerset
Bristol
Chippenham
Marlborough
North Somerset
Weston-super-Mare
Bath
Devizes
Wiltshire
Wells
Ilfracombe — Minehead
Somerset Glastonbury
Salisbury
Barnstaple
Taunton
Bideford
Yeovil
Bude
Devon
Dorset
Launceston
Exeter
Dorchester
Poole
Padstow
Exmouth
Weymouth
Bournemouth
Cornwall
Swanage
Newquay
Bodmin
Totnes
Plymouth
Torquay
Dartmouth
St Ives
Truro
Penzance
Falmouth

Isles of Scilly
Hugh Town

HIGHLIGHTS FOR 2012/13 IN THE SOUTH WEST

- **Tintagel Castle:** dramatic birthplace of the legend of King Arthur.
- **Pendennis Castle:** fantastic views & family fun at Cornwall's greatest fortress.
- **Stonehenge:** discover the mystery of the great stone circle.

BRISTOL & BATH

Church of St Thomas the Martyr, Bristol
Bristol – BS1 6QR

© David Martyn

Located in Bristol city centre, this handsome Georgian building replaced a medieval church deemed unsafe for use. The light-filled Classical interior is elegantly presented and there is a fine ring of eight bells, all cast by local founders.

Owned and managed by The Churches Conservation Trust.

OPENING TIMES
Wed   10.30am-2.30pm

Other days by appointment, please call 0117 929 1766 before your visit

HOW TO FIND US
Train: Nearest 🚉 Bristol Temple Meads ¼ mile

Bus: Close to bus routes to city centre and bus station. Bus and coach terminus 1 mile. Routes 51/54/57/57A/70/178/339/349/379/672

2 mins walk from Temple Church

MAP Page 313 (3H)
OS Map 172, 154/155: ST591727

Sir Bevil Grenville's Monument
Bath & NE Somerset

Erected to commemorate the heroism of a Royalist commander and his Cornish pikemen at the Battle of Lansdown, 1643.

OPENING TIMES
Any reasonable time

HOW TO FIND US
Direction: Located 4 miles NW of Bath on the N edge of Lansdown Hill, near the road to Wick

Train: Bath Spa 4½ miles

Bus: Wessex Connect service 620 Bath Spa – Tetbury

 P Parking (in lay-by).

MAP Page 313 (3H)
OS Map 172, 155: ST722703

Stanton Drew Circles and Cove
Bath & NE Somerset

Though the third largest collection of prehistoric standing stones in England, the three circles and three-stone 'cove' of Stanton Drew are surprisingly little-known. Recent surveys have revealed that they were only part of a much more elaborate ritual site.

OPENING TIMES
Cove: any reasonable time.
Two main stone circles: access at the discretion of the landowner, who may levy a charge

HOW TO FIND US
Direction: Cove: in the garden of the Druid's Arms public house. Circles: E of Stanton Drew village

Train: Bristol Temple Meads 7 miles

Bus: Somerbus 640 (Fri) & 754 (Mon), A Bus service 683 (Wed), BANES 752 (Wed), Coombs 834 (Tues), Eurotaxis/CT Travel 672

Stanton Drew Circles and Cove

🐕

MAP Page 313 (3H)
OS Map 172/182, 154/155
Cove: ST597631
Circles: ST601633

Stoney Littleton Long Barrow
Bath & NE Somerset

One of the finest accessible examples of a Neolithic chambered tomb, with its multiple burial chambers open to view.

OPENING TIMES
Any reasonable daylight hours

HOW TO FIND US
Direction: 1 mile S of Wellow off A367

Train: Bath Spa 6 miles

Bus: Somerbus 757 (Wed); First 173, 178 or 184 to Peasedown St John then 2½ mile walk

P Parking (limited).
Note: visitors are advised to bring a torch, and that there may be mud on approach and interior floor.

MAP Page 313 (3H)
OS Map 172, 142: ST735572

Temple Church
Bristol

The 'leaning tower' and walls of this large, late medieval church survived bombing during World War II. The graveyard is now a public garden.

OPENING TIMES
Exterior only: any reasonable time

HOW TO FIND US
Direction: Located in Temple St, off Victoria St

Train: Bristol Temple Meads ¼ mile

Bus: From surrounding areas

MAP Page 313 (3H)
OS Map 172, 154/155: ST593727

Ballowall Barrow
Cornwall

In a spectacular cliff-edge position, this unique Bronze Age tomb has a long and complex history as a sacred site. Seen as excavated in 1878 by Cornish antiquarian William Borlase.

Managed by the National Trust.

OPENING TIMES
Any reasonable time

HOW TO FIND US
Direction: 1 mile W of St Just, near Carn Gloose

Train: Penzance 8 miles

Bus: First 10, 300 (summer only); Western Greyhound 504, 507, 509

MAP Page 312 (7A)
OS Map 203, 102: SW355312

Carn Euny Ancient Village
Cornwall

Among the best preserved ancient villages in the South West, occupied from the Iron Age until late Roman times. It includes the foundations of stone houses and an intriguing 'fogou' underground passage.

Managed by the Cornwall Heritage Trust.

OPENING TIMES
Any reasonable time

HOW TO FIND US
Direction: 1¼ miles SW of Sancreed off A30

Carn Euny Ancient Village

Train: Penzance 6 miles

Bus: Western Greyhound service 509 to Grumbla

Parking 600 metres (660 yards) away in Brane.

MAP Page 312 (7A)
OS Map 203, 102: SW402288

Chysauster Ancient Village
Cornwall – TR20 8XA

This Romano-British settlement was originally occupied 2000 years ago. The village consisted of stone-walled homesteads known as 'courtyard houses', found only on the Land's End peninsula and the Isles of Scilly. The houses line a 'village street', and each had an open central courtyard surrounded by a number of thatched rooms. There are also the remains of an enigmatic 'fogou' underground passage.
www.english-heritage.org.uk/ chysauster

NON-MEMBERS
Adult	£3.50
Concession	£3.20
Child	£2.10

OPENING TIMES
1 Apr-30 Jun, daily	10am-5pm
1 Jul-31 Aug, daily	10am-6pm
1-30 Sep, daily	10am-5pm
1 Oct-4 Nov, daily	10am-4pm
5 Nov-28 Mar	Closed

Chysauster Ancient Village

HOW TO FIND US
Direction: Located 2½ miles NW of Gulval, off B3311

Train: Penzance 3½ miles

Bus: Western Greyhound 508 then 1½ mile walk; Western Greyhound 516 then 1¾ mile walk

Tel: 07831 757934

MAP Page 312 (7B)
OS Map 203, 102: SW472350

Dupath Well
Cornwall

This charming well-house of c. 1500 stands over an ancient spring believed to cure whooping cough. Built by the Augustinian canons of nearby St Germans priory, it houses the remains of an immersion pool for cure-seekers.

Managed by the Cornwall Heritage Trust.

OPENING TIMES
Any reasonable time

HOW TO FIND US
Direction: 1 mile E of Callington off A388

Train: Gunnislake 4½ miles

Bus: Main services to Callington are First 76 or Western Greyhound 576 then ½ mile

MAP Page 312 (6D)
OS Map 201, 108: SX375692

Halliggye Fogou
Cornwall

Roofed and walled in stone, this complex of passages is the largest and best-preserved of several mysterious underground tunnels associated with Cornish Iron Age settlements. The purpose of such 'fogous' – a Cornish-language word meaning 'cave' – is unknown. Refuges, storage chambers or ritual shrines have all been suggested.

Free entry to the fogou. Entry to the rest of the Trelowarren Estate is charged.

Managed by the Trelowarren Estate.

OPENING TIMES
Reasonable daylight hours May-Sep, but completely blocked Oct-Apr inclusive

HOW TO FIND US
Direction: 5 miles SE of Helston off B3293. E of Garras on Trelowarren Estate. There is a lay-by at the side of the lane through the Trelowarren Estate. Walk up hill and the entrance to the fogou is signposted through a gate

Train: Penryn 10 miles

Bus: Western Greyhound 538 to Garras and then c. 1 mile walk

Parking (free to members).

Visitors are strongly advised to bring a torch.

MAP Page 312 (7B)
OS Map 203, 103: SW713239

Hurlers Stone Circles
Cornwall

Three fine late Neolithic or early Bronze Age stone circles arranged in a line, a grouping unique in England. Probably the best examples of ceremonial circles in the South West, they are traditionally reputed to be the remains of men petrified for playing 'hurling' on a Sunday.

Managed by the Cornwall Heritage Trust.

OPENING TIMES
Any reasonable time

HOW TO FIND US
Direction: Located ½ mile NW of Minions, off B3254

Train: Liskeard 7 miles

Bus: Western Greyhound 574 from Liskeard to Minions or 574 to Darite or Upon Cross then 1 mile walk, DAC Coaches 261, Group Travel 236

Parking ¼ mile walk.

MAP Page 312 (6D)
OS Map 201, 109: SX258714

King Doniert's Stone
Cornwall

Two richly carved pieces of a 9th-century 'Celtic' cross, with an inscription commemorating Dumgarth, British King of Dumnonia, who drowned in c. AD 875.

Managed by the Cornwall Heritage Trust.

OPENING TIMES
Any reasonable time

HOW TO FIND US
Direction: 1 mile NW of St Cleer, off B3254

Train: Liskeard 7 miles

Bus: DAC 79B & Western Greyhound 574

Parking (in lay-by).

MAP Page 312 (6D)
OS Map 201, 109: SX236688

Launceston Castle
Cornwall – PL15 7DR

Set on a large natural mound, Launceston Castle dominates the surrounding landscape. Begun soon after the Norman Conquest, its focus is an unusual keep consisting of a 13th-century round tower built by Richard, Earl of Cornwall, inside an earlier circular shell-keep. The tower top is now reached via a dark internal staircase.

The castle long remained a prison and George Fox, founder of the Quàkers, suffered harsh confinement here in 1656. An exhibition traces 1000 years of history, with finds from site excavations.

www.english-heritage.org.uk/launceston

NON-MEMBERS
Adult	£3.50
Concession	£3.20
Child	£2.10

OPENING TIMES
1 Apr-30 Jun, daily	10am-5pm
1 Jul-31 Aug, daily	10am-6pm
1-30 Sep, daily	10am-5pm
1 Oct-4 Nov, daily	10am-4pm
5 Nov-28 Mar	Closed

HOW TO FIND US
Direction: In Launceston

Bus: First 76; Jackets X85 (Sat only); Western Greyhound 510, 576 & 577, Group Travel 223, 225 & 236

Tel: 01566 772365

Disabled access (outer bailey, exhibition and shop).

MAP Page 312 (5D)
OS Map 201, 112: SX331846

Pendennis Castle
See feature – Page 102

Penhallam Manor
Cornwall

The low and grass-covered but complete ground-plan of a moated 13th-century manor house, in a delightful woodland setting.

OPENING TIMES

Any reasonable time

HOW TO FIND US

Direction: Signposted from Week St Mary, off a minor road off A39 from Treskinnick Cross (10 minute walk from the car park on the forest track)

Bus: Western Greyhound service 595 stops at Treskinnick Cross (2 miles). Webber Coaches service 208 (Mon/Wed/Thu/Fri) and 220 (Tues) to the nearby village of Week St Mary

🐕 🅿 Parking (limited).

MAP Page 312 (5D)
OS Map 190, 111: SX224974

Restormel Castle
Cornwall – PL22 0EE

The great 13th-century circular shell-keep of Restormel still encloses the principal rooms of the castle in remarkably good condition. It stands on an earlier Norman mound surrounded by a deep dry ditch, atop a high spur beside the River Fowey. Twice visited by the Black Prince, son of Edward III, it finally saw action during the Civil War in 1644. It commands fantastic views and is a favourite picnic spot.

Restormel Castle

www.english-heritage.org.uk/restormel

NON-MEMBERS

Adult	£3.50
Concession	£3.20
Child	£2.10

OPENING TIMES

1 Apr-30 Jun, daily	10am-5pm
1 Jul-31 Aug, daily	10am-6pm
1-30 Sep, daily	10am-5pm
1 Oct-4 Nov, daily	10am-4pm
5 Nov-28 Mar	Closed

HOW TO FIND US

Direction: Located 1½ miles N of Lostwithiel, off A390

Train: Lostwithiel 1½ miles

Bus: Western Greyhound 523, Roselyn 293, 296, Gorran Community Bus G4, Jackets X5 to Lostwithiel then 1½ walk.

Tel: 01208 872687

🐕 🍴 🚶 🅿 🅿 📷 ⚠ OVP

Access via a stock grazing area, appropriate footwear is advisable. There are steps on the entrance path. Disabled visitors may wish to call the site in advance to arrange alternative access.

MAP Page 312 (6C)
OS Map 200, 107: SX104614

St Breock Downs Monolith
Cornwall

St Breock Downs Monolith

Originally 5 metres (16 feet) high and weighing some 16.75 tonnes, this is Cornwall's largest and heaviest prehistoric monolith. It stands on the summit of St Breock Downs, offering wonderful views.

Managed by the Cornwall Heritage Trust.

OPENING TIMES

Any reasonable time

HOW TO FIND US

Direction: Located on St Breock Downs; 3½ miles SW of Wadebridge off unclassified road to Rosenannon

Train: Roche 5½ miles

Bus: Closest bus service is the Tuesday and Friday Travel Cornwall route 405 to Rosenannon (2 mile). Alternatively Western Greyhound services 510 or 594 to St Jidgey from whence you should walk along the Saints Trail (2½ mile)

🐕

MAP Page 312 (6C)
OS Map 200, 106: SW968683

St Catherine's Castle
Cornwall

One of a pair of small artillery forts built by Henry VIII in the 1530s to defend Fowey Harbour, consisting of two storeys with gun ports at ground level.

OPENING TIMES

Any reasonable time

HOW TO FIND US

Direction: 1½ miles SW of Fowey, along a woodland footpath off A3082

Train: Par 4 miles

Bus: Western Greyhound 524 & 525 to within ¾ mile walk of the castle

🐕 🅿
Parking (Ready Money Cove Car Park, Fowey, ¾ mile walk).

MAP Page 312 (6C)
OS Map 200/204, 107: SX119509

Pendennis Castle Cornwall – TR11 4LP

Constructed between 1540 and 1545, Pendennis and its sister, St Mawes Castle, form the Cornish end of the chain of coastal castles built by Henry VIII to counter a threat from France and Spain. Thereafter Pendennis was frequently adapted to face new enemies over 400 years, right through until World War II.

Pendennis Castle is home to a collection of wartime cartoons by George Butterworth. The acclaimed cartoons, which appeared daily throughout World War II, lampooned both Hitler and Mussolini, enraging the Nazi leader so much that the cartoonist was put on his 'hit-list'. During your visit to Pendennis, set aside some time to view the cartoons, generously given to English Heritage by George Butterworth's widow, a neighbour of the castle.

Check opening times at www.english-heritage.org.uk

In 1598, during Elizabeth I's reign, a new type of defensive rampart was added around the original fort. The castle was strengthened again prior to the Civil War and played host to the future Charles II in 1646, before he sailed to the Isles of Scilly. It then withstood five months of siege, before becoming the penultimate Royalist garrison on the British mainland to surrender.

Pendennis continued to play a vital role in Cornwall's defences throughout the late 19th and early 20th centuries, and saw significant action during World War II. Evidence of its fascinating history is on show throughout the site, and the Guardhouse has been returned to its World War I appearance. You can also visit the Half Moon Battery, including the underground magazine (by guided tour only), as well as the original 16th-century gun tower with its recreated Tudor gun deck.

The refurbished 1901 Royal Artillery Barracks houses an interactive exhibition, tracing the history of the castle, its people, and its links with Falmouth and the trade routes of the British Empire. A key feature is a hands-on scale model of the castle: with the aid of special effects, children can step into the shoes of a soldier on kit parade.

After a busy day exploring, sample the delicious selection of refreshments, snacks and light meals in the tearoom situated within the Royal Garrison Artillery Barracks.

The pre-bookable education suite, with two rooms and a wet room for creative workshops, can accommodate up to 120 children. The fully-equipped hospitality area serves as both a conference centre and a stunning wedding venue, with the Fal Estuary in the backdrop

www.english-heritage.org.uk/pendennis

 www.facebook.com/pendenniscastle

NON-MEMBERS

Adult	£6.50
Concession	£5.90
Child	£3.90
Family	£16.90

Additional charges for members and non-members may apply on event days

OPENING TIMES

1 Apr-30 Jun, daily	10am-5pm*
1 Jul-31 Aug, daily	10am-6pm*
1-30 Sep, daily	10am-5pm*
1 Oct-4 Nov, daily	10am-4pm
5 Nov-17 Feb, Sat-Sun	10am-4pm
18-22 Feb, daily	10am-4pm
23 Feb-28 Mar, Sat-Sun	10am-4pm
24-26 Dec and 1 Jan	Closed

*Closes at 4pm on Saturdays

The keep will close for 1 hour at lunch on Saturdays if an event is booked

Free guided tours of the Half Moon Battery, check availability on arrival

Free members' guided tours
6 Nov, 5 Dec, 24 Jan, 7 Feb, 21 Mar
10.30am-12.30pm/1.30pm-3.30pm

HOW TO FIND US

Direction: On Pendennis Headland, 1 mile SE of Falmouth

Train: Falmouth Docks ½ mile

Bus: Western Greyhound service 500; First service 41 also passes nearby

Tel: 01326 316594

Local Tourist Information: 01326 312300

Disabled access (wheelchair access to the grounds, but steep slopes or drops in places. There is also full wheelchair access to the shop, tearoom, Discovery Centre and the Barracks, which contains a virtual tour of the whole site).

Dogs on leads (in grounds only).

Tearoom open daily, Apr-Oct (closes ½ hour before the castle), Nov-Mar: Sat-Sun, 12pm-3.30pm.

MAP Page 312 (7C)
OS Map 204, 103/105: SW824318

- Available for corporate and private hire
- Licensed for civil wedding ceremonies
- Holiday cottages available to let

Enjoy the castle grounds in private after it closes to the public when you stay in the Custodian's House or Callie's Cottage

Tintagel Castle Cornwall – PL34 0HE

With its spectacular location on one of Britain's most dramatic coastlines, Tintagel is an awe-inspiring and romantic spot, a place of legends.

Take time to browse in the superb castle shop which specialises in books, medieval and Arthurian themed gifts and toys, tapestries, jams and chutneys.

Joined to the mainland by a narrow neck of land, Tintagel Island faces the full force of the Atlantic. On the mainland itself, the gaunt remains of the medieval castle represent only one phase in a long history of occupation. Even before Richard, Earl of Cornwall, built his castle, Tintagel was already associated with the conception of King Arthur. This connection was later renewed by Alfred, Lord Tennyson, in his *Idylls of the King*.

After a period as a Roman settlement and military outpost, Tintagel is thought to have been a trading settlement of Celtic kings during the 5th and 6th centuries. Legend has it that one of these was King Mark, whose nephew Tristan fell in love with Yseult (or Isolde). Their doomed romance is part of Tintagel's story.

The remains of the 13th-century castle are breathtaking. Steep stone steps, stout walls and rugged windswept cliff edges encircle the Great Hall, where Richard, Earl of Cornwall, once feasted.

There are many unanswered questions and legends surrounding Tintagel. The castle has an amazing capacity to surprise us, even after years of investigation.

In 1998, excavations were undertaken under the direction of Professor Chris Morris of the University of Glasgow, on a relatively sheltered and small site on the eastern side of the island, first excavated in the 1930s. Pottery from the 5th and 6th centuries was found, as well as some fine glass fragments believed to be from 6th or 7th-century Málaga in Spain. Even more remarkable was a 1500-

year-old piece of slate on which remained two Latin inscriptions. The second inscription reads: 'Artognou, father of a descendant of Coll, has had (this) made'. Who exactly Artognou was continues to be a subject for lively speculation.

Searching for King Arthur, a short audio visual tour through the ages, introduces visitors to the castle, its legends and history.

During the summer you can also enjoy special introductory talks. The site offers a shop and visitor facilities, and the café, set above the beach, serves a delicious selection of hot and cold snacks and light meals – all sourced from the finest local Cornish ingredients.

Access to the castle is difficult for disabled visitors (via over 100 steep steps). There is a Land Rover service from the village which can take visitors to the exhibition and shop (Apr-Oct only). Contact the site for service information. **www.english-heritage.org.uk/tintagel**

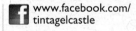

www.facebook.com/tintagelcastle

HOW TO FIND US

Direction: On Tintagel Head, 600m (660 yards) along uneven track from Tintagel; no vehicles except Land Rover service, extra charge

Bus: Western Greyhound 594 (with connections available at Wadebridge, Camelford and Boscastle)

Tel: 01840 770328

Local Tourist Information: Boscastle Visitor Centre: 01840 250010; Camelford (summer only): 01840 212954; Padstow: 01841 533449

Disabled access is limited. A Land Rover service to the castle (Apr-Oct) is available at a separate charge. Please call the site for more details.

Parking (600 metres (660 yards) in the village) – not managed by EH.

MAP Page 312 (5C)
OS Map 200, 111: SX049891

NON-MEMBERS

Adult	£5.70
Concession	£5.10
Child	£3.40
Family	£14.80

OPENING TIMES

1 Apr-30 Sep, daily	10am-6pm
1 Oct-4 Nov, daily	10am-5pm
5 Nov-17 Feb, Sat-Sun	10am-4pm
18-22 Feb, daily	10am-4pm
23 Feb-28 Mar, Sat-Sun	10am-4pm
24-26 Dec and 1 Jan	Closed

Beach Café open Apr-Oct daily (closes ½ hour before the castle), Nov-Mar, Sat-Sun 11am-3.30pm

Free members' guided tours 16 Nov, 23 Jan, 18 Feb, 14 Mar 11am-12.30pm/1.30pm-3pm

St Mawes Castle Cornwall – TR2 5DE

St Mawes Castle is among the best-preserved of Henry VIII's coastal artillery fortresses, and the most elaborately decorated of them all. One of the chain of forts built between 1539 and 1545 to counter an invasion threat from Catholic France and Spain, it guarded the important anchorage of Carrick Roads, sharing the task with Pendennis Castle on the other side of the Fal estuary.

A charming clover-leaf shape surrounded by outer defences, St Mawes was designed to mount heavy 'ship-sinking' guns. But particular care was also taken with its embellishment, and it is still bedecked with carved Latin inscriptions in praise of Henry VIII and his son Edward VI. It owes its fine preservation for modern visitors to the fact that, unlike Pendennis Castle, it was little developed after its completion. Easily falling to landward attack by Civil War Parliamentarian forces in 1646, it remained neglected until partial re-arming during the 19th and early 20th centuries. Other coastal forts built by Henry VIII include Portland, Deal and Walmer Castles.

www.english-heritage.org.uk/ stmawes

⊤ Available for corporate and private hire

▲ Licensed for civil wedding ceremonies

⌂ Holiday cottage available to let

NON-MEMBERS

Adult	£4.40
Concession	£4.00
Child	£2.60

OPENING TIMES

1 Apr–30 Jun, Sun–Fri	10am–5pm
1 Jul–31 Aug, Sun–Fri	10am–6pm
1–30 Sep, Sun–Fri	10am–5pm
1 Oct–4 Nov, daily	10am–4pm
5 Nov–28 Mar, Sat–Sun	10am–4pm

Property may close at 3.30pm on Fridays, Saturdays (when open) and Sundays and for 1 hour during other days for private events

The Keep will close for 1 hour on Saturday if an event is booked

24–26 Dec and 1 Jan	Closed

HOW TO FIND US

Direction: In St Mawes on A3078

Train: Penmere (Falmouth), 4 miles via Prince of Wales Pier and ferry

Bus: Western Greyhound service 550 ½ mile, but better to catch ferry from Falmouth

Tel: 01326 270526

Dogs on leads (grounds only).

MAP Page 312 (7C)
OS Map 204, 105: SW841328

Enjoy panoramic views from the holiday cottage at **St Mawes Castle**

Tintagel Castle
See feature – Page 104

Tregiffian Burial Chamber
Cornwall

A Neolithic or early Bronze Age chambered tomb with an entrance passage, walled and roofed with stone slabs, leading into the central chamber.

Managed by the Cornwall Heritage Trust.

OPENING TIMES
Any reasonable time

HOW TO FIND US

Direction: Located 2 miles SE of St Buryan, on B3315

Train: Penzance 5½ miles

Bus: Western Greyhound service 501, 504, First 1, 1A, 300

Parking (in lay-by).

MAP Page 312 (7B)
OS Map 203, 102: SW431244

Trethevy Quoit
Cornwall

This well-preserved and impressive Neolithic 'dolmen' burial chamber stands 2.7 metres (8.9 ft) high. There are five standing stones, surmounted by a huge capstone.

Managed by the Cornwall Heritage Trust.

OPENING TIMES
Any reasonable time

HOW TO FIND US

Direction: 1 mile NE of St Cleer, near Darite; off B3254

Train: Liskeard 3½ miles

Bus: Western Greyhound 574

MAP Page 312 (6D)
OS Map 201, 109: SX259688

Bayard's Cove Fort:
see Dartmouth, Bayard's Cove Fort

Berry Pomeroy Castle
Devon – TQ9 6LJ

Tucked away in a steep wooded valley, Berry Pomeroy Castle is the perfect romantic ruin. Within the 15th-century defences of the Pomeroy family castle, still displaying a wall painting of the Three Kings in its gatehouse chamber, looms the dramatic ruined shell of its successor, the great mansion of the Seymours. Begun in the 1560s and ambitiously enlarged from c. 1600, their mansion was intended to become the most spectacular house in Devon, a match for Longleat and Audley End.

Never completed, and abandoned by 1700, it became the focus of blood-curdling ghost stories, recounted in the audio tour.

www.english-heritage.org.uk/berrypomeroy

Berry Pomeroy Castle

NON-MEMBERS

Adult	£4.80
Concession	£4.30
Child	£2.90

OPENING TIMES

1 Apr-30 Jun, daily	10am-5pm
1 Jul-31 Aug, daily	10am-6pm
1-30 Sep, daily	10am-5pm
1 Oct-4 Nov, daily	10am-4pm
5 Nov-28 Mar, Sat-Sun	10am-4pm
24-26 Dec and 1 Jan	Closed

HOW TO FIND US

Direction: 2½ miles E of Totnes off A385

Train: Totnes 3½ miles

Bus: Stagecoach in Devon 111, 112

Tel: 01803 866618

Disabled access (grounds and ground floor only).

Parking (no coach access) at end of long drive (approx. ¾ mile).

Café (not managed by EH) open Tue-Sun, Thu-Sun in Oct.

MAP Page 313 (6F)
OS Map 202, OL20/110: SX839623

Blackbury Camp
Devon

An Iron Age hillfort with impressive ramparts, now surrounded by woodland.

OPENING TIMES
Any reasonable time

HOW TO FIND US
Direction: Off B3174/A3052

Train: Honiton 6½ miles

Bus: Stagecoach Devon 52A, First X53 & X54 alight at Three Horseshoes on A3052 between Sidford & Seaton and then public footpath (steep climb c. 1 mile)

MAP Page 313 (5G)
OS Map 192/193, 115: SY187924

Dartmouth, Bayard's Cove Fort
Devon

Small Tudor artillery fort guarding Dartmouth's inner harbour, picturesquely sited on the quayside.

OPENING TIMES
Any reasonable time

HOW TO FIND US
Direction: Located in Dartmouth, on the riverside

Train: Paignton 8 miles via ferry

Bus: First 90, 93 & X81, alternatively Stagecoach bus 22, 24 or 120 to Kingswear Banjo then cross the River Dart Lower or passenger ferry

MAP Page 313 (6F)
OS Map 202, OL20: SX879509

Dartmouth Castle
See feature – page 108

Grimspound
Devon

The best known of many Dartmoor prehistoric settlements, Grimspound dates from the late Bronze Age. The remains of 24 stone houses survive within a massive boundary wall.

Managed by the Dartmoor National Park Authority.

OPENING TIMES
Any reasonable time

HOW TO FIND US
Direction: 6 miles SW of Moretonhampstead, off B3212

Bus: First summer only Transmoor Link service 82 Exeter St David's–Plymouth. Alight at Challacombe Cross then walk 1¼ mile. There is also a year-round service 98 operated by Beacon Bus between Tavistock and Bellever (Postbridge) which is 5 mile walk from Grimspound

MAP Page 312 (5E)
OS Map 191, OL28: SX701809

Dartmouth Castle Devon – TQ6 0JN

OPENING TIMES

1 Apr-30 Jun, daily		10am-5pm
1 Jul-31 Aug, daily		10am-6pm
1-30 Sep, daily		10am-5pm
1 Oct-4 Nov, daily		10am-4pm
5 Nov-28 Mar, Sat-Sun	10am-4pm
24-26 Dec and 1 Jan		Closed

HOW TO FIND US

Direction: 1 mile SE of Dartmouth off B3205, narrow approach road. No coach access

Train: Paignton 8 miles via ferry

Bus: First service 90, 93 & X81, alternatively Stagecoach bus 22, 24 or 120 to Kingswear Banjo then cross the River Dart Lower or passenger ferry

Tel: 01803 833588

Parking (not owned by EH, charged).

Tearooms (not managed by EH).

Toilets (not managed by EH).

MAP Page 313 (6F)
OS Map 202, OL20: SX887503

One of the most picturesquely-sited forts in England. For over six hundred years Dartmouth Castle has guarded the narrow entrance to the Dart Estuary and the busy port of Dartmouth.

This fascinating complex of defences was begun in 1388 by John Hawley, privateering mayor of Dartmouth and the prototype of the flamboyant 'Shipman' in Chaucer's *Canterbury Tales*. About a century later the townsmen added the imposing and well-preserved 'gun tower', probably the very first fortification in Britain purpose-built to mount 'ship-sinking' heavy cannon. Climb to the top for breathtaking views across the estuary, and see how this could be blocked in wartime by a heavy chain.

Unusually incorporating the fine church of St Petrox, the castle saw action during the Civil War and continued in service right up until World War II. Successive up-dating included the Victorian 'Old Battery' with its remounted heavy guns, guardrooms and maze of passages to explore. Here, a dramatic film-sequence recreates a Victorian gun-firing, and throughout the fortress displays retell the castle's six centuries of history.

You can enjoy a boat trip from the castle to the picturesque quay.

www.english-heritage.org.uk/dartmouth

NON-MEMBERS

Adult	£4.80
Concession	£4.30
Child	£2.90

Hound Tor
Deserted Medieval Village
Devon

The remains of four 13th-century stone farmsteads, on land originally farmed in the Bronze Age. This isolated Dartmoor hamlet was probably abandoned in the early 15th century. A free downloadable audio tour is available from the English Heritage website.

Managed by the Dartmoor National Park Authority.

OPENING TIMES
Any reasonable time

HOW TO FIND US
Direction: 1½ miles S of Manaton, ½ mile from the Ashburton road

Bus: Countrybus Saturday service 271 to Harefoot Cross then 1½ mile walk. Otherwise the closest you will get by bus are the Wednesday only Country Bus 672 to Widecombe In The Moor (3 mile) or the Carmel Coaches service 671 to Manaton (2¼ mile).

Parking (½ mile walk across moor to monument).

MAP Page 312 (5E)
OS Map 191, OL28: SX746788

Kirkham House, Paignton
Devon

Kirkham House, Paignton

This late medieval stone house, afterwards split into three cottages, was restored in the 1960s. Furnished with modern furniture, illustrating traditional craftsmanship and the original use of the rooms.

Managed in association with the Paignton Preservation & Local History Society.

OPENING TIMES
6 & 9 Apr, 7 May, 4 Jun, 27 Aug & every Sun in Jul–Aug   2pm–5pm

Heritage Open Days   11am–4pm

HOW TO FIND US
Direction: Located in Kirkham St, off Cecil Rd, Paignton

Train: Paignton ½ mile

Bus: From surrounding areas

MAP Page 313 (6F)
OS Map 202, OL20/110: SX885610

Lydford Castle and Saxon Town
Devon

Beautifully sited on the fringe of Dartmoor, Lydford boasts three defensive features. Near the centre is a small-scale Norman keep on a mound, built as a prison. It later became notorious for harsh punishments – 'the most annoyous, contagious and detestable place within this realm'. To the south is an earlier Norman earthwork castle; to the north, Saxon town defences. A free downloadable audio tour is available from the English Heritage website.

Lydford Castle and Saxon Town

OPENING TIMES
Any reasonable time

HOW TO FIND US
Direction: In Lydford off A386; 8½ miles S of Okehampton

Bus: Beacon Bus 118

MAP Page 312 (5E)
OS Map 191/201, OL28: SX509848

Merrivale Prehistoric Settlement – Devon

The remains of a Bronze Age settlement, side-by-side with several sacred sites, including three stone rows, a stone circle, standing stones and burial cairns, probably constructed over a long period between c. 2500 BC and 1000 BC.

Managed by the Dartmoor National Park Authority.

OPENING TIMES
Any reasonable time

HOW TO FIND US
Direction: 1 mile E of Merrivale

Train: Gunnislake 10 miles

Bus: Beacon Bus service 98 Yelverton-Tavistock (with connections from Plymouth)

MAP Page 312 (6E)
OS Map 191, OL28: SX554748

Okehampton Castle
Devon – EX20 1JA

The remains of the largest castle in Devon, in a picturesque setting on a wooded spur above the rushing River Okement. Begun soon after the Norman Conquest as a motte and bailey castle with a stone keep, it was converted into a sumptuous residence in the 14th century by Hugh Courtenay, Earl of Devon, much of whose work survives. After the last Courtenay owner fell foul of Henry VIII in 1538, it declined into an allegedly haunted ruin. Riverside picnic area and woodland walks nearby.

www.english-heritage.org.uk/ okehampton

NON-MEMBERS

Adult	£3.80
Concession	£3.40
Child	£2.30

OPENING TIMES

1 Apr-30 Jun, daily	10am-5pm
1 Jul-31 Aug, daily	10am-6pm
1-30 Sep, daily	10am-5pm
1 Oct-28 Mar	Closed

HOW TO FIND US

Direction: Located 1 mile SW of Okehampton town centre (signposted)

Train: Okehampton (summer Sundays only) ½ mile

Bus: First Atlantic Coast Express service X9, Beacon Bus service 118, Western Greyhound service 510 & 599 & Carmel service 318

Tel: 01837 52844

Audio Guide (also available for the visually impaired).
Woodland Walk Guide available from kiosk.

MAP Page 312 (5E)
OS Map 191, OL28/113: SX583942

Royal Citadel, Plymouth
Devon

A dramatic 17th-century fortress built to defend the coastline from the Dutch, and keep watch on a recently rebellious town. Still in use by the military today.

ENTRY

Non-member	£5.00
EH members and children	£4.00

OPENING TIMES

By guided tour only, May-Sep: Tue & Thu only	2.30pm

The Citadel is an operational military establishment, tours may be curtailed without notice. Photography is not permitted

HOW TO FIND US

Direction: At E end of Plymouth Hoe

Train: Plymouth 1 mile

Bus: Plymouth Citybus 25

Local Tourist Information
Plymouth: 01752 304849

Viewing is only by Blue Badge Guide tour – parties of 10 or more contact Barbican TIC 01752 306330 for authorised guide details.

MAP Page 312 (6E)
OS Map 201, OL20/108: SX480538

St Martin's Church, Exeter
Devon – EX1 1EZ

© CCT

This 1,000-year-old church in the shadow of the cathedral is one of the oldest buildings in Exeter. Its tiny parish – smaller than a football pitch – included workers and traders from the surrounding streets. The distinctive red and white exterior complements the light and simple interior.

Owned and managed by The Churches Conservation Trust.

OPENING TIMES

Mon-Fri	9.30am-4.30pm
Sat	10am-5pm

HOW TO FIND US

Train: Nearest Exeter Central 5 mins walk

Bus: Routes 173/360. Exeter bus and coach station approx 7 mins walk. Exeter St Davids 15 mins walk or a 5 mins bus ride

30 mins from Hound Tor deserted medieval village

MAP Page 313 (5F)
OS Map 192, 114: SX922926

Totnes Castle
Devon –TQ9 5NU

A classic Norman motte and bailey castle, founded soon after the Conquest to overawe the Saxon town. A later stone shell-keep crowns its steep mound, giving sweeping views across the town rooftops to the River Dart.

www.english-heritage.org.uk/ totnes

Totnes Castle

NON-MEMBERS

Adult	£3.50
Concession	£3.20
Child	£2.10

OPENING TIMES

1 Apr-30 Jun, daily	10am-5pm
1 Jul-31 Aug, daily	10am-6pm
1-30 Sep, daily	10am-5pm
1 Oct-4 Nov, daily	10am-4pm
5 Nov-28 Mar, Sat-Sun	10am-4pm
24-26 Dec and 1 Jan	Closed

HOW TO FIND US

Direction: In centre of Totnes, at Castle Street, off Station Road opposite railway station. From town centre, turn north off High Street

Train: Totnes ¼ mile

Bus: From surrounding areas

Tel: 01803 864406

🐕 🖐 🅿 📷 ⚠ OVP

Parking (charged, 64 metres (70 yards); cars only, narrow approach roads).

Keep accessible only via steep steps.

MAP Page 312 (6E)
OS Map 202, OL20/110: SX800605

Upper Plym Valley
Devon

Some 300 Bronze Age and medieval sites, covering 15½ square kilometres (6 square miles) of Dartmoor landscape.

OPENING TIMES

Any reasonable time

HOW TO FIND US

Direction: 4 miles E of Yelverton

🐕

MAP Page 312 (6E)
OS Map 202, OL20/OL28: SX580660

DORSET

Abbotsbury Abbey Remains
Dorset

Part of a monastic building, perhaps the abbot's lodging, of the Benedictine Abbey of Abbotsbury. St Catherine's Chapel is within half a mile.

OPENING TIMES

Any reasonable time

HOW TO FIND US

Direction: Located in Abbotsbury, off B3157, near the churchyard

Train: Upwey 7½ miles

Bus: First X53 & 253; Damory 61 (Wed only)

🐕 🅿

Parking (charged).

MAP Page 313 (5H)
OS Map 194, OL15: SY578852

Abbotsbury, St Catherine's Chapel
Dorset

Set high on a hilltop overlooking Abbotsbury Abbey, this sturdily buttressed and barrel-vaulted 14th-century chapel was built by the monks as a place of pilgrimage and retreat.

Abbotsbury, St Catherine's

OPENING TIMES

Any reasonable time

HOW TO FIND US

Direction: ½ mile S of Abbotsbury; by path from village, off B3157. Path leads off signposted lane to Swannery

Train: Upwey 7 miles

Bus: First X53 & 253; Damory 61 (Wed only)

🐕 ⚠

MAP Page 313 (5H)
OS Map 194, OL15: SY573848

Christchurch Castle and Norman House
Dorset

The remains of Christchurch Castle include parts of the mound-top keep and, more unusually, the 12th-century riverside chamber block or 'Constable's House'. This very early example of domestic architecture includes a rare Norman chimney. There is an important 12th-century priory church nearby.

OPENING TIMES

Any reasonable time

HOW TO FIND US

Direction: Located in Christchurch, near the Priory

Train: Christchurch ¾ mile

Bus: From surrounding area

🐕 ⚠

MAP Page 313 (5K)
OS Map 195, OL22: SZ160927

Fiddleford Manor
Dorset

The principal parts of a small stone manor house, probably begun c. 1370 for William Latimer, Sheriff of Somerset and Dorset. The hall and solar chamber display outstandingly fine timber roofs.

Please note: The adjoining building is a private residence and is not open to visitors.

OPENING TIMES

1 Apr-30 Sep, daily	10am-6pm
1 Oct-28 Mar, daily	10am-4pm
24-26 Dec and 1 Jan	Closed

HOW TO FIND US

Direction: 1 mile E of Sturminster Newton off A357

Bus: Damory 310 & 368; Wilts & Dorset X8

Disabled access (ground floor only – with 1 step).

Parking (no coach access).

MAP Page 313 (4H)
OS Map 194, 129: ST801136

Jordan Hill Roman Temple
Dorset

The foundations of a 4th-century Romano-Celtic temple.

OPENING TIMES

Any reasonable time

HOW TO FIND US

Direction: Located 2 miles NE of Weymouth, off A353

Train: Upwey or Weymouth, both 2 miles

Bus: First 4/4B, 31, X53 & 503

MAP Page 313 (5H)
OS Map 194, OL15: SY699821

Kingston Russell Stone Circle
Dorset

A late Neolithic or early Bronze Age circle of 18 fallen stones, on a hilltop overlooking Abbotsbury and the sea.

Kingston Russell Stone Circle

OPENING TIMES

Any reasonable time

HOW TO FIND US

Direction: Located 2 miles N of Abbotsbury; 1 mile along a footpath off minor roads, not signposted, 1¾ miles

Train: Weymouth (10½ miles) or Dorchester South or West (both 8 miles)

Bus: First X53; Damory 61 (Wed), 253 then 2 mile walk

Limited parking on road verge at access to farm. Access to Stone Circle on foot only via public footpaths, off minor roads. 1¾ mile. No off-road vehicle access.

MAP Page 313 (5H)
OS Map 194, OL15: SY578878

Knowlton Church and Earthworks
Dorset

The siting of this ruined medieval church at the centre of a Neolithic ritual henge earthwork symbolises the transition from pagan to Christian worship.

OPENING TIMES

Any reasonable time

HOW TO FIND US

Direction: SW of Cranborne on B3078

Bus: Damory service 300 serves Knowlton. Damory service 319 serve the nearby villages of Wimborne St Giles and Gussage All Saints

MAP Page 313 (4J)
OS Map 195, 118: SU024103

Maiden Castle
Dorset

Maiden Castle

Among the largest and most complex Iron Age hillforts in Europe, Maiden Castle's huge multiple ramparts enclose an area equivalent to 50 football pitches, protecting several hundred residents. Excavations in the 1930s and 1980s revealed the site's 4000-year history, from a Neolithic causewayed enclosure to a small Roman temple built on the site in the 4th century AD. They also produced evidence of an extensive late Iron Age cemetery, where many of the burials had suffered horrific injuries in attacks or skirmishes. Information panels guide you around the hillfort and illustrate its long history. A free downloadable audio tour is available from the English Heritage website.

OPENING TIMES

Any reasonable time

HOW TO FIND US

Direction: 2 miles S of Dorchester, off A354, N of bypass

Train: Dorchester South or West, both 2 miles

Bus: Damory service 2 to Maiden Castle Lane and then walk ½ m. Alternatively First service 31 or Damory/South West Coaches service 212 or Damory service 216 and alight between Poundbury and Martinstown and use footpath 1 mile

MAP Page 313 (5H)
OS Map 194, OL15: SY669884

The Nine Stones
Dorset

Now in a wooded glade, this small prehistoric circle of nine standing stones was constructed around 4000 years ago. Winterbourne Poor Lot Barrows (p.115) are nearby.

The Nine Stones

OPENING TIMES

Any reasonable time

HOW TO FIND US

Direction: 1½ miles SW of Winterbourne Abbas, on A35

Train: Weymouth 4½ miles

Bus: First 31 Weymouth – ⇌ Axminster (passing ⇌ Dorchester South)

⚑ P ⚠

Park in Little Chef car park in Winterbourne Abbas and use permissive path parallel to A35.

MAP Page 313 (5H)
OS Map 194, OL15/117: SY611904

Portland Castle

See feature – page 114

St Catherine's Chapel, Abbotsbury: see Abbotsbury,

St Catherine's Chapel – Page 111

Sherborne Old Castle
Dorset – DT9 3SA

Built by Bishop Roger of Salisbury in the 12th century as a strongly-defended palace, Sherborne Old Castle became a powerful Royalist base during the Civil War. Described as 'malicious and mischievous' by Cromwell, it fell in 1645 after a fierce eleven-day siege. Sherborne 'New' Castle is nearby (see p.137).

www.english-heritage.org.uk/sherborne

NON-MEMBERS

Adult	£3.50
Concession	£3.20
Child	£2.10

Sherborne Old Castle

OPENING TIMES

1 Apr-30 Jun, daily	10am-5pm
1 Jul-31 Aug, daily	10am-6pm
1-30 Sep, daily	10am-5pm
1 Oct-4 Nov, daily	10am-4pm
5 Nov-28 Mar	Closed

HOW TO FIND US

Direction: Located ½ mile E of Sherborne, off B3145

Train: Sherborne ¾ mile

Bus: First 57, 58 & 58A, South West Coaches 3, 7, 15, 36, 40, 40A, 42, 74 and Damory services 216, 330 & 368

Tel: 01935 812730

⚑ ♨ ⚐ ⚑ P ⚑ ⚑ ⚑ ⚠ OVP

Refreshments available.
Secure cycle parking available.
National network route 26.

MAP Page 313 (4H)
OS Map 183, 129: ST648168

St George's Church, Portland
Dorset – DT5 2JP

© CCT

This vast solitary church rises from a rocky peninsula. Inspired by St Paul's Cathedral, it is one of Dorset's most magnificent 18th-century buildings. The interior is fabulously preserved, and the headstones in the sprawling churchyard are a treasure trove of tales of murder, piracy and adventure.

Owned and managed by The Churches Conservation Trust.

St George's Church, Portland

OPENING TIMES

May-Sept	2.30pm-5pm

At other times keyholder nearby

HOW TO FIND US

Train: Nearest ⇌ Weymouth 4½ miles

Bus: Route 1

5 mins from Portland Castle

MAP Page 313 (6H)
OS Map 194, OL15: SY686720

Whitcombe Church, Whitcombe
Dorset – DT2 8NY

© CCT

The setting of this medieval church evokes the rustic atmosphere of old Dorset life. Its great treasures are the stunning medieval wall paintings inside. However, the church still holds on to its final secret – its name – the dedication is lost in time.

Owned and managed by The Churches Conservation Trust.

OPENING TIMES

Open daily during daylight hours

HOW TO FIND US

Train: Nearest ⇌ Dorchester West 2 miles

Bus: Route 101

10 mins from Maiden Castle

MAP Page 313 (5H)
OS Map 194, OL15: SY716884

Portland Castle Dorset – DT5 1AZ

NON-MEMBERS

Adult	£4.70
Concession	£4.20
Child	£2.80
Family	£12.20

OPENING TIMES

1 Apr-30 Jun, daily	10am-5pm
1-22 Jul, daily	10am-6pm
23 Jul-12 Aug Please see the website for up-to-date opening times	
13-31 Aug, daily	10am-6pm
1-30 Sep, daily	10am-5pm
1 Oct-4 Nov, daily	10am-4pm
5 Nov-28 Mar	Closed

Parts of the castle may be unavailable for short periods during private events

HOW TO FIND US

Direction: Overlooking Portland Harbour in Castletown, Isle of Portland

Train: Weymouth 4½ miles

Bus: First summer service 501 serves the castle direct. At other times South West Coaches service 210 & First service 1 pass close by

Ferry: From Weymouth Harbour, Good Fri-end Oct (weather permitting). Call the castle for details

Tel: 01305 820539

Disabled access – Captain's House, ground floor of castle and Governor's Garden. Disabled toilet.

Captain's House Tearoom, 11am-4pm, variable closing in Oct.

Audio tours available.

MAP Page 313 (6H)
OS Map 194, OL15: SY685744

The history of this fort, which overlooks Portland harbour, is diverse and fascinating. Built by Henry VIII to defend the anchorage against possible French and Spanish invasion, its squat appearance is typical of the artillery forts built in the early 1540s.

Unusually for a fort of this period, the castle has seen much interior alteration, though the exterior remains largely unchanged. It first witnessed serious fighting during the Civil War, when it was seized by Parliamentarians and Royalists.

It became a Seaplane Station during World War I, and was in the forefront of the D-Day preparations which helped to end World War II.

The Governor's Garden, designed by Christopher Bradley-Hole as part of the Contemporary Heritage Garden series, contains an impressive circular amphitheatre made from local Portland stone, with two-level seating for about 200 people. This perfectly sheltered spot is a great place to enjoy the dramatic sea and harbour views.

www.english-heritage.org.uk/portland

Enjoy a refreshing sea journey to Portland Castle from Weymouth aboard *My Girl*, a World War II veteran boat. 10% discount for EH members – valid 6 Apr to 31 Oct 2012. Tel 01305 785000 or visit whitemotorboat.freeuk.com

☐ Available for corporate and private hire

◢ Licensed for civil wedding ceremonies

NEW FOR 2012

Explore the long and fascinating history of the castle, as many characters and stories from the past are brought to life with new presentations and hands-on exhibits.

Winterbourne Poor Lot Barrows
Dorset

A 'cemetery' of 44 Bronze Age burial mounds of varying types and sizes, straddling the A35 main road.

OPENING TIMES
Any reasonable time

HOW TO FIND US

Direction: 2 miles W of Winterbourne Abbas, S of junction of A35 with a minor road to Compton Valence. Access via Wellbottom Lodge – 180 metres (200 yards) E along A35 from junction

Train: Dorchester West or South, both 7 miles

Bus: First 31 Weymouth – Axminster (passes ⟦train⟧ Dorchester South)

⟦symbols⟧
No adjacent parking. Warning: cross road with care.

MAP Page 313 (5H)
OS Map 194, OL15/117: SY590907

GLOUCESTERSHIRE

Belas Knap Long Barrow
Gloucestershire

A particularly fine example of a Neolithic long barrow of c. 3800 BC, featuring a false entrance and side chambers. Excavated in 1863 and 1865, when the remains of at least 38 people were found in the chambers. The barrow has since been restored. Managed by Gloucestershire County Council.

OPENING TIMES
Any reasonable time

HOW TO FIND US

Direction: Near Charlton Abbots; ½ mile on Cotswold Way

Train: Cheltenham 9 miles

Bus: Mikes Travel (Wed and Sat only), Villager Community Bus service V10 (Wed only) stops within ½ mile of the site. Otherwise Castleways service 606 & 656 to within 1¾ miles or Castleways 559 to Winchcombe village then walk

MAP Page 313 (1J)
OS Map 163, OL45: SP021254

Blackfriars, Gloucester:
see Gloucester, Blackfriars – See right

Cirencester Amphitheatre
Gloucestershire

The earthwork remains of one of the largest Roman amphitheatres in Britain, built in the early 2nd century. It served the Roman city of Corinium (now Cirencester), then second only in size and importance to London, and had a capacity of around 8000 spectators. Later fortified against Saxon invaders.

Cirencester Amphitheatre

OPENING TIMES
Any reasonable time

HOW TO FIND US

Direction: Located W of Cirencester, next to the bypass. Access from the town, or along Chesterton Lane from the W end of the bypass, on to Cotswold Ave

Train: Kemble 4 miles

Bus: Pulham's 855 (Fosse Link); Stagecoach 59; Stagecoach 51; 51A (Sun only)

MAP Page 313 (2J)
OS Map 163, OL45/169: SP020014

Gloucester, Blackfriars
Gloucestershire

One of the most-complete surviving friaries of Dominican 'black friars' in England, later converted into a Tudor house and cloth factory. Notable features include the church and the fine scissor-braced dormitory roof, as well as the earliest surviving purpose-built library in England, in the south range.

OPENING TIMES
For opening times and prices please check the website for more details www.english-heritage.org.uk/blackfriars

HOW TO FIND US

Direction: In Blackfriars Lane, off Ladybellegate St, off Southgate St, Gloucester

Train: Gloucester ½ mile

Bus: Short walk from Gloucester Bus Station

⟦symbols⟧
Parking (adjacent. Charge applies, not managed by EH).

MAP Page 313 (2J)
OS Map 162, 179: SO829184

Gloucester, Greyfriars
Gloucestershire

Substantial remains of an early Tudor friary church of Franciscan 'grey friars'.

OPENING TIMES
Any reasonable time

HOW TO FIND US
Direction: On Greyfriars Walk

Train: Gloucester ½ mile

Bus: Gloucester Bus Station ½ mile

MAP Page 313 (2J)
OS Map 162, 179: SO832184

Great Witcombe Roman Villa
Gloucestershire

The remains of a large and luxurious villa built c. AD 250, with a bathhouse complex and possibly the shrine of a water spirit.

OPENING TIMES
Exterior: Reasonable daylight hours

HOW TO FIND US
Direction: Located 5 miles SE of Gloucester off A46; ½ mile S of reservoir in Witcombe Park; 400 metres (440 yards) from Cotswold Way National Trail

Train: Gloucester 6 miles

Bus: Stagecoach service 46 to Green Street then 1 mile walk, or Stagecoach 10 to Brockworth and 2 mile walk. Also infrequent Swanbrook service 852 serves Witcombe

Parking (no access for coaches. No parking permitted in the lane to or beyond the car park).

MAP Page 313 (2J)
OS Map 163, 179: SO899142

Don't forget your membership card

Hailes Abbey
Gloucestershire – GL54 5PB

The Cistercian abbey of Hailes was founded in 1246 by Richard of Cornwall, King Henry III's brother, in thanksgiving for deliverance from shipwreck, and dissolved on Christmas Eve 1539. Though never housing large numbers of monks, it had extensive and elaborate buildings, financed by pilgrims visiting its renowned relic, 'the Holy Blood of Hailes' – allegedly a phial of Christ's own blood.

Eleven interpretation panels guide you around the abbey buildings, and an audio tour brings the site to life. Sculptures, stonework and other site finds are displayed in the museum. The adjacent parish church displays notable medieval wall-paintings. Hot drinks and snacks available in the shop.

www.english-heritage.org.uk/hailes

Owned by the National Trust, managed and maintained by English Heritage.

NON-MEMBERS

Adult	£4.30
Concession	£3.90
Child	£2.60

National Trust members free, but charged for audio tour (£1) and special events

Hailes Abbey

OPENING TIMES

1 Apr-30 Jun, daily	10am-5pm
1 Jul-31 Aug, daily	10am-6pm
1-30 Sep, daily	10am-5pm
1 Oct-4 Nov, daily	10am-4pm
5 Nov-31 Mar	Closed

HOW TO FIND US
Direction: 2 miles NE of Winchcombe off B4632. On the Cotswold Way National Trail

Train: Cheltenham 10 miles

Bus: Castleways service 606 from Cheltenham to within 1 mile

Tel: 01242 602398

Disabled access (ramp to museum, disabled toilet).

Refreshments available.

MAP Page 313 (1J)
OS Map 150/163, OL45: SP050300

Kingswood Abbey Gatehouse
Gloucestershire

This 16th-century gatehouse, one of the latest monastic buildings in England, displays a richly sculpted mullioned window. It is the sole survivor of this Cistercian abbey.

OPENING TIMES
Exterior: open any reasonable time

Interior: key available from 3 Wotton Road, Abbey St 10am-3.30pm weekdays only

HOW TO FIND US
Direction: In Kingswood, off B4060; 1 mile SW of Wotton-under-Edge

Train: Yate 8 miles

Bus: First 311 or Wessex Connect 84

Public toilets near to monument.

MAP Page 313 (2H)
OS Map 162/172, 167: ST747920

Notgrove Long Barrow
Gloucestershire

A grassed-over Neolithic long barrow containing stone-lined burial chambers, on the crest of a high Cotswold ridge.

Managed by Gloucestershire County Council.

OPENING TIMES
Any reasonable time

HOW TO FIND US
Direction: Located 1½ miles NW of Notgrove, on A436

Bus: Pulham's 801 Moreton-in-Marsh – Cheltenham (passes close to ⊞ Moreton-in-Marsh)

MAP Page 313 (1J)
OS Map 163, OL45: SP096212

Nympsfield Long Barrow
Gloucestershire

A large Neolithic burial mound with spectacular vistas over the Severn Valley. Its internal burial chambers are uncovered for viewing.

Managed by Gloucestershire County Council.

OPENING TIMES
Any reasonable time

HOW TO FIND US
Direction: Located 1 mile NW of Nympsfield on B4066

Train: Stroud 5 miles

Bus: Cotswold Green 35 (weekdays). Stagecoach 264 (Tue & Fri) to ¾ mile from the site

MAP Page 313 (2H)
OS Map 162, 167/168: SO794013

Odda's Chapel
Gloucestershire

One of the most complete surviving Saxon churches in England, this chapel was built in 1056 by Earl Odda, and rediscovered in 1865 subsumed into a farmhouse. Nearby is the equally famous Saxon parish church.

OPENING TIMES
1 Apr–4 Nov, daily	10am-6pm
5 Nov–28 Mar, daily	10am-4pm
24-26 Dec and 1 Jan	Closed

HOW TO FIND US
Direction: Located in Deerhurst off B4213, at Abbots Court; SW of parish church

Train: Cheltenham 8 miles

Bus: Service 652 (Thu only) passes the site; Veolia (Astons) 351, then 1½ mile walk from Apperley

Parking (not EH, charges apply).

MAP Page 313 (1J)
OS Map 150, 179: SO869298

Offa's Dyke
Gloucestershire

A three-mile section of the great earthwork boundary dyke built along the Anglo-Welsh border by Offa, King of Mercia, probably during the 780s. This especially impressive wooded stretch includes the Devil's Pulpit, with fine views of Tintern Abbey.

OPENING TIMES
Any reasonable time

HOW TO FIND US
Direction: Located 3 miles NE of Chepstow, off B4228. Via Forest Enterprise Tidenham car park, 1 mile walk (waymarked) down to The Devil's Pulpit on Offa's Dyke (access is suitable only for those wearing proper walking shoes and is not suitable for the very young, old or infirm)

Train: Chepstow 7 miles

Bus: Chepstow Classic Bus service 69 to Tintern then 1 mile walk

Offa's Dyke

MAP Page 313 (2H)
OS Map 162, OL14/167
SO546011-ST549975

Over Bridge
Gloucestershire

A single-arch stone bridge spanning the River Severn, built in 1825-30 by the great engineer Thomas Telford.

OPENING TIMES
Any reasonable time

HOW TO FIND US
Direction: 1 mile NW of Gloucester, at junction of A40 (Ross) and A417 (Ledbury)

Train: Gloucester 2 miles

Bus: Stagecoach 24, 24A, 30, 31, 32, 33, 73, 132; Veolia Astons 351

Parking (in lay-by).

MAP Page 313 (1H)
OS Map 162, 179: SO816196

St Briavels Castle
Gloucestershire

The fine twin-towered gatehouse of this castle, built by Edward I in 1292, once defended a crossbow bolt factory which used local Forest of Dean iron. Once a prison, it is now a youth hostel in wonderful walking country.

OPENING TIMES
Exterior: Any reasonable time
Bailey
1 Apr–30 Sep, daily   1pm-4pm

HOW TO FIND US
Direction: In St Briavels; 7 miles NE of Chepstow off B4228

Train: Chepstow 8 miles

Bus: KWT Coaches 705, Chepstow Classic Bus 707, 708 and Geoff Willetts Coaches 787

Tel: 01594 530272

MAP Page 313 (2H)
OS Map 162, OL14: SO559042

St Mary's Church, Kempley
Gloucestershire

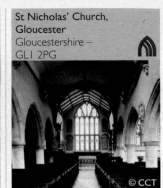

A delightful Norman church, displaying one of the most outstandingly complete and well-preserved sets of medieval wall-paintings in England, dating from the 12th–15th centuries.

Managed by the Friends of Kempley Church.

OPENING TIMES
1 Mar-4 Nov, daily   10am-6pm

Please call for an appointment in winter

All group visits must be pre-booked, please visit the website for details

HOW TO FIND US
Direction: 1 mile N of Kempley off B4024; 6 miles NE of Ross-on-Wye

Train: Ledbury 8 miles

Bus: George Youngs Coaches 677 (Tue & Fri)

Tel: 01531 660214

MAP Page 313 (1H)
OS Map 149, 189: SO670313

St Nicholas' Church, Gloucester
Gloucestershire – GL1 2PG

© CCT

This church beside Gloucester's (now vanished) west gate is known for its leaning, truncated white stone spire (damaged during the Siege of Gloucester in 1643). Formerly one of Gloucester's most prosperous parish churches, it was built for merchant traders, many of whom have memorials within.

Owned and managed by The Churches Conservation Trust.

OPENING TIMES
Tue-Sat   10am-5pm

Keys from Gloucester Folk Museum, opposite church on Westgate

HOW TO FIND US
Train: Nearest ⊠ Gloucester ½ mile

Bus: Route 351

5 mins walk from Greyfriars and Blackfriars; 10 mins walk from Over Bridge

MAP Page 313 (1H)
OS Map 162, 179: SO829188

Uley Long Barrow (Hetty Pegler's Tump)
Gloucestershire

A partly reconstructed Neolithic chambered mound, 37 metres (120 ft) long, atmospherically sited overlooking the Severn Valley. 'Hetty Pegler' was its 17th-century landowner.

Managed by Gloucestershire County Council.

OPENING TIMES
Exterior viewing only

HOW TO FIND US
Direction: Located 3½ miles NE of Dursley, on B4066

Train: Stroud 6 miles

Bus: Stagecoach in the Cotswolds 20 Stroud – Uley (passes close to ⊠ Stroud); Cotswold Green 281 (Mon & Wed) from Dursley. All to within 1 mile

MAP Page 313 (2H)
OS Map 162, 167/168: SO790000

Windmill Tump Long Barrow, Rodmarton
Gloucestershire

A Neolithic chambered tomb with an enigmatic 'false entrance'. Managed by Gloucestershire County Council.

OPENING TIMES
Any reasonable time

HOW TO FIND US
Direction: 1 mile SW of Rodmarton

Train: Kemble 5 miles

Bus: Stagecoach in the Cotswolds 881 from ⊠ Kemble

Map Page 313 (2J)
OS Map 163, 168: ST933973

Members' events

Check our website for details of our programme of members' events throughout the year, designed and available exclusively for members.

www.english-heritage.org.uk/events

All Saints' Church, Langport
Somerset – TA10 9QF

© CCT

All Saints' stands on a hill, overlooking the remains of a Benedictine abbey. Its bold pinnacled tower, bedecked with gargoyles known locally as 'Hunky Punks', is a local landmark. However, the church's special treasure is the largest collection of medieval stained glass in Somerset.

Owned and managed by The Churches Conservation Trust.

OPENING TIMES
Keyholder nearby

HOW TO FIND US
Train: Nearest 🚉 Bridgwater 9½ miles

Bus: Route 16

3 mins from Muchelney Abbey

MAP Page 313 (4G)
OS Map 193, 129: ST423267

Butter Cross, Dunster:
see Dunster, Butter Cross
– Page 120

Cleeve Abbey   Somerset – TA23 0PS

The picturesque Cistercian abbey of Cleeve boasts the most impressively complete and unaltered set of monastic cloister buildings in England. Standing roofed and two storeys high, they include the gatehouse; the 15th-century refectory with its glorious angel roof; an unusual 'painted chamber'; and the floor of an earlier refectory, decked from end to end with 13th-century heraldic tiles, the protection of which was the subject of a recent high profile English Heritage research project. The great dormitory is one of the finest examples in the country. Beneath it are the newly-vaulted warming room, and the sacristy with more early 13th-century tilework and decoration.

An exhibition and virtual tour tell the story of abbey life, and a story bag, *Brother Cedric and the Missing Sheep*, is a fun way for families to explore the abbey together.

www.english-heritage.org.uk/cleeve

NON-MEMBERS
Adult	£4.30
Concession	£3.90
Child	£2.60

OPENING TIMES
1 Apr-31 Aug – Please check website for details or contact Customer Services 0870 333 1181	
1-30 Sep, daily	10am-5pm
1 Oct-4 Nov, daily	10am-4pm
5 Nov-28 Mar	Closed

HOW TO FIND US
Direction: Located in Washford, ¼ mile S of A39

Train: Washford ½ mile (West Somerset Railway)

Bus: First 28 & Webber 18

Tel: 01984 640377

🍴▣♿♿♿📷P🚐🔒♿⚠
OVP

Disabled access (grounds and ground floor only, plus toilet).

Dogs on leads (in grounds only).

Refreshments available.

MAP Page 313 (4F)
OS Map 181, OL9: ST047407

Church of St Mary the Virgin, Stocklinch Ottersey
Somerset – TA19 9JN

© CCT

This hillside landmark, made of golden Ham stone, is an atmospheric gem. St Mary's is linked to its sister church, St Mary Magdalene, by an old legend of two sisters who both fell in love with a vicar, each building a church for him.

Owned and managed by The Churches Conservation Trust.

OPENING TIMES
Open daily during daylight hours

HOW TO FIND US
Train: Nearest ⊠ Crewkerne 6½ miles

Bus: No bus nearby

20 mins from Muchelney Abbey

MAP Page 313 (4G)
OS Map 193, 128: ST388172

Dunster, Butter Cross
Somerset

The transplanted stump of a medieval stone cross, once a meeting-place for butter-sellers.

Managed by the National Trust.

OPENING TIMES
Any reasonable time

HOW TO FIND US
Direction: Beside minor road to Alcombe, 350 metres (400 yards) NW of Dunster parish church

Train: Dunster (West Somerset Railway) 1 mile

Bus: Beacon Bus service 398 and WebberBus service 107 & 564 (both Mon, Wed & Fri only). Also Quantock Motor Services summer service 400. First service 28 and WebberBus services 18 & 106 serve Dunster Steep from whence it is about a ½ mile walk

Dunster, Butter Cross

🐕

MAP Page 313 (4F)
OS Map 181, OL9: ST823604

Dunster, Gallox Bridge
Somerset

This ancient stone bridge – originally 'gallows bridge'– once carried packhorses bringing fleeces to Dunster market.

Managed by the National Trust.

OPENING TIMES
Any reasonable time

HOW TO FIND US
Direction: Located off A396 at the S end of Dunster village

Train: Dunster ¾ mile (West Somerset Railway)

Bus: Beacon Bus service 398 and WebberBus service 107 & 564 (both Mon/Wed/Fri). Also Quantock Motor Services summer service 400. First service 28 and WebberBus services 18 & 106 serve Dunster Steep from whence it is about a ½ mile

🐕 ♿

MAP Page 313 (4F)
OS Map 181, OL9: SS989432

Dunster, Yarn Market
Somerset

This fine 17th-century timber-framed octagonal market hall is a monument to Dunster's once-flourishing cloth trade.

Managed by the National Trust.

OPENING TIMES
Any reasonable time

HOW TO FIND US
Direction: In Dunster High St

Train: Dunster (West Somerset Railway) ½ mile

Bus: Beacon Bus service 398 and WebberBus service 107 & 564 (both Mon, Wed & Fri only). Also Quantock Motor Services summer service 400. First service 28 and

Dunster, Yarn Market

WebberBus services 18 & 106 serve Dunster Steep from whence it is about a ½ mile walk

🐕 ♿

MAP Page 313 (4F)
OS Map 181, OL9: SS992438

Farleigh Hungerford Castle
See feature opposite

Gallox Bridge, Dunster:
see Dunster, Gallox Bridge – See left

Glastonbury Tribunal
Somerset – BA6 9DP

A fine, late-15th-century stone town house, with an early Tudor façade and panelled interiors. Now contains a Tourist Information Centre and the Glastonbury Lake Village Museum.

Managed by Glastonbury Tribunal Ltd.

NON-MEMBERS
Museum:

Adult	£2.50
Concession	£2.00
Child	£1.00

OPENING TIMES

Mon-Sat (last entry 3.30pm)	10am-4pm
Sun	Closed
25-26 Dec and 1 Jan	Closed

Opening hours may be varied during winter season

HOW TO FIND US
Direction: In Glastonbury High St

Bus: Bakers-Dolphin service 668 passes site.
First 29, 375, 376 & 377 and Frome Minibuses pass within ½ mile

Tel: 01458 832954

🏛 🅿 ♿

Disabled access (ground floor – 2 steps).

Parking (charged).

MAP Page 313 (4H)
OS Map 182/183, 141: ST499389

Farleigh Hungerford Castle

Somerset – BA2 7RS

Farleigh Hungerford was begun in the 1370s by Sir Thomas Hungerford, Speaker of the Commons, and extended in the 15th century by his son Walter, Lord Hungerford, distinguished soldier and statesman. The remains of their fortified mansion include two tall corner towers and a complete castle chapel, crowded with family monuments and bedecked with wall-paintings. In the chapel's crypt the coffins of many Hungerfords are still visible, several with attached 'death masks'.

The colourful Hungerford family included two members executed during the Wars of the Roses and another – who imprisoned his wife here for four years – beheaded by Henry VIII. A Tudor Lady Hungerford burnt her murdered husband's body in the castle's oven.

The story of Farleigh and its owners is told in extensive displays in the Priest's House and through an audio tour. There is a touch-screen virtual tour for disabled visitors and family and educational facilities including a 'book box', schools base and historic costumes.

www.english-heritage.org.uk/ farleigh

NON-MEMBERS

Adult	£4.00
Concession	£3.60
Child	£2.40

OPENING TIMES

1 Apr-30 Jun, daily	10am-5pm
1 Jul-31 Aug, daily	10am-6pm
1-30 Sep, daily	10am-5pm
1 Oct-4 Nov, daily	10am-4pm
5 Nov-28 Mar, Sat-Sun	10am-4pm
24-26 Dec and 1 Jan	Closed

HOW TO FIND US

Direction: In Farleigh Hungerford, 9 miles SE of Bath; 3½ miles W of Trowbridge on A366

Train: Avoncliffe 2 miles; Trowbridge 3½ miles

Bus: Libra 96 from Trowbridge (pass close to ⚑ Trowbridge) to within 1½ miles

Tel: 01225 754026

⊘ ■ ⚒ ⌂ ⟟ ⟟ ✕ P ⧉ ⌕ ♿
⚠ OVP

Disabled access (Chapel and Priest's House, ground floor only. Disabled toilet).
Refreshments available.

MAP Page 313 (3H)
OS Map 173, 143/156: ST801576

Meare Fish House
Somerset

The only surviving building of comparable purpose in England, this housed Glastonbury Abbey's official in charge of the (then) adjacent lake fishery. Its design, miniaturising the components of larger medieval houses, is also unique.

OPENING TIMES

Any reasonable time. Key available from Manor House farm

HOW TO FIND US

Direction: In Meare village, on B3151

Bus: Bakers-Dolphin service 668 Cheddar – Street

✕

MAP Page 313 (4G)
OS Map 182, 141: ST458417

Muchelney Abbey
Somerset – TA10 0DQ

This atmospheric and once-remote 'great island' amid the Somerset Levels has many rewards for visitors. Beside the clearly laid out foundations of the wealthy medieval Benedictine abbey (and its Anglo-Saxon predecessor) stands a complete early Tudor house in miniature. Originally the abbots' lodgings, this charming building includes a magnificent great chamber with ornate fireplace, carved settle and stained glass; two rooms with time-faded walls painted to resemble cloth hangings; and a

Muchelney Abbey

pair of kitchens with fine timber roof. Parts of the richly decorated cloister walk and refectory are incorporated, and nearby is the thatched two-storey monks' lavatory, unique in Britain.

Exhibitions illustrate monastic life with a fascinating collection of site finds, including decorated tiles and stonework. Much improved facilities for disabled visitors include a touch-screen tour. A 'story bag' is a fun way for families to explore the abbey together.

www.english-heritage.org.uk/muchelney

The adjacent parish church and medieval Priest's House are not managed by English Heritage.

NON-MEMBERS

Adult	£4.30
Concession	£3.90
Child	£2.60

OPENING TIMES

1 Apr–30 Jun, daily	10am–5pm
1 Jul–31 Aug, daily	10am–6pm
1–30 Sep, daily	10am–5pm
1 Oct–4 Nov, daily	10am–4pm
5 Nov–28 Mar	Closed

HOW TO FIND US

Direction: In Muchelney, 2 miles S of Langport via Huish Episcopi

Bus: South West Coaches 10 (Wed only); Somerset County 850 (Thu only); First 54 then 1 mile walk from Huish Episcopi

Tel: 01458 250664

Dogs on leads (in grounds only).

Disabled access (grounds and most of ground floor, adapted toilet).

Light refreshments available.

MAP Page 313 (4G)
OS Map 193, 129: ST429249

Nunney Castle
Somerset

The striking and picturesque moated castle of Nunney was built in the 1370s by Sir John de la Mere, a local knight who was beginning to enjoy royal favour. Extensively modernised in the late 16th century, the castle was held for the King during the Civil War, but quickly fell to Parliamentarian cannon in 1645: not until Christmas Day 1910, however, did the gun-damaged portion of the wall finally collapse.

OPENING TIMES

Any reasonable time

HOW TO FIND US

Direction: Located in Nunney, 3½ miles SW of Frome, off A361 (no coach access)

Train: Frome 3½ miles

Bus: First 161 Frome – Wells

Parking by nearby church (not EH).

Disabled access (exterior only).

MAP Page 313 (3H)
OS Map 183, 142: ST737457

St Martin of Tours, Elworthy
Somerset – TA4 3PY

© Robert Cutts

Tucked into the hillside above the road, this church has a distinctive battlemented tower with an unusual outside stairway. Inside, there is charming stained glass, and medieval and Jacobean woodwork, including a carved screen across the chancel arch.

Owned and managed by The Churches Conservation Trust.

OPENING TIMES

Open daily during daylight hours

HOW TO FIND US

Train: Nearest ⬆ Taunton 10¾ miles

Bus: No bus nearby

10 mins from Cleeve Abbey

MAP Page 313 (4F)
OS Map 181, OL09: ST082352

Yarn Market, Dunster: see Dunster, Yarn Market – Page 120

Free App

Plan your day out or find events at our properties. Use the 'Near Me' feature to find properties nearby, view opening times, directions and even search for properties by type. See page 21 for details or go to www.english-heritage.org.uk/daysout/app

Bradford-on-Avon Tithe Barn
Wiltshire

A spectacular 14th-century monastic stone barn, 51 metres (168 ft) long, with a sophisticated timber-cruck roof.

OPENING TIMES
Daily	10.30am-4pm
25 Dec	Closed

HOW TO FIND US
Direction: Located ½ mile S of town centre off B3109

Train: Bradford-on-Avon ¼ mile

Bus: Libra Travel service 96, Frome Minibuses service 98 & X96 to Frome Road canal bridge and then short walk. First 264 & 265

Parking (adjacent, not managed by EH – charge applies).

MAP Page 313 (3H)
OS Map 173, 156: ST823604

Bratton Camp and White Horse
Wiltshire

Below an Iron Age hillfort, enclosing a much earlier long barrow, stands the Westbury White Horse. Cut into the hillside in 1778, this replaced a slightly older horse, commemorating King Alfred's legendary victory over the Danes nearby.

OPENING TIMES
Any reasonable time

Bratton Camp and White Horse

HOW TO FIND US
Direction: 2 miles E of Westbury off B3098, 1 mile SW of Bratton

Train: Westbury 3 miles

Bus: Faresaver 87 Trowbridge-Devizes (passes ⮂ Westbury)

MAP Page 313 (3J)
OS Map 184, 143: ST900516

Chisbury Chapel
Wiltshire

A pretty thatched and flint-walled 13th-century chapel, later used as a barn.

OPENING TIMES
Any reasonable time

HOW TO FIND US
Direction: Off unclassified road, ¼ mile E of Chisbury, off A4; 6 miles E of Marlborough

Train: Bedwyn 1 mile

Bus: Wiltshire Bus services 20 & 22 to Chisbury turn then ½ mile walk

MAP Page 313 (3K)
OS Map 174, 157: SU280660

Hatfield Earthwork (Marden Henge)
Wiltshire

The earthworks of a Neolithic henge and monumental mound, by a loop in the River Avon.

OPENING TIMES
Any reasonable time

HOW TO FIND US
Direction: 5½ miles SE of Devizes, off A342; NE of village of Marden

Train: Pewsey 5 miles

Bus: Tourist Coaches 210 (Thu & Sat), 249; Wiltshire Connect 2 bookable bus L1. Ring 08456 525 255

MAP Page 313 (3J)
OS Map 173, 130: SU092583

Ludgershall Castle and Cross
Wiltshire

The ruins and earthworks of a royal castle dating mainly from the 12th and 13th centuries, frequently used as a hunting lodge. The remains of the medieval cross stand in the centre of the village.

OPENING TIMES
Any reasonable time

HOW TO FIND US
Direction: Located on the N side of Ludgershall, off A342

Train: Andover 7 miles

Bus: Stagecoach 8, 80

Disabled access (part of site only and village cross).
Parking (limited).

MAP Page 313 (3K)
OS Map 184/185, 131: SU264512

Netheravon Dovecote
Wiltshire

A charming 18th-century brick dovecote, still with most of its 700 or more nesting boxes.

OPENING TIMES
Exterior viewing only from nearby roadside, as there is no access to the field in which dovecote is situated.

HOW TO FIND US
Direction: In Netheravon, 4½ miles N of Amesbury on A345

Train: Pewsey 9 miles, Grateley 11 miles

Bus: Wilts & Dorset X5 Salisbury – Swindon (passes close to ⮂ Salisbury and Swindon)

MAP Page 313 (3J)
OS Map 184, 130: SU147484

Old Sarum Wiltshire – SP1 3SD

The great earthwork of Old Sarum stands near Salisbury on the edge of Wiltshire's chalk plains. Its mighty ramparts were raised in about 500 BC by Iron Age peoples, and later occupied by the Romans, the Saxons and, most importantly, the Normans.

William the Conqueror paid off his army here in 1070, and in 1086 summoned all the great landowners of England here to swear an oath of loyalty. A Norman castle was built on the inner mound, and joined soon afterwards by a royal palace. By the middle of the 12th century a new town occupied much of the great earthwork, complete with a noble new Norman cathedral, the mother church of a huge diocese.

But Norman Sarum was not destined to thrive. Soldiers and priests quarrelled and life on the almost waterless hilltop became intolerable. The solution was a move downhill to the new settlement now known as Salisbury, where a new cathedral was founded in 1220. Thereafter

Old Sarum went into steep decline. Its cathedral was demolished and its castle was eventually abandoned. But the largely uninhabited site continued to 'elect' two MPs, becoming the most notorious of the 'Rotten Boroughs' swept away by the 1832 Reform Act.

Today, the remains of the prehistoric fortress and of the Norman palace, castle and cathedral evoke memories of thousands of years of history, which are interpreted by graphic panels throughout the site.

Visit the website for details of special events.

www.english-heritage.org.uk/oldsarum

NON-MEMBERS

Adult	£3.80
Concession	£3.40
Child	£2.30

OPENING TIMES

1 Apr-30 Jun, daily	10am-5pm
1 Jul-31 Aug, daily	9am-6pm
1-30 Sep, daily	10am-5pm
1 Oct-4 Nov, daily	10am-4pm
5 Nov-31 Jan, daily	11am-3pm
1-28 Feb, daily	11am-4pm
1-28 Mar, daily	10am-4pm
24-26 Dec and 1 Jan	Closed

HOW TO FIND US

Direction: 2 miles N of Salisbury, off A345

Train: Salisbury 2 miles

Bus: Wilts & Dorset service X5, 8, 69, 69A and Stonehenge Tour service See www.thestonehengetour.info

Tel: 01722 335398

Local Tourist Information Salisbury: 01722 334956

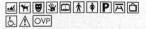

Disabled access (outer bailey and grounds only, disabled toilet).

Refreshments available.

MAP Page 313 (4J)
OS Map 184, 130: SU138327

Old Wardour Castle Wiltshire – SP3 6RR

Beautifully sited beside a lake, Old Wardour Castle was built in the late 14th century by John Lord Lovel as a lightly fortified but showy and luxurious residence. A hexagonal tower house ranged round a central courtyard, its form is very unusual in England.

Substantially updated by the staunchly Roman Catholic Arundell family after c. 1570, the castle saw much fighting

during the Civil War. In 1643 the 60-year-old Lady Arundell was forced to surrender it to Parliament. But the new garrison was almost immediately besieged in turn by Royalist forces led by her son. After an eventful 10 months of bombardment and undermining, they finally capitulated in March 1644.

The badly damaged castle became a romantic ruin, and was incorporated in the 18th century into the landscaped grounds of Lord Arundell's New Wardour House (not managed by English Heritage, no public access). The castle's setting in a Registered Landscape enhances the significance of this hidden jewel.

Visit the website for details of special events.

www.english-heritage.org.uk/oldwardour

🔆 Licensed for civil wedding ceremonies

NON-MEMBERS

Adult	£4.00
Concession	£3.60
Child	£2.40

OPENING TIMES

1 Apr-30 Jun, daily	10am-5pm
1 Jul-31 Aug, daily	10am-6pm
1-30 Sep, daily	10am-5pm
1 Oct-4 Nov, daily	10am-4pm
5 Nov-28 Mar, Sat-Sun	10am-4pm
24-26 Dec and 1 Jan	Closed

HOW TO FIND US

Direction: Located off A30 2 miles SW of Tisbury. Also accessible from A350 (narrow rural roads), coaches approach with care

Train: Tisbury 2½ miles

Bus: Wilts & Dorset service 26 Salisbury – Shaftesbury (passes 🚉 Tisbury).

Tel: 01747 870487

Disabled access (grounds and ground floor only), disabled toilet.

Refreshments available.

MAP Page 313 (4J)
OS Map 184, 118: ST939263

Old Church St Mary's, Wilton
Wiltshire – SP2 0HQ

© Fergus McNeill

This 'old' church was partially demolished, leaving the surviving building standing surrounded by the romantic ruins of its arcades and tower arch. Apart from the charming 18th-century ceiling, there are some fascinating memorials to the people of Wilton inside.

Owned and managed by The Churches Conservation Trust.

OPENING TIMES
Keyholder nearby

HOW TO FIND US
Train: Nearest ≋ Salisbury 2½ miles

Bus: Regular buses from Salisbury, route 13/25/27/84/R3

10 mins from Old Sarum, 20 mins from Stonehenge

MAP Page 313 (4J)
OS Map 184, 130: SU097313

Old Sarum
See feature – page 124

Old Wardour Castle
See feature – page 125

The Sanctuary: see Avebury
– Page 128

Silbury Hill: see Avebury
– Page 128

St Andrew's Church, Rollestone
Wiltshire – SP3 4HG

© Cameron Newham

This tiny, charming church, overlooking the River Till, was built of flint and stone chequerwork and has two large Perpendicular windows. The church was owned by the religious crusading order of the Knights Hospitaller for 350 years, and still contains its original font.

Owned and managed by The Churches Conservation Trust.

OPENING TIMES
Open daily during daylight hours

HOW TO FIND US
Train: Nearest ≋ Salisbury 9 miles

Bus: Routes 2/4/U4

5 mins from Stonehenge

MAP Page 313 (4J)
OS Map 184, 130: SU073431

Stonehenge
See feature – Page 130

West Kennet Avenue:
see Avebury – Page 129

West Kennet Long Barrow:
see Avebury – Page 129

Windmill Hill: see Avebury,
– Page 129

Woodhenge
Wiltshire

Neolithic monument, dating from about 2500 BC, with concrete markers indicating the location of six concentric rings of timber posts. The timber structure is surrounded by a circular bank and ditch (henge) whose entrance is aligned north-east towards the summer solstice sunrise, like Stonehenge. A small central flint cairn marks the location of a child burial.

Part of the Stonehenge and Avebury World Heritage Site.

OPENING TIMES
Any reasonable time

Usual facilities may not be available around the summer solstice 20-22 June. Please call 0870 333 1181 before your visit

HOW TO FIND US
Direction: 1½ miles N of Amesbury, off A345, just S of Durrington

Train: Salisbury 9 miles

Bus: Wilts & Dorset services X5

MAP Page 313 (4J)
OS Map 184, 130: SU151434

Avebury Wiltshire

Avebury rivals – some would say exceeds – Stonehenge as the largest, most impressive and complex prehistoric site in Britain. The henge, built and altered over the centuries from about 2600 BC to 2400 BC, now appears as a huge circular bank and ditch, enclosing an area of approximately 25 acres (10 hectares), including part of Avebury village. Within this 'henge' ditch is an inner circle of great standing stones, enclosing two more stone circles, each with a central feature.

The site's present appearance owes much to the marmalade heir Alexander Keiller, who excavated and re-erected many stones during the 1930s, and whose archaeological collections are displayed in the nearby museum. Many stones had been broken or buried in medieval and later times, one crushing its destroyer as it fell.

Avebury is part of a wider complex of Neolithic and Bronze Age monuments, with many other ceremonial and ritual sites in English Heritage care. West Kennet Avenue joined it to the Sanctuary, and another stone avenue connected it with Beckhampton. West Kennet Long Barrow and Windmill Hill are also nearby, as is the huge and mysterious Silbury Hill. This extraordinary assemblage of sites seemingly formed a huge 'sacred landscape', whose use and purpose can still only be guessed at. Avebury and its surroundings have, with Stonehenge, achieved international recognition as a World Heritage Site.

Avebury Henge and Stone Circles are in the freehold ownership of the National Trust and in English Heritage guardianship. They are managed by the National Trust on behalf of English Heritage, and the two organisations share the cost of managing and maintaining the property.

127

OPENING TIMES

Any reasonable time

Usual facilities may not be available around the summer solstice 20-22 June. Please call 01672 539250 before you visit

HOW TO FIND US

See Alexander Keiller Museum

🚇 **P** ♿

Parking (see Alexander Keiller Museum).

MAP Page 313 (3J)
OS Map 173, 157: SU102700

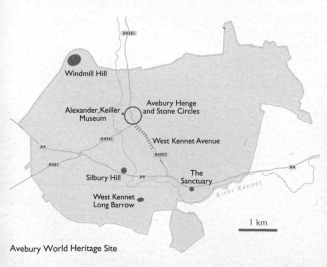

Avebury World Heritage Site

◎ Stonehenge and Avebury World Heritage Site

Avebury, Alexander Keiller Museum Wiltshire – SN8 1RF

One of the most important prehistoric archaeological collections in Britain, housed in the Stables Gallery, includes many artefacts from the World Heritage Site (WHS) monuments. The admission fee includes access to both the Stables and Barn Galleries. The Barn Gallery (belonging to the National Trust) tells the story of the WHS, its monuments, and the people associated with it.

The Museum, which sits within the Avebury WHS, is in the freehold ownership of the National Trust and in English Heritage guardianship on behalf of the Secretary of State for the DCMS; the museum collection is on loan from the DCMS.

NON-MEMBERS

Adult	£4.40
Child	£2.20
Family (2+2)	£12.20
Family (1+3)	£7.90

Reduced price when arriving by cycle or public transport

OPENING TIMES

1 Apr-31 Oct, daily	10am-6pm
1 Nov-28 Mar, daily	10am-4pm
24-26 Dec and 1 Jan	Closed

HOW TO FIND US

Direction: In Avebury, 7 miles W of Marlborough

Train: Pewsey 10 miles; Swindon 11 miles

Bus: Stagecoach in Swindon service 49. Connect2 line 43; Wilts & Dorset service 96

🅴♿♿✉🎣🅿♿

Parking (Visitor car park free to EH members. S of Avebury off A4361. Free disabled visitors' parking in village car park).

MAP Page 313 (3J)
OS Map 173, 157: SU099700

Avebury, The Sanctuary Wiltshire

Begun around 3000 BC, The Sanctuary was originally a complex circular arrangement of timber posts, with the later addition of stone settings. These components are now indicated by concrete slabs and posts. Its function remains a mystery: possibly it enshrined the dwelling place of some revered person, and certainly numbers of human bones were found here, accompanied by food remains suggesting elaborate death rites and ceremonies. Later, the West Kennet Avenue was constructed to connect it with newly-built Avebury, reinforcing the status of this enigmatic but clearly very important site.

The Sanctuary is in DCMS ownership and in English Heritage guardianship. It is managed by the National Trust on behalf of English Heritage, and the two organisations share the cost of managing and maintaining the property.

OPENING TIMES

Any reasonable time

Usual facilities may not be available around the summer solstice 20-22 June. Please call 01672 539250 before you visit

HOW TO FIND US

Train: Pewsey 9 miles, Bedwyn 12 miles

Bus: Wilts & Dorset service 96; A.D.Rains/Bodmans X76

🎣🅿

Parking (in lay-by).

MAP Page 313 (3J)
OS Map 173, 157: SU118680

Avebury, Silbury Hill Wiltshire

The largest man-made prehistoric mound in Europe, mysterious Silbury Hill compares in height and volume to the roughly contemporary Egyptian pyramids.

Built in about 100 years around 2400 BC, it apparently contains no burial. Though clearly important in itself, its purpose and significance remain unknown.

There is no access to the Hill itself. This is to prevent erosion of archaeological deposits and rare chalk grassland (the Hill is a Site of Special Scientific Interest).

Find out more about the recent conservation project (2000-2008) at **www.english-heritage. org.uk/silbury**

OPENING TIMES

Viewing area during reasonable daylight hours. Strictly no access to the hill itself

Usual facilities may not apply around the summer solstice 20-22 June. Please call 0870 333 1181 before you visit

HOW TO FIND US

Direction: 1 mile W of West Kennet on A4

Train: Pewsey 9 miles, Swindon 13 miles

Bus: Stagecoach in Swindon service 49; Wilts & Dorset service 96. Both pass within ¾ mile of the site. Also A.D.Rains/Bodmans X76

🎣🅿♿

Disabled access (viewing area).

MAP Page 313 (3J)
OS Map 173, 157: SU100685

Usual facilities may not be available around the summer solstice 20-22 June. Please call 01672 539250 before you visit.

Avebury, West Kennet Avenue
Wiltshire

Avebury, West Kennet Long Barrow
Wiltshire

Avebury, Windmill Hill
Wiltshire

129

An 'avenue', originally of around 100 pairs of prehistoric standing stones, raised to form a winding 1½ mile ritual link between the pre-existing monuments of Avebury and The Sanctuary.

West Kennet Avenue is in the freehold ownership of the National Trust and in English Heritage guardianship. It is managed by the National Trust on behalf of English Heritage, and the two organisations share the cost of managing and maintaining the property.

OPENING TIMES
Any reasonable time

HOW TO FIND US
Direction: Runs alongside B4003

Train: Pewsey 9 miles, Swindon 12 miles

Bus: Stagecoach in Swindon service 49, Wilts & Dorset services 96. Both pass within ¾ mile of the site. Also A.D.Rains/Bodmans X76

🐕 ♿ 🅿

Parking (in lay-by).

Disabled access (on roadway).

MAP Page 313 (3J)
OS Map 173, 157: SU105695

One of the largest, most impressive and most accessible Neolithic chambered tombs in Britain. Built around 3650 BC, it was used for a short time as a burial chamber, nearly 50 people being buried here before the chambers were blocked.

West Kennet Long Barrow is in private ownership and in English Heritage guardianship. It is managed by the National Trust on behalf of English Heritage, and the two organisations share the cost of managing and maintaining the property.

OPENING TIMES
Any reasonable time

HOW TO FIND US
Direction: ¾ mile SW of West Kennet, along footpath off A4

Train: Pewsey 9 miles, Swindon 13 miles

Bus: Stagecoach in Swindon service 49; Wilts & Dorset services 96. Both pass within ¾ mile of the site. Also A.D.Rains/Bodmans X76

🐕 🅿

Parking (in lay-by).

MAP Page 313 (3J)
OS Map 173, 157: SU105677

The classic Neolithic 'causewayed enclosure', built around 3675 BC, with three concentric but intermittent ditches covering an area of approximately nine hectares (22 acres). Large quantities of animal bones, cereal crops, stone tools, artefacts and pottery were found here, suggesting the communal gathering of people to feast, trade and carry out ritual activities.

Windmill Hill is in the freehold ownership of the National Trust and in English Heritage guardianship. It is managed by the National Trust on behalf of English Heritage, and the two organisations share the cost of managing and maintaining the property.

OPENING TIMES
Any reasonable time

HOW TO FIND US
Direction: 1¼ miles NW of Avebury

Train: Swindon 11 miles

Bus: Stagecoach in Swindon service 49; Wilts & Dorset service 96. Both pass within ¾ mile of the site. Also A.D.Rains/Bodmans X76

MAP Page 313 (3J)
OS Map 173, 157: SU087714

Usual facilities may not be available around the summer solstice 20-22 June. Please call 01672 539250 before you visit.

Stonehenge Wiltshire – SP4 7DE

The great and ancient stone circle of Stonehenge is unique; an exceptional survival from a prehistoric culture now lost to us. The monument was begun around 3000 BC in the Neolithic period and construction activities continued until about 1600 BC in the Bronze Age. It is aligned with the rising and setting of the sun at the solstices, but its exact purpose remains a mystery.

Opening times from 20-22 June may be subject to change due to summer solstice. Please call 0870 333 1181 before your visit.

Check opening times at www.english-heritage.org.uk

Over many centuries, there has been intense debate about the significance and uses of Stonehenge. Certainly it became the focal point of a landscape filled with prehistoric ceremonial and burial structures. It also represented an enormous investment of labour and time. A huge effort and great organisation was needed to carry the stones tens – and on occasion hundreds – of miles by land and water, and then to shape and raise them. Only a sophisticated society could have mustered so large a workforce, and produced the design and construction skills necessary to build Stonehenge and its surrounding monuments.

Stonehenge's orientation in relation to the rising and setting sun has always been one of its most remarkable features. Yet it remains uncertain whether this was because its builders came from a sun-worshipping culture, or because the sun had some other meaning for them.

What cannot be denied is the ingenuity of the builders of Stonehenge. With only very basic tools such as antler picks at their disposal, they dug the enclosing ditch and erected the bank, later using similar tools to dig the holes for the stones. Other stone tools were used to shape the mortises and tenons linking the upright stones with the horizontal lintels.

Some of these tools can be seen, together with other artefacts including personal material from graves, on display in the museums at Salisbury and Devizes.

The first monument at Stonehenge (around 3000 BC) consisted of a circular ditch and bank (c. 120m in diameter), possibly with a ring of 56 wooden or stone posts, the pits for which are now called Aubrey Holes. Some 500 years later the first stones were brought to the site. These were small bluestones, transported over 240km (150 miles) from the Preseli Hills in Pembrokeshire, and larger sarsen stones, from the Marlborough Downs over 27km (16 miles) to the north. The bluestones were probably erected as a double circle, and the sarsens were placed in an outer circle, composed of 30 sarsen uprights with joining lintels.

A World Heritage Site, Stonehenge and its surrounding prehistoric monuments remain powerful witnesses to the once great civilisations of the Stone and Bronze Ages, between 6000 and 3000 years ago.

132

Within this were five sarsen trilithons (pairs of uprights with a lintel across each) arranged in a horsehoe shape, with an open end towards midsummer sunrise. Later the bluestones were re-arranged to form an outer setting and an inner oval setting.

The remains that can be seen today are a remarkable survival of this ancient monument in its final phase.

In the landscape immediately around Stonehenge there are visible remains of many different types of monuments, and many more have been detected. Neolithic monuments include long barrows, the long rectangular earthwork known as the Cursus (once thought to resemble a Roman chariot racecourse) and the henge monuments at Woodhenge (p.126) and Durrington Walls, contemporary with the stone phases at Stonehenge. There are also hundreds of Bronze Age round barrows, which were built during the period after the large sarsens were erected at Stonehenge. Stonehenge is surrounded by 827 hectares of land owned by the National Trust, with excellent walks to some of the monuments

mentioned above. Stonehenge and Avebury became a World Heritage Site in 1986 for their outstanding prehistoric monuments from the Neolithic to the Bronze Age periods.

www.english-heritage.org.uk/stonehenge

NON-MEMBERS

Adult	£7.80
Concession	£7.00
Child	£4.70
Family	£20.30
NT members admitted free	

Please note: All education groups must be pre-booked

OPENING TIMES

1 Apr-31 May, daily	9.30am-6pm
1 Jun-31 Aug, daily	9am-7pm
1 Sep-15 Oct, daily	9.30am-6pm
16 Oct-15 Mar, daily	9.30am-4pm
16-31 Mar, daily	9.30am-6pm
26 Dec and 1 Jan	10am-4pm
24-25 Dec	Closed

Opening times from 20-22 June may be subject to change due to summer solstice. Please call 0870 333 1181 before your visit

Recommended last admission time no later than 30 minutes before the advertised closing time

When weather conditions are bad, access may be restricted and visitors may not be able to use the walkway around the stone circle

Stone Circle Access outside normal opening hours by advance booking only. Book during weekday office hours on telephone 01722 343834

HOW TO FIND US

Direction: 2 miles W of Amesbury on junction of A303 and A344/A360

Train: Salisbury 9½ miles, Andover 15½ miles (but taxi links only)

Bus: Wilts & Dorset Stonehenge Tour service (alight Salisbury train or bus station)
See www.thestonehengetour.info

Tel: 0870 333 1181 (Customer Services)

Local Tourist Information
Amesbury: 01980 622833; and Salisbury: 01722 334956

Audio tours (complimentary – available in ten languages and hearing loop: subject to availability).

Catering, hot and cold refreshments available throughout the year.

Guidebooks (also available in French, German, Japanese and Spanish; large print and braille guides in English only).

No dogs allowed (except guide and hearing dogs).

Parking (Seasonal parking is charged, refundable on entry).

MAP Page 313 (4J)
OS Map 184, 130: SU122422

The Heritage of Scilly Isles of Scilly

The stunningly beautiful Isles of Scilly hold vast arrays of archaeological riches both above and below sea level. English Heritage recognises the importance of promoting this unique cultural landscape, and provides expert advice and significant funding to regeneration and conservation projects throughout the Isles.

Bryher
King Charles's Castle
Cromwell's Castle
Old Blockhouse
New Grimsby
Tresco
St Martin's
Eastern Isles
Bant's Carn Burial Chamber
Innisidgen Burial Chambers
Samson
St Mary's
Harry's Walls
Porth Hellick Down Burial Chamber
Garrison Walls
Hugh Town
Annet
Gugh
St Agnes

Images:
(top) Harry's Walls
(middle) King Charles's Castle
(bottom) Cromwell's Castle

This compact archipelago of about 100 islands lies around 28 miles to the south-west of Land's End. None of them is any bigger than three miles across and only five are inhabited. Despite their landmass of only 16 square kilometres (6.18 square miles), these islands contain a remarkable number of historic sites. These range from traditional farmhouses and dwellings to ritual burial monuments, cist grave cemeteries and Romano-Celtic shrines. Early settlements provide evidence of a distinctive Scillonian culture which thrived in the island group 2000 years ago. More recently, defensive monuments constructed during the Civil War and World War II stand as testament to the strategic importance of the islands. The Gulf Stream keeps the climate warm, enabling exotic plants and wildlife to thrive.

OPENING TIMES

All EH properties on the Scillies are open at any reasonable time

HOW TO FIND US

Direction: See individual property entries (p.134) for access details

Bus: Details from St Mary's TIC on 01720 422536

Tel: 0117 9750700 (Regional office)

Bant's Carn Burial Chamber and Halangy Down Ancient Village
St Mary's, Isles of Scilly

The remains a Romano-British village in a wonderfully scenic location. On the hill above stands a Bronze Age burial mound with entrance passage and inner chamber.

OPENING TIMES
Any reasonable time

HOW TO FIND US
Direction: 1 mile N of Hugh Town

MAP Page 312 (5B)
OS Map 203, 101: SV910123

Cromwell's Castle
Tresco, Isles of Scilly

Standing on a rocky promontory guarding the lovely anchorage between Bryher and Tresco, this round tower is one of the few surviving Cromwellian fortifications in Britain, built after the conquest of the Royalist Scillies in 1651.

OPENING TIMES
Any reasonable time

HOW TO FIND US
Direction: On the shoreline, approach with care, ¾ mile NW of New Grimsby

MAP Page 312 (4A)
OS Map 203, 101: SV882159

Garrison Walls
St Mary's, Isles of Scilly

You can enjoy a two-hour walk alongside the ramparts of these defensive walls and earthworks, dating from the 16th to 18th centuries. Other remains include Elizabethan Star Castle and defences from both World Wars.

Garrison Walls

OPENING TIMES
Any reasonable time

HOW TO FIND US
Direction: Around the headland W of Hugh Town

MAP Page 312 (5A)
OS Map 203, 101: SV898104

Harry's Walls
St Mary's, Isles of Scilly

An unfinished artillery fort, built above St Mary's Pool harbour in 1552-53.

OPENING TIMES
Any reasonable time

HOW TO FIND US
Direction: ¼ mile NE of Hugh Town

MAP Page 312 (5B)
OS Map 203, 101: SV909109

Innisidgen Lower and Upper Burial Chambers
St Mary's, Isles of Scilly

Two Bronze Age communal burial cairns of Scillonian type, with fine views. The upper cairn is the best preserved on the islands.

OPENING TIMES
Any reasonable time

HOW TO FIND US
Direction: 1¾ miles NE of Hugh Town

MAP Page 312 (5B)
OS Map 203, 101: SV922127

King Charles's Castle
Tresco, Isles of Scilly

The ruins of a mid 16th-century coastal artillery fort, later garrisoned – hence the name – by Civil War Royalists. Reached from New Grimsby by footpath.

King Charles's Castle

OPENING TIMES
Any reasonable time

HOW TO FIND US
Direction: Located ¾ mile NW of New Grimsby. Coastal location, approach with care

MAP Page 312 (4A)
OS Map 203, 101: SV882161

Old Blockhouse
Tresco, Isles of Scilly

Substantial remains of a small 16th-century gun tower protecting Old Grimsby harbour, vigorously defended during the Civil War.

OPENING TIMES
Any reasonable time

HOW TO FIND US
Direction: Located on Blockhouse Point, at the S end of Old Grimsby harbour

MAP Page 312 (4A)
OS Map 203, 101: SV897155

Porth Hellick Down Burial Chamber
St Mary's, Isles of Scilly

A large and imposing Scillonian Bronze Age entrance grave, with kerb, inner passage and burial chamber all clearly visible.

OPENING TIMES
Any reasonable time

HOW TO FIND US
Direction: 1¾ miles E of Hugh Town

MAP Page 312 (5B)
OS Map 203, 101: SV928108

Associated attractions in the South West

These visitor attractions, all independent of EH, offer discounts to our members. Please call before you visit to confirm details. A valid EH membership card must be produced for each member.

The Arthurian Centre
Cornwall PL32 9TT

Walk through newly exposed archaeology to the unique, 1500-year-old 'King Arthur's Stone' on the site of Arthur and Mordred's last battle of 'Camlann'

- Land of Arthur Exhibition
- Great visit for all ages

10 mins from Tintagel Castle
Tel: 01840 213947
www.arthur-online.co.uk

20% discount on entry

Bodmin & Wenford Railway
Bodmin, Cornwall PL31 1AQ

The Bodmin & Wenford Railway is the only standard gauge (full size) heritage railway in Cornwall still regularly worked by steam locomotives. A great family attraction.

5 miles from Restormel Castle
Tel: 01208 73555
www.bodminrailway.co.uk

10% discount on entry
(Not valid on event days)

Bowood House and Gardens
Wiltshire SN11 0LZ

Magnificent family home of the Marquis and Marchioness of Lansdowne, set in beautiful 'Capability' Brown parkland. Families love the amazing Adventure Playground and Soft Play Palace. Rhododendron Walks April–mid-June.

10 miles from J17 of M4
Tel: 01249 812102
www.bowood.org

25% discount on Adult & Senior Citizen tickets
(May not be valid on event days)

Coldharbour Mill Working Wool Museum
Devon EX15 3EE

This 200-year-old spinning mill still produces knitting yarns and weaves tartan cloth as it tells the story of the once flourishing West Country woollen industry. Restored water wheel and two steam engines also on show.

2 miles from J27 of M5
Tel: 01884 840960
www.coldharbourmill.org.uk

25% discount on entry

The Fashion Museum
Bath BA1 2QH

A world class collection of contemporary and historical dress, housed in Bath's magnificent 18th century Assembly Rooms. 2012 exhibitions include *Sport & Fashion*. Café and fashion gift shop.

20 mins from M4
Tel: 01225 477785
www.fashionmuseum.co.uk

10% discount on entry

Kents Cavern Prehistoric Caves
Devon TQ1 2JF

An extensive labyrinth of caverns with spectacular natural formations, widely used by prehistoric people. The human archaeology discovered here dates back over 500,000 years, making it Britain's premier prehistoric cave.

11 miles from Totnes Castle
Tel: 01803 215136
www.kents-cavern.co.uk

50% discount on entry
(Adult and child price)

⊞ EH Members   OVP OVP Holders   Discounted Child Places Included

Lulworth Castle & Park
Dorset BH20 5QS

Enjoy wide open spaces, historic buildings, stunning landscapes, park and woodland walks. Castle displays, children's activity room and unrivalled Castle Tower views. Pay and display parking. Picnic areas.

50 mins from Portland Castle

Tel: 0845 450 1054

www.lulworth.com

Free entry to
the castle

National Maritime Museum Cornwall
Cornwall TR11 3QY

This award-winning museum delivers something for everyone. Family activities every school holiday, changing exhibitions and a host of events. A new generation of museum offering more than you might expect.

1 mile from Pendennis Castle

Tel: 01326 313388

www.nmmc.co.uk

10% discount
on entry

Porthcurno Telegraph Museum
Cornwall TR19 6JX

A family-friendly attraction set in secret WWII tunnels where the world's largest telegraph cable station linked the British Empire. Discover how the telegraph changed the world. Featured on BBC's Coast.

25 mins from Chysauster Ancient Village

Tel: 01736 810966

www.porthcurno.org.uk

10% discount on entry
(Not valid on event days)

Powderham Castle
Devon EX6 8JQ

Take time to enjoy the 600-year-old home of the Earl & Countess of Devon. Fascinating tours, stunning views, deer park safari, play castle, friendly animals, shops, tearoom and special events.

10 miles from J30 of M5

Tel: 01626 890243

www.powderham.co.uk

20% discount on entry
(Not valid on event days)

The Roman Baths
Bath BA1 1LZ

One of Britain's finest monuments, built around England's only hot springs 2000 years ago and still flowing with natural hot water. Brought vividly to life with the best of modern interpretation.

20 mins from M4

Tel: 01225 477785

www.romanbaths.co.uk

10% discount
on entry

Salisbury and South Wiltshire Museum
Wiltshire SP1 2EN

Salisbury Museum is the home of the award-winning Stonehenge Gallery and the famous 'Amesbury Archer'. Displays also reveal the history of medieval Salisbury and Old Sarum.

10 mins from Old Sarum

Tel: 01722 332151

www.salisburymuseum.org.uk

50% discount on standard
museum entry ticket

Sherborne Castle
Dorset DT9 5NR

Original house built by Sir Walter Raleigh in 1594. Splendid decorative interiors and collections. 'Capability' Brown lake and landscaped lakeside gardens. Home of the Digby family since 1617. Tearoom and gift shop.

½ mile from Sherborne Old Castle
Tel: 01935 812072

www.sherbornecastle.com

£1.50 off 'Gardens Only' ticket
Castle Interior extra charge.
(not valid on special
event days)   ⊞ OVP 👪4

Sudeley Castle
Gloucestershire GL54 5JD

Nestled in the Cotswold Hills, Sudeley is surrounded by 1200 acres of grounds, award-winning gardens and historic ruins. Tours of the Castle apartments on selected weekdays. Former home of Katherine Parr.

10 miles from J9 of M5
Tel: 01242 602308

www.sudeleycastle.co.uk

25% discount
on entry   ⊞

Wheal Martyn
Cornwall PL26 8XG

Woodland walks; Cornwall's largest working waterwheel; preserved Victorian China clay works; mining heritage; vintage commercial vehicles; modern mining in action; lovely café and gift shop. Dogs welcome throughout.

2 miles N of St Austell
Tel: 01726 850362

www.wheal-martyn.com

2 for 1
entry   ⊞ OVP 👪6

Wiltshire Heritage Museum
Wiltshire SN10 1NS

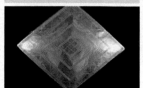

The best Bronze Age archaeology collections in Britain, including objects from Stonehenge and Avebury. The Museum traces the story of Wiltshire, its environment and people over the last 6000 years.

8 miles from Avebury
Tel: 01380 727369

www.wiltshireheritage.org.uk

50% discount
on entry   ⊞ OVP 👪6

Woodchester Mansion
Gloucestershire GL10 3TS

Abandoned by its builders before completion, Woodchester Mansion has been virtually untouched by time since the mid-1870s. Enjoy a unique opportunity to explore a neo-Gothic building 'frozen' in mid-assembly.

10 mins from J13 of M5
Tel: 01453 861541

www.woodchestermansion.org.uk

£1.00 off
admission   ⊞ OVP 👪6

Wrest Park

EAST OF ENGLAND

PROPERTIES

East of England properties consist of:

50	English Heritage
9	The Churches Conservation Trust
8	Associated Attractions

Remember to check opening times before you visit any of our properties www.english-heritage. org.uk/daysout

Details of local public transport information in England are available from Traveline www.traveline.org.uk or call 0871 200 2233.

Chinese Bridge at Wrest Park

BEDFORDSHIRE
Bushmead Priory
De Grey Mausoleum, Flitton
Houghton House
Wrest Park

CAMBRIDGESHIRE
Denny Abbey and the Farmland Museum
Duxford Chapel
Isleham Priory Church
Longthorpe Tower

ESSEX
Audley End House and Gardens
Colchester, St Botolph's Priory
Colchester, St John's Abbey Gate
Hadleigh Castle
Hill Hall
Lexden Earthworks and Bluebottle Grove
Mistley Towers
Prior's Hall Barn, Widdington
Tilbury Fort
Waltham Abbey Gatehouse and Bridge

HERTFORDSHIRE
Abbotsbury Abbey Remains
Berkhamsted Castle
Old Gorhambury House
Roman Wall, St Albans

NORFOLK
Baconsthorpe Castle
Berney Arms Windmill
Binham Market Cross
Binham Priory
Blakeney Guildhall
Burgh Castle
Caister Roman Fort
Castle Acre Priory
Castle Acre Priory, Castle and Bailey Gate
Castle Rising Castle
Cow Tower, Norwich
Creake Abbey
Great Yarmouth Row Houses & Greyfriars' Cloisters
Grime's Graves – prehistoric flint mine
North Elmham Chapel
St Olave's Priory
Thetford, Church of the Holy Sepulchre
Thetford Priory
Thetford Warren Lodge
Weeting Castle

SUFFOLK
Bury St Edmunds Abbey
Framlingham Castle
Landguard Fort
Leiston Abbey
Lindsey St James's Chapel
Moulton Packhorse Bridge
Orford Castle
Saxtead Green Post Mill

EAST OF ENGLAND

Cromer
King's Lynn
Norfolk
Norwich
Great Yarmouth
Wisbech
Downham Market
Peterborough
Lowestoft
Cambridgeshire
Ely
Southwold
Huntingdon
Bury St Edmunds
Cambridge
Newmarket
Suffolk
Aldeburgh
Bedford
Ipswich
Bedfordshire
Saffron Walden
Felixstowe
Luton
Stevenage
Harwich
Hertford
Colchester
St Albans
Harlow
Chelmsford
Hemel Hempstead
Essex
Clacton
Hertfordshire
Basildon
Southend
Tilbury

HIGHLIGHTS FOR 2012/13 IN THE EAST OF ENGLAND

■ **Audley End House & Gardens:** a spectacular stately home explores life above and below stairs.

■ **Wrest Park:** discover the magnificent newly restored gardens.

■ **Framlingham Castle:** a fascinating castle day out.

BEDFORDSHIRE

Bushmead Priory
Bedfordshire – MK44 2LD

A rare survival of the complete refectory of an Augustinian priory, with fine timber roof and notable 14th-century wall paintings.

NON-MEMBERS

Adult	£5.50
Concession	£5.00
Child	£3.30

OPENING TIMES
1 May-31 Aug, entry on the first Sat of the month only. Tel: 01525 860000 (Option 2) to book

HOW TO FIND US
Direction: Located off B660, 2 miles S of Bolnhurst

Train: St Neots 6 miles

Bus: Grant Palmer 28 & 29

MAP Page 316 (4E)
OS Map 153, 225: TL115607

Church of St Margaret of Antioch, Knotting
Bedfordshire – MK44 1AF

© CCT

This small rural church tucked into the landscape is quintessentially English. The spiked chancel gates were added in 1637 to stop cockfighting and betting, for which the rector of the day was de-frocked! In the churchyard stands a World War I memorial to the men of Knotting.

Church of St Margaret of Antioch, Knotting

Owned and managed by The Churches Conservation Trust.

OPENING TIMES
Open daily during daylight hours

HOW TO FIND US
Train: Nearest ≋ Wellingborough 6¾ miles

Bus: Route number R16

15 mins from Chichele College

MAP Page 316 (4E)
OS Map 153, 224: TL004636

De Grey Mausoleum, Flitton
Bedfordshire

Among the largest sepulchral chapels attached to any English church, this cruciform mausoleum houses a remarkable sequence of 17 sculpted and effigied monuments, spanning nearly three centuries (1615-1859), to the De Grey family of Wrest Park. You can download the audio tour prior to visiting from the English Heritage website.

OPENING TIMES
Weekends only. Contact the key keeper in advance: Mrs Stimson, 3 Highfield Road, Flitton. Tel: 01525 860094

De Grey Mausoleum, Flitton

HOW TO FIND US
Direction: Attached to Flitton church; through Flitton, on an unclassified road 1½ miles W of A6 at Silsoe

Train: Flitwick 2 miles

Bus: A limited service is provided by Flittabus (of Ampthill); Cedar service 146 & K4; Centrebus 20; Grant Palmer service 44 & 77

MAP Page 316 (5E)
OS Map 153, 193: TL059359

Houghton House
Bedfordshire – MK45 2EZ

The shell of a 17th-century mansion commanding magnificent views, reputedly the inspiration for the 'House Beautiful' in John Bunyan's *Pilgrim's Progress*. Built around 1615 for Mary, Dowager Countess of Pembroke, in a mixture of Jacobean and Classical styles; the ground floors of two Italianate loggias survive, possibly the work of Inigo Jones.

Information panels describe the house, its owners and the surrounding hunting estate. A free downloadable audio tour is available from the English Heritage website.

OPENING TIMES
Any reasonable time

HOW TO FIND US
Direction: 1 mile NE of Ampthill off B530, 8 miles S of Bedford

Train: Flitwick or Stewartby, both 3 miles

Bus: Stagecoach in Northants service 42; Grant Palmer service 42, 44, 197 & 200; Flittbus F5, F6B, F8; Cedar 146

MAP Page 316 (5E)
OS Map 153, 193: TL039395

Wrest Park

Ranking among the most vastly impressive of all English gardens, yet until recently little visited, magnificent Wrest Park is English Heritage's latest star attraction. Wrest Park is one of the great gardens of England, which tells the story of England's love affair with landscape. It is a unique place capturing over two hundred years of garden history and design. Wrest's 92-acre gardens were developed over more than two centuries by the aristocratic De Grey family, and have now been re-awakened by an ambitious £4m restoration project supported by the Heritage Lottery Fund. Set against the backdrop of a great French-style chateau, they are also now equipped with extensive visitor facilities.

Don't miss our St George's Day Festival event here, the largest in the country.

Check opening times at www.english-heritage.org.uk

Check opening times at www.english-heritage.org.uk

The gardens are enlivened throughout by charming architectural features, unexpected vistas and a wealth of statuary. Visitors can stroll beside the Long Water to the beautiful Baroque 'Archer Pavilion' the focus of the main garden walks. The ultimate garden dining room, it still retains its outstanding interior decoration. The intricate woodland paths of the 18th century Great Garden reveal Classical altars, a Chinese Temple and a secluded Dogs' Cemetery for De Grey family pets. And yet more walks lead to the splendid 1830s Orangery; the colonnaded Bowling Green House; and Jemima, Marchioness Grey's enchanting Bath House, disguised as a thatched Classical ruin.

Nearer the great mansion are the recently restored Rose Garden and vibrantly-planted Italian Garden. Although Wrest Park primarily offers a garden visit, the huge French-style mansion designed and built by Thomas, Earl de Grey in 1834-9 is partly open to visitors. Its unfurnished but opulently decorated State Rooms include the imposing Staircase Hall; the Library which served as the De Grey family's living room; and the Drawing Room with its ceiling painting of wispily-draped 1830s ladies. Countess Henrietta's Sitting Room, chintzily furnished as

WREST PARK AND THE DE GREY FAMILY

Wrest Park was home to the de Grey family from the 13th century until the early 20th century. In this exhibition you can discover how different generations left their mark on the landscape, and discover what happened to Wrest after the family left in 1917.

it may have appeared in the 1840s, looks through to a lofty glass-roofed Conservatory, unusually built as an integral part of the mansion. An interactive exhibition traces the history of the De Grey family and the development and working of their estate.

The new Visitor Centre in the Walled Garden offers introductory displays, plant sales – and not least a spacious café with indoor and outdoor tables, overlooking a children's play area inspired by the house and gardens.

Please note: No flash photography or stiletto heels in the house.

www.english-heritage.org.uk/ wrestpark

www.facebook.com/ wrestpark

Available for corporate and private hire

Licensed for civil wedding ceremonies

NEW FOR 2012

From April, see the French Parterre restored to its appearance as originally envisaged by Earl de Grey. From June, you can also view previously unseen sculptures in a gallery housed in the former dairy.

NON-MEMBERS

Adult	£8.50
Concession	£7.70
Child	£5.10
Family	£22.10

OPENING TIMES

1 Apr-3 Jun, Thu-Mon & Bank Hols	10am-6pm
4-8 Jun, daily	10am-6pm
9-30 Jun, Thu-Mon & Bank Hols	10am-6pm
1 Jul-30 Sep, daily	10am-6pm
1-26 Oct, Thu-Mon	10am-5pm
27 Oct-4 Nov, daily	10am-5pm
5 Nov-17 Feb, Sat-Sun	10am-4pm
18-22 Feb, daily	10am-4pm
23 Feb-28 Mar, Sat-Sun	10am-4pm
24-26 Dec and 1 Jan	Closed

Last entry 1 hour before closing

The house may be closed if an event is booked. Entry to the gardens may also be restricted earlier than the usual '1 hour before closing' time, although access to the gardens for those who have already arrived will continue until normal closing times. Please call to check

Free members' guided tours
5 Nov, 3 Dec, 7 Jan, 4 Feb, 4 Mar 11am & 2pm

HOW TO FIND US

Direction: ¾ mile E of Silsoe off A6, 10 miles S of Bedford

Train: Flitwick 4 miles

Bus: Grant Palmer 44 & 77 (Tue only); Stagecoach in Northants service 81 Bedford – Luton; Cedar 146 (Fri only); Flittabus

Tel: 01525 860000

Mobility cart available for disabled visitors. New guidebook.

MAP Page 316 (5E)
OS Map 153, 193: TL091355

CAMBRIDGESHIRE

All Saints' Church, Cambridge
Cambridgeshire – CB5 8BP

© Paul Raeside.
BBC Homes & Antiques magazine

The pale stone spire of All Saints' is a prominent landmark in the heart of Cambridge. The interior is a dramatic blast of colour and pattern – light gleams through stained-glass windows by leading Arts and Crafts artists and almost every surface has painted, stencilled or gilded decoration.

Owned and managed by The Churches Conservation Trust.

OPENING TIMES
Open daily during daylight hours

HOW TO FIND US
Train: Nearest ⬛ Cambridge 1 mile

Bus: Route numbers 1, 2, 5, 55

15 mins from Denny Abbey and the Farmland Museum

MAP Page 317 (4F)
OS Map 154, 209: TL453587

Don't forget to check opening times online before you visit

www.english-heritage.org.uk/ daysout/properties

Denny Abbey and the Farmland Museum
Cambridgeshire – CB25 9PQ

Denny Abbey has a unique and fascinating history. Founded in 1159 as a Benedictine monastery, it then became a retirement home for elderly Knights Templars. After the Templars' suppression for alleged heresy in 1308, it next passed to the Countess of Pembroke, who converted part into a house and established in the rest a convent of 'Poor Clare' Franciscan nuns. This in turn was dissolved by Henry VIII in 1539, whereafter the buildings became a farm until the 1960s, with the nuns' great refectory as its barn. Among its tenants was Thomas Hobson, the horse-hirer whose refusal to allow customers to select their mounts gave rise to the expression 'Hobson's choice'.

All these changes are still traceable in the building: they are now interpreted for visitors by graphic panels illustrated by local artist Anne Biggs, together with a time-line tracing the site's history from 4000 BC, a viewing platform and displays of site finds. Family-friendly activities include imaginative hands-on interactives about medieval tiles, stained glass and arches.

Denny's later farming story is continued by Walnut Tree Cottage, furnished as a labourer's home of the 1940s. The site's Farmland Museum also features a fenman's hut, farrier's hut and wheelwright's workshops, a village shop display and many other aspects of Cambridgeshire rural life.

Managed by the Farmland Museum Trust.

NON-MEMBERS

Museum and Abbey
Adult	£4.50	Concession	£3.50
Child	£2.50	Family	£12.00

Free entry for children under 5

Museum charge
Adult	£3.50	Concession	£2.50
Child	£1.50	Family	£8.00

Free entry for children under 5

The abbey is free to members but there is a discounted charge for the museum (inc. life members). The charge is mandatory for special event days. Please contact the museum for further details

OPENING TIMES
1 Apr-1 Nov, Mon-Fri 12pm-5pm
Sat-Sun & Bank Hols 10.30am-5pm

HOW TO FIND US
Direction: Located 6 miles N of Cambridge on A10

Train: Waterbeach 3 miles

Bus: Stagecoach Cambridge 9

Tel: 01223 860489/860988

⚠ OVP

Disabled access (museum and abbey ground floor only).

Dogs on leads (restricted areas only).

Tearoom/restaurant (weekends only).

MAP Page 317 (4F)
OS Map 154, 226: TL492685

Duxford Chapel
Cambridgeshire

A modest but complete and attractive 14th-century chantry chapel, perhaps originally a hospital.

Managed by South Cambridgeshire District Council.

OPENING TIMES
Any reasonable time

HOW TO FIND US
Direction: Adjacent to Whittlesford station off A505

Train: Whittlesford, adjacent

Bus: Stagecoach Cambridge Citi7. Also Myall service 101 (Tue only) & 132 (Sun only)

MAP Page 317 (4F)
OS Map 154, 209: TL485473

Isleham Priory Church
Cambridgeshire

The best example in England of a small Norman Benedictine priory church, surviving in a surprisingly unaltered state despite later conversion into a barn.

OPENING TIMES
Any reasonable time. Contact the key keeper, Mrs R Burton, 18 Festival Road, Isleham – 5 min walk

HOW TO FIND US
Direction: Located in centre of Isleham, 16 miles NE of Cambridge on B1104

Train: Newmarket 8½ miles, Ely 9 miles

Bus: Freedom Travel service 203 (Tue and Sat only) & 204

MAP Page 317 (4G)
OS Map 143, 226: TL642743

Get our free app
www.english-heritage.org.uk/ daysout/app

Longthorpe Tower
Cambridgeshire – PE3 6LU

Longthorpe Tower displays one of the most complete and important sets of 14th-century domestic wall paintings in northern Europe. This varied 'spiritual encyclopaedia' of worldly and religious subjects includes the Wheel of Life, the Nativity and King David.
www.vivacity-peterborough.com

Managed by Vivacity Culture & Leisure Trust.

NON-MEMBERS
Adult	£3.50
Concession	£2.50
Child	£2.00

OPENING TIMES
6 Apr-31 Oct, Sat-Sun & Bank Hols   10am-4pm

Guided tours will be available on the first Saturday of every month and are included in the entrance fee. Call during office hours to book

HOW TO FIND US
Direction: Located 2 miles W of Peterborough on A47

Train: Peterborough 1½ miles

Bus: Location is a short walk from Peterborough Bus Station. Centrebus R47; Kimes service 9, Peterborough City Transport service 406 and Stagecoach service 2 bus nearby

Tel: 01733 864663

Parking (not at site).

MAP Page 316 (3E)
OS Map 142, 227/235: TL162984

St Peter's Church, Cambridge
Cambridgeshire – CB3 0AJ

© Cameron Newham

Tiny, tall-spired St Peter's is tucked into a quiet corner of Cambridge, a haven of tranquillity amid the busy streets around it. Mermen, carved into the stone font, may have an ancient link to St Peter, patron saint of fishermen.

Owned and managed by The Churches Conservation Trust.

OPENING TIMES
Open Mon-Fri during the morning; other times key available from Kettle's Yard Gallery next door

HOW TO FIND US
Train: Nearest ≡ Cambridge 2 miles

Bus: Route 1A, 2, 5, 6, 55. Drummer Street Bus Station 10 mins walk from church

30 mins from Audley End House and Gardens

MAP Page 317 (4F)
OS Map 154, 209: TL445592

Audley End House and Gardens

Essex – CB11 4JF

Among the the most delightful of English Heritage's treasures, Audley End is probably the best place in the country to experience not only the sumptuous lifestyle enjoyed by the aristocratic owners of a great country house – but also how their indoor and outdoor servants made it happen.

Please note: In some rooms, light levels are reduced to preserve vulnerable textiles and other collections. No photography or stiletto heels allowed in the house.

Incorporating research into the real lives of the 25 or so indoor servants employed here, the Service Wing presentation illustrates how familiar household tasks were conducted on a near-industrial scale for the Braybrooke family and their retinue. Watch out for special days when visitors can see and hear from costumed interpreters cooking, washing and ironing in traditional ways.

The house takes its name from Sir Thomas Audley, Henry VIII's Lord Chancellor, who adapted the buildings of suppressed Walden Abbey as his mansion. His grandson Thomas Howard, first Earl of Suffolk and James I's Lord Treasurer, rebuilt the house on a massive scale between 1603 and 1614. This immense double-courtyard 'Palace of Audley End' was three times its present size, and one of the largest mansions in England: 'too big for a king', quipped James during a visit in 1614, 'though it might suit a Lord Treasurer'. But in 1618 Suffolk fell from favour, and his vast mansion went into decline.

Charles II bought Audley End in 1668 as a base for attending Newmarket races: his Queen Catherine of Braganza held court here that autumn. When repairs proved ruinously costly, William III returned Audley End to the Suffolk family in 1701. The witty and accomplished Henrietta Howard lived here, before leaving her 'obstinate, drunken and brutal' husband, the 9th Earl, for a royal lover and her new Thames-side villa, Marble Hill House (see p.36).

After the Suffolk line died out in 1745, the estate was bought by the Countess of Portsmouth for her nephew and heir, later first Baron Braybrooke. He made extensive changes, adding a suite of neo-Classical rooms designed by Robert Adam and a Gothick chapel. Meanwhile, 'Capability' Brown was employed to remodel the grounds. Today the house's interior largely represents the taste of the third Baron Braybrooke, who redecorated many of its rooms in the Jacobean style during the 1820s. He installed his extensive picture collection and filled the rooms with inherited furnishings.

The Service Wing

The Victorian Service Wing gives a unique insight into the 'below stairs' working of this great household during the 1880s. The kitchens, dairy, dry larder and laundries are fully equipped with original and reproduction Victorian fixtures and fittings, and vividly animated with lifelike sights and sounds, film projection and even examples of foods eaten in the era. They provide a strikingly atmospheric picture of daily life for the people who once toiled here – from butler down to dairy maid and lowly houseboy.

The Stables

The lovely gabled red-brick early 17th century stables, recently re-opened after many decades, are the latest of Audley End's many attractions. Once housing the horses, grooms, coaches, and other equipment needed to service the demands of this great country house, they are now set as in the 1880s. The horses are back, and there are daily riding displays, plus talks, stables tours and hands-on demonstrations of grooming and horse-care, in which children can take part.

Lively interactive displays here trace the development of the estate, and allow visitors to 'virtually' meet the Victorian outdoor staff of Audley End, including the land steward, head gardener, gamekeeper, cowman and groom.

The Gardens

Audley End's park and fine gardens also offer a series of varied delights. Visitors can stroll by the lake through the cascaded Elysian Garden; walk up to the Classical Temple of Concord to view

Audley End House and Gardens   continued

the house in its wonderful setting; visit the memorial to Polish 'underground' resistance soldiers who trained here in World War II; or admire the restored 19th-century formal parterre garden at the back of the house. For practical gardeners, Audley End's massive and renowned walled organic kitchen garden, growing fruit and vegetable varieties from Victorian times, is also an unmissable attraction. Next to it are the new Children's Play area and Cart Yard Café.

www.english-heritage.org.uk/audleyend

www.facebook.com/audleyend

Holiday cottage available to let

Book a relaxing break in Cambridge Lodge here. Enjoy stunning views of the tranquil lake and manicured lawns, and stroll through the grounds in private once the gates have closed to the public.

NON-MEMBERS

Full Estate

Adult	£13.00
Concession	£11.70
Child	£7.80
Family	£33.80

Stables, Service Wing & Gardens
(not available on event days)

Adult	£9.00
Concession	£8.10
Child	£5.40
Family	£23.40

OPENING TIMES

House

1-15 Apr, daily	12pm-5pm
16 Apr-3 Jun, Wed-Sun & Bank Hols	12pm-5pm
4-8 Jun, daily	12pm-5pm
9 Jun-30 Sep, Wed-Sun & Bank Hols	12pm-5pm
1-28 Oct, Wed-Sun	12pm-4pm
29 Oct-4 Nov, daily	12pm-4pm
5 Nov-28 Mar (House closed)	

Gardens, Stables and Service Wing

1-15 Apr, daily	10am-6pm
16 Apr-3 Jun, Wed-Sun & Bank Hols	10am-6pm
4-8 Jun, daily	10am-6pm
9-30 Jun, Wed-Sun & Bank Hols	10am-6pm
1 Jul-30 Sep, daily	10am-6pm
1-28 Oct, Wed-Sun	10am-5pm
29 Oct-2 Nov, daily	10am-5pm
3 Nov-17 Feb, Sat-Sun	10am-4pm
18-22 Feb, daily	10am-4pm
23 Feb-28 Mar, Sat-Sun	10am-4pm
24-26 Dec and 1 Jan	Closed

Last entry to the house and estate is 1 hour before closing

The house will be accessible for guided tours only on certain days. Please call or check our website for more details

Free members' guided tours

8 Nov, 6 Dec, 3 Jan, 7 Feb, 7 Mar	11am & 2pm

HOW TO FIND US

Direction: 1 mile W of Saffron Walden on B1383 (M11 exit 8 or 10)

Train: Audley End 1¼ miles. Note: Footpath is beside busy main road

Bus: First 302; Hedingham 417, 418, 419; Stephensons 1, 5, 301. C.J.Myall service 101; 132; Stephensons 59; Excel 5,301; Four Counties Buses 59, 313; Freedom Travel 18; Regal 322; Viceroy 11, 34, 59, 443, 444, 445, 590; Walden Travel 91, 94 all pass within ¼ mile of entrance

Tel: 01799 522842 (info line)

Local Tourist Information
Saffron Walden: 01799 524002
Cambridge: 01223 464732

Disabled access (grounds, Great Hall, Stable Yard and Service Wing only. Please call for more information).

MAP Page 317 (5F)
OS Map 154, 195: TL525382

Colchester, St Botolph's Priory
Essex

The remains of one of the first Augustinian priories in England, founded c. 1100. An impressive example of early Norman architecture, built in flint and re-used Roman brick, the church displays massive circular pillars and round arches and an elaborate west front. Later badly damaged by cannon fire during the Civil War siege of 1648.

Managed by Colchester Borough Council.

OPENING TIMES
Any reasonable time

HOW TO FIND US
Direction: Nr Colchester Town station

Train: Colchester Town, adjacent

Bus: Bus services to/from Colchester are provided by Beestons (of Hadleigh), Chambers (of Bures), First Essex, Hedingham Omnibuses and Network Colchester. Priory is 2 minutes walk from the bus station

Tel: 01206 282931

MAP Page 317 (5H)
OS Map 168, 184: TL999249

Colchester, St John's Abbey Gate
Essex

This pinnacled gatehouse, elaborately decorated in East Anglian 'flushwork', is the sole survivor of the wealthy Benedictine abbey of St John. It was built c. 1400 to strengthen the abbey's defences following the Peasants' Revolt. Later part of the mansion of the Royalist Lucas family, the gatehouse was bombarded and stormed by Parliamentarian soldiers during the Civil War siege.

Managed by Colchester Borough Council.

OPENING TIMES
Any reasonable time

HOW TO FIND US
Direction: S side of central Colchester

Train: Colchester Town ¼ mile

Bus: Bus services to/from Colchester are provided by Beestons (of Hadleigh), Chambers (of Bures), First Essex, Hedingham Omnibuses and Network Colchester

Tel: 01206 282931

MAP Page 317 (5H)
OS Map 168, 184: TL998248

Hadleigh Castle
See feature – Page 153

Hill Hall
Essex – CM16 7QQ

This fine Elizabethan mansion features some of the earliest external Renaissance architectural detail in the country, and two rare and outstanding sets of 16th-century wall paintings of mythical and Biblical subjects. Hill Hall has now been divided into private houses, but parts remain open to the public by prior arrangement.

NON-MEMBERS
Adult	£5.50
Concession	£5.00
Child	£3.30

OPENING TIMES
1 Apr-30 Sep. Pre-booked guided tours on Wednesdays only

Tel: 01799 522842 to book

HOW TO FIND US
Direction: 3 miles SE of Epping. Entrance ½ mile N of Theydon Mount Church

Bus: Closest bus services are Arriva 375; Travel With Hunny 33 & Blue Triangle 575 to Passingford Bridge (2¾ miles)

Train: Epping or Theydon Bois 2½ miles

MAP Page 317 (6F)
OS Map 167/177, 174: TQ489995

Check *Heritage Today* or visit our website for the latest events listings in your area.

www.english-heritage.org.uk/events

Lexden Earthworks and Bluebottle Grove
Essex

The banks and ditches of a series of late Iron Age defences protecting the western side of Camulodunum – pre-Roman Colchester. There are also many pre-Roman graves hereabouts, including Lexden Tumulus, allegedly the burial place of the British chieftain Cunobelinus.

Managed by Colchester Borough Council.

OPENING TIMES
Any reasonable time

HOW TO FIND US
Direction: 2 miles W of Colchester off A604. Lexden Earthworks are on Lexden Straight Rd. To visit Bluebottle Grove from Lexden, turn left into Heath Rd, left into Church Lane, right into Beech Hill and follow the signs to the site

Train: Colchester or Colchester Town, both 2½ miles

Bus: Hedingham 4 and Network Colchester services 5 & 15

Tel: 01206 282931

MAP Page 317 (5H) OS Map 168,184
Lexden Earthworks: TL965246
Bluebottle Grove: TL975245

Mistley Towers
Essex

Mistley Towers

Two porticoed Classical towers, which stood at each end of a grandiose but highly unconventional Georgian church, designed by Robert Adam in 1776.

Managed by Mistley Thorn Residents' Association.

OPENING TIMES
Daily   10am-4pm
Key available from Mistley Quay Workshops: 01206 393884
Please call in advance

HOW TO FIND US
Direction: Located on B1352, 1½ miles E of A137 at Lawford, 9 miles E of Colchester

Train: Mistley ¼ mile

Bus: Hedingham service 2, 85, Carters 92, 93C, 96; First 102, 103, 104, 193; Network Colchester 102 & 104

Disabled access (exterior only).
Dogs on leads (restricted areas).

MAP Page 317 (5H)
OS Map 168/169,184/197: TM116320

Prior's Hall Barn, Widdington
Essex

One of the finest surviving medieval barns in eastern England, tree-ring dated to the mid-15th century, with a breathtaking aisled interior and crown-post roof, the product of some 400 oaks.

OPENING TIMES
1 Apr-30 Sep, Sat-Sun   10am-6pm

HOW TO FIND US
Direction: In Widdington, on unclassified road 2 miles SE of Newport, off B1383

Train: Newport 2 miles

Bus: Excel 301; Regal 322

MAP Page 317 (5F)
OS Map 167, 195: TL537318

St Botolph's Priory
Essex: see Colchester,
St Botolph's Priory – Page 151

St John's Abbey Gate
Essex: see Colchester,
St John's Abbey Gate – Page 151

Waltham Abbey Gatehouse and Bridge
Essex – EN9 1XQ

A fine 14th-century gatehouse, bridge and other remains of the abbey refounded by Harold, last Saxon King of England.

Managed by Lee Valley Park.

OPENING TIMES
Any reasonable time

HOW TO FIND US
Direction: In Waltham Abbey off A112

Train: Waltham Cross 1¼ miles

Bus: Regal 211, 212, 213 & 240; Regal/Arriva 250 & 251, Network Harlow 505; Roadrunner 255; TWH 555

Tel: 01992 702200

Sensory trail guide.

MAP Page 317 (6F) OS Map 166,174
Gatehouse: TL381007
Harold's Bridge: TL382009

Hadleigh Castle Essex

The romantic ruins of a royal castle on a ridge overlooking the Essex marshes and the Thames estuary. The first castle was begun in about 1215 by Hubert de Burgh, King John's powerful Justiciar, probably as a towered octagonal enclosure. But in 1239 it was confiscated by Henry III, and thereafter remained in royal ownership or gift for over three centuries.

Conveniently accessible from London by royal barge, Hadleigh Castle was extensively rebuilt by Edward III during the 1360s, to which period most of the surviving remains belong. Edward's refurbished castle was intended partly to reinforce the defences of the Thames Estuary against French invasion: the towers looking towards the estuary would have presented a strong impression of power and security. Yet the now ageing king's main use of the castle was probably as a personal retreat, where he could stay in privacy and comfort: excavated

remains of Edward's great hall, with its 'solar' or private withdrawing room, can still be seen here.

After Edward III's death in 1377 his successors took little interest in Hadleigh, whose tenancy passed to a series of mainly absentee royal relations, including three of Henry VIII's queens. Eventually the castle was sold in 1551, and substantially demolished for building materials. Yet Edward III's two big eastern drum towers still remain, the south-east tower – allegedly used by Georgian revenue men looking out for smugglers – still commandingly standing three storeys high.

OLYMPICS 2012

The London 2012 Olympic Mountain Bike Event will take place at nearby Hadleigh Farm, with the castle as its backdrop.

OPENING TIMES
Any reasonable time

HOW TO FIND US
Direction: ¾ mile S of A13 at Hadleigh

Train: Leigh-on-Sea 1½ miles by footpath

Bus: First, First/Regal and Arriva from surrounding areas to within ½ mile

Access to the castle is restricted as entry is via a 'kissing gate' only.

MAP Page 317 (7G)
OS Map 178, 175: TQ810860

Tilbury Fort Essex – RM18 7NR

The great artillery fort at Tilbury on the Thames estuary defended London's seaward approach from the 16th century through to World War II. Henry VIII built the first fort here, and Queen Elizabeth I famously rallied her army nearby to face the threat of the Armada. The present fort was begun in 1672 under Charles II: it is much the best example of its type in England, with its complete circuit of moats and bastioned outworks still substantially surviving. The fort mounted powerful artillery to command the river, as well as landward defences. The east magazine houses an exhibition which traces its role in the defence of London.

Visitors can now enter the north-east bastion. There are displays of guns and gunpowder barrels, and information on advances in military engineering. The audio tour includes Elizabeth I's Armada speech, and a description of life at Tilbury by 'Nathan Makepiece', the fort's Master Gunner. Our interactive oral history programme provides a fascinating insight into Tilbury, and also includes 360 degree views of inaccessible areas.

🎬 *Sharpe*, the TV historical drama set during the Napoleonic Wars.

NON-MEMBERS

Adult	£4.50
Concession	£4.10
Child	£2.70
Family	£11.70

OPENING TIMES

1 Apr-4 Nov, Thu-Mon	10am-5pm
5 Nov-28 Mar, Sat-Sun	10am-4pm
24-26 Dec and 1 Jan	Closed

HOW TO FIND US

Direction: Located ½ mile E of Tilbury off A126, close to the Port of Tilbury

Train: Tilbury Town 1½ miles

Bus: Cintona service 99 connects with trains at Tilbury Town and passes the fort

Ferry: Gravesend – Tilbury Ferry, then ¼ mile

Tel: 01375 858489

Disabled access (exterior, magazines and fort square).

Dogs on leads (restricted areas).

MAP Page 317 (7G)
OS Map 177/178,162/163: TQ651753

Berkhamsted Castle
Hertfordshire

The substantial remains of a strong and important motte and bailey castle dating from the 11th to 15th centuries, with surrounding walls, ditches and earthworks. Lived in by Thomas Becket in the 12th century: Richard Earl of Cornwall added a 13th-century palace complex.

OPENING TIMES

Summer, daily	10am-6pm
Winter, daily	10am-4pm
25 Dec and 1 Jan	Closed

HOW TO FIND US

Direction: Near ⇥ Berkhamsted

Train: Berkhamsted, adjacent

Bus: From surrounding areas

MAP Page 316 (6D)
OS Map 165, 181: SP995082

Church of St Mary the Virgin, Little Hormead
Hertfordshire – SG9 0LS

© CCT

A 1,000-year-old haven of tranquillity set in a churchyard encircled by trees. Atmospheric St Mary's is a rare and precious survival with a rare Norman

Church of St Mary the Virgin, Little Hormead

chancel arch, and some wonderful craftsmanship in wood and ironwork, including an original Norman door.

Owned and managed by The Churches Conservation Trust.

OPENING TIMES

Please see Churches Conservation Trust website for current opening times

HOW TO FIND US

Train: Nearest ⇥ Bishop's Stortford 7½ miles, Stansted Airport 7¾ miles, Royston 8 miles

Bus: No bus route nearby

25 mins from Audley End House and Gardens

MAP Page 317 (5F)
OS Map 166, 194: TL398291

Old Gorhambury House
Hertfordshire

The remains of a once immense mansion built in 1563-8 by Sir Nicholas Bacon, Queen Elizabeth's Lord Keeper, and visited by the queen on at least four occasions. Its elaborately decorated Classical two-storey porch survives, with parts of the hall, chapel and clock-tower.

Old Gorhambury House

OPENING TIMES

All year (except 1 Jun & Saturdays 1 Sep–1 Feb), any reasonable time

HOW TO FIND US

Direction: Just off A4147 on western outskirts of St Albans. Walk up 2 mile drive on permissive path. Access by car is limited

Train: St Albans Abbey 3 miles, St Albans 3½ miles

Bus: Arriva/Uno services 300, 301 pass start of drive

MAP Page 316 (6E)
OS Map 166, 182: TL110076

Roman Wall, St Albans
Hertfordshire

A section of the two-mile-long wall built between AD 265 and 270 to defend the Roman city of Verulamium, including the foundations of towers and the London Gate.

OPENING TIMES

Any reasonable time

HOW TO FIND US

Direction: Located on the S side of St Albans, ½ mile from the centre, off the A4147

Train: St Albans Abbey ½ mile, St Albans 1¼ miles

Bus: Uno services S8 & S9 operate close to the Roman Wall site

MAP Page 316 (6E)
OS Map 166, 182: TL137066

Baconsthorpe Castle
Norfolk

Surrounded by a reedy moat and a wildfowl-haunted mere, the evocative ruins of this fortified manor house chronicle the rise and fall of the ambitious Heydon family over two centuries. The wealthy but 'crafty and quarrelsome' John Heydon built the imposing inner gatehouse and first castle in the 1450s, during the troubled Wars of the Roses period, and his son Sir Henry extended the gunport-defended castle to include a garden court. Subsequent generations converted part of the site into a textile factory, and added the turreted Elizabethan outer gatehouse, but the family eventually succumbed to bankruptcy and sold their mansion for salvage.

The castle stands astride walking and cycle trails. Download a free audio tour from our website before you visit.

OPENING TIMES
Any reasonable time

HOW TO FIND US
Direction: ¾ mile N of village of Baconsthorpe off unclassified road, 3 miles E of Holt

Train: Sheringham 4½ miles

Bus: Sanders service 16 (Tue and Fri only) or 17 (Thu and Sat only) and the Baconsthorpe Community Bus (Wed and Fri only) serve the village.

🐕 🅿️

MAP Page 317 (1H)
OS Map 133, 252: TG121382

Don't forget your membership card

Berney Arms Windmill
Norfolk

One of Norfolk's best and largest extant marsh mills, built to grind a constituent of cement and in use until 1951, finally pumping water to drain surrounding marshland.

For access information to Berney Arms Windmill please call the Great Yarmouth Row Houses on 01493 857900.

OPENING TIMES
Please ring 01493 857900

HOW TO FIND US
Direction: 3½ miles NE of Reedham on the N bank of River Yare. Accessible by hired boat, or by footpath from Halvergate (3½ miles)

Train: Berney Arms ¼ mile

Tel: 01493 857900

🐕 ⚠️

MAP Page 317 (3K)
OS Map 134, OL40: TG465049

Binham Market Cross
Norfolk

The tall shaft of a 15th-century cross, on the site of an annual fair held from the 1100s until the 1950s.

Managed by Binham Parochial Church Council.

OPENING TIMES
Any reasonable time

Binham Market Cross

HOW TO FIND US
Direction: Located on the Binham village green adjacent to the Priory

Bus: Sanders service 13 (Thu only) and 46 otherwise nearest service is Norfolk Green 29 to Wighton (2 mile walk)

MAP Page 317 (1H)
OS Map 132, 251: TF984396

Binham Priory
Norfolk

Among the most impressive monastic sites in East Anglia, Binham Priory retains its nave – now the parish church – virtually complete, with a striking 13th-century west front and triple tiers of late Norman arches within, along with screens revealing medieval saints peeping through later overpainting. The extensive ruins beyond, notably the massive piers of the fallen church tower, emphasise the original size of this Benedictine priory.

Major recent enhancements, carried out by local initiatives with English Heritage support, make a visit even more worthwhile. They include much improved disabled access, a fascinating display of site finds, toilets, and a children's activity area.

Managed by Binham Parochial Church Council.

Binham Priory

OPENING TIMES
Binham Priory (monastic ruins):
Any reasonable time

Priory Church:
Summer, daily	9am-6pm
Winter, daily	9am-4pm

HOW TO FIND US
Direction: ¼ mile NW of village of Binham on road off B1388

Bus: Sanders service 13 (Thu only) & 46 otherwise nearest service is Norfolk Green 29 to Wighton (2 mile walk)

Tel: 01328 830362

E ⚲ ⚲ P ♿

MAP Page 317 (1H)
OS Map 132, 251: TF982399

Blakeney Guildhall
Norfolk

A relic of Blakeney's medieval prosperity, the remains of a flint 15th-century merchant's house with complete brick-vaulted undercroft. Later the guildhall of the port's fish merchants.

Managed by Blakeney Parish Council.

OPENING TIMES
Any reasonable time

HOW TO FIND US
Direction: In Blakeney off A149

Train: Sheringham 9 miles

Bus: Norfolk Green Coasthopper service (CH3), Sanders service 13 (Thu only) and 46

Tel: 01263 741106

MAP Page 317 (1H)
OS Map 133, 251: TG028441

Burgh Castle
Norfolk

The imposing stone walls, with added towers for catapults, of a Roman 3rd-century 'Saxon Shore' fort. Panoramic views over Breydon Water, into which the fourth wall long since collapsed.

Burgh Castle

Managed by Norfolk Archaeological Trust.

OPENING TIMES
Any reasonable time

HOW TO FIND US
Direction: At far W end of Breydon Water on unclassified road, 3 miles W of Great Yarmouth

Train: Great Yarmouth 5 miles

Bus: First 5 from Great Yarmouth then a short walk

MAP Page 317 (3K)
OS Map 134, OL40: TG475047

Caister Roman Fort
Norfolk – NR30 5JS

The partial excavated remains of a Roman 'Saxon Shore' fort, including wall and ditch sections and building foundations. Built around AD 200 for a unit of the Roman army and navy, and occupied until the end of the 4th century.

Managed by Great Yarmouth Borough Council.

OPENING TIMES
Any reasonable time

HOW TO FIND US
Direction: From Great Yarmouth, follow the A149 northbound and then the A149 Caister Bypass. Follow brown tourist signs for Caister Roman Fort. From other directons follow signs for Great Yarmouth and then brown tourist signs from the Caister Bypass roundabout. Parking and the entrance to the Fort are situated off a lay-by on Norwich Road ¼ mile from the roundabout

Train: Great Yarmouth 3 miles

Bus: First services 1, 1A, 4; Sanders 6

MAP Page 317 (2K)
OS Map 134, OL40: TG517123

Castle Rising Castle
Norfolk – PE31 6AH

One of the biggest, most complete and most lavishly decorated Norman keeps in England, with an impressive entrance forebuilding, surrounded by stupendous earthworks. Begun in 1138 by William d'Albini for his wife, the widow of Henry I, in the 14th century it became the luxurious prison of Queen Isabella, widow (and alleged murderess) of Edward II.
www.castlerising.co.uk

Owned and managed by Lord Howard of Rising.

NON-MEMBERS
Adult	£4.00
Concession	£3.30
Child	£2.50

OPENING TIMES
1 Apr-1 Nov, daily (or dusk if earlier in Oct)	10am-6pm
2 Nov-28 Mar, Wed-Sun	10am-4pm
24-26 Dec	Closed

HOW TO FIND US
Direction: Located 4 miles NE of King's Lynn off A149

Train: King's Lynn 4½ miles

Bus: Norfolk Green 11 to Castle Rising

Tel: 01553 631330

⌂ ⚲ ⚲ ⚲ P ⚲ ♿ ⚠

Audio tours (charged).

Disabled access (exterior only, toilets).

Dogs on leads (restricted areas).

MAP Page 317 (2G)
OS Map 132, 250: TF666246

Castle Acre Priory, Castle and Bailey Gate

Norfolk – PE32 2XD

The delightful village of Castle Acre boasts an extraordinary wealth of history.

Situated on the Peddar's Way, a major trade and pilgrim route to Thetford, Bromholm Priory and Walsingham, it is a very rare and complete survival of a Norman planned settlement, including a castle, town, fine parish church and associated monastery. All this is the work of a powerful Norman baronial family, the Warennes, mainly during the 11th and 12th centuries.

First came the castle, founded soon after the Conquest by the first William de Warenne, probably as a stone 'country house'. During the first half of the 12th century, however, more disturbed conditions prompted its progressive conversion into a strong keep, further defended by stone walls and an immense system of earthworks. These massive ramparts and ditches are perhaps the finest castle earthworks anywhere in England.

Meanwhile, the 'planned town', deliberately established outside the castle, was also protected by ditched earthwork defences with stone gates. The north or Bailey Gate survives, with the main road into the village still running between its towers.

Visitors to Castle Acre can likewise trace the ancient street layout of this now peaceful village, lined with attractive flint or brick houses, before exploring both the great castle earthworks and the extensive priory remains.

A village and castle trail can be downloaded from the Castle Acre Priory page of the English Heritage website.

Castle Acre Castle and Bailey Gate
Norfolk

OPENING TIMES
Any reasonable time

HOW TO FIND US
Direction: Located at the E end of Castle Acre, 5 miles N of Swaffham

Bus: West Norfolk Community Transport (weekdays), Freestone Coaches 32; Peelings 1 (Tue)

🍴🐕⚠ (Castle only)

MAP Page 317 (2G)
OS Map 132, 236/238
Bailey Gate: TF819152
Castle: TF819152

Castle Acre Priory Norfolk – PE32 2XD

Among the largest and best preserved monastic sites in all England, Castle Acre Priory often surprises new visitors by its immense size and variety. Its foundation in about 1090 by William de Warenne II reflected his family's devotion to the famous French monastery of Cluny: the Cluniac order's love of architectural decoration is displayed in the beautiful west front of the great 12th-century priory church, bedecked with tiers of intersecting round arches. Beyond extend the impressive remains of the cloister and monks' living quarters, including a gigantic two-storey 24-seater toilet block.

Best preserved of all is the west range, virtually complete and fully roofed. Its timber-framed and flint-chequered porch and oriel-windowed prior's lodging form an outstandingly attractive grouping with the church's west front.

A mansion in itself, the lodging includes a chamber sumptuously revamped in early Tudor times for one of the last priors; with decorated fireplace, ceiling painted with Tudor roses, and two massive timber chests still in place. The adjacent prior's chapel was once even more elaborately adorned, with traces of medieval wall paintings still visible.

There is much more to see, including our exhibition and display of archaeological finds, site model and audio tour featuring a 15th-century chant from a Castle Acre song book. The recreated herb garden grows plants the monks would have used for medicinal and culinary purposes. There is also a large activities barn for schools. A priory terrain guide can be downloaded from the Castle Acre Priory page of the English Heritage website.

NON-MEMBERS

Adult	£5.80
Concession	£5.20
Child	£3.50
Family	£15.10

OPENING TIMES

1 Apr-4 Nov, daily	10am-5pm
5 Nov-28 Mar, Sat-Sun	10am-4pm
24-26 Dec and 1 Jan	Closed

HOW TO FIND US

Direction: ¼ mile W of village of Castle Acre, 5 miles N of Swaffham

Bus: West Norfolk Community Transport (weekdays), Freestone Coaches 32; Peelings 1 (Tue)

Tel: 01760 755394

Disabled access (ground floor and grounds only).

Toilets (a short walk. Not accessible for wheelchairs; 50 metres from entrance, with single step for access).

MAP Page 317 (2G)
OS Map 132, 236/238: TF814148

Check opening times at www.english-heritage.org.uk

Church of St John, Maddermarket, Norwich
Norfolk – NR2 1DS

© CCT

500-year-old St John's, which survived a gas explosion in 1876, is squeezed ingeniously into a cramped site. The almost square, light-filled interior is crowded with marvellous monuments, furnishings and rich stained glass. One of three CCT churches in Norwich.

Owned and managed by The Churches Conservation Trust.

OPENING TIMES
Please see Churches Conservation Trust website for current opening times

HOW TO FIND US
Train: Nearest 🚆 Norwich ½ mile

Bus: Route number 160

1 mile from Cow Tower

MAP Page 317 (2J)
OS Map 134, 237: TG229087

Church of the Holy Sepulchre, Thetford, Norfolk:
see Thetford, Church of the Holy Sepulchre – Page 163

Cow Tower, Norwich
Norfolk

One of the earliest purpose-built artillery blockhouses in England, this brick tower was built in c.1398-9 to command a strategic point in Norwich's city defences External viewing only.

Managed by Norwich City Council.

OPENING TIMES
Any reasonable time

HOW TO FIND US
Direction: In Norwich, near cathedral (approx. 1 mile walk)

Bus: From surrounding areas

Train: Norwich ½ mile

Tel: 01603 213434

🕎

MAP Page 317 (2J)
OS Map 134, OL40/237: TG240092

Creake Abbey
Norfolk

Tranquil ruins of an Augustinian abbey church, unusual because visibly reduced in size after a serious fire in the 15th century.

Managed by Mrs A C Scott.

OPENING TIMES
Any reasonable time

HOW TO FIND US
Direction: N of North Creake off B1355

Bus: Norfolk Green 27

🕎

MAP Page 317 (1H)
OS Map 132, 251: TF856395

Grime's Graves
See feature – Page 162

North Elmham Chapel
Norfolk

A place with an unusual story, illustrated on graphic panels. The small Norman chapel here stands on the site of an earlier timber church, probably the Saxon cathedral of East Anglia. In the 14th century it was converted into a fortified manor house by Henry Despenser, the unpopular Bishop of Norwich who brutally suppressed the Peasants' Revolt of 1381.

Managed by North Elmham Parish Council.

OPENING TIMES
Any reasonable time

HOW TO FIND US
Direction: Located 6 miles N of East Dereham on B1110

Bus: Konectbus service 7, 7A & 18. Carters service 9 (Wed only). Also National Express service 496

🕎

MAP Page 317 (2H)
OS Map 132, 238: TF988216

Great Yarmouth Row Houses and Greyfriars' Cloisters Norfolk – NR30 2RG

other now-demolished Row dwellings, a treasure trove for lovers of period decoration.

Nearby stands Greyfriars' Cloisters, the remains of a 13th-century friary of Franciscan 'grey friars', later swallowed up by Row development and converted into a number of dwellings large and small. Traces of their interior features can still be seen on the brick-built walls of parts of the cloister and church, laid bare by wartime bombing. Early 14th-century wall-paintings were discovered here in the 1960s.

NON-MEMBERS

Adult	£4.20
Concession	£3.80
Child	£2.50
Family	£10.90

OPENING TIMES

1 Apr-30 Sep, Mon-Fri 11am-4pm

Access to Greyfriars' Cloisters is by pre-arrangement only

HOW TO FIND US

Direction: Great Yarmouth, follow signs for Historic Quay. The houses are directly behind the Norfolk Nelson Museum on the Historic South Quay

Train: Great Yarmouth ½ mile

Bus: Bus services to Great Yarmouth are operated by Anglian (of Beccles), Ambassador Travel and First

Tel: 01493 857900

MAP Page 317 (2K)
OS Map 134, OL40
Houses: TG525072
Cloisters: TG524073

Living space was very much at a premium in early 17th-century Great Yarmouth, then among the most prosperous fishing port in England. Hence the inhabitants crowded into the town's distinctive 'Rows', a network of narrow alleyways linking Yarmouth's three main thoroughfares. Many 'Row houses' were damaged by World War II bombing or demolished during post-War clearances, but two surviving properties in the care of English Heritage show what these characteristic dwellings looked like at various stages in their history.

Both Row 111 and the Old Merchant's House were originally built in the early 17th century as wealthy merchants' residences, but later sub-divided into tenements. The Old Merchant's House, which has spectacular Jacobean plaster ceilings in two of its rooms, is presented as it was in about 1870, when the Atkins and Rope families of fishermen – represented by models of family members at work or rest – shared the property. Adjacent Row 111 house is shown as it was in about 1942 (just before it received a direct hit from an incendiary bomb), likewise with figures of the three families which then occupied parts of it. Both houses also display a wonderful collection of fixtures and fittings – including painted panels, elaborate wall-ties and door-knockers – rescued from

Grime's Graves – prehistoric flint mine

Norfolk – IP26 5DE

Grime's Graves is the only Neolithic flint mine open to visitors in Britain. A grassy lunar landscape of over 400 shafts, pits, quarries and spoil dumps, they were first named Grim's Graves by the Anglo-Saxons – meaning the pagan god Grim's quarries, or 'the Devil's holes'.

It was not until one of them was excavated by Canon Greenwell in 1870 that they were identified as flint mines dug over 5000 years ago, during the later Neolithic and Early Bronze Ages.

What the prehistoric miners sought here was the fine quality, jet-black flint floorstone, which occurs some nine to twelve metres below surface level. Digging with red-deer antler picks, they sank shafts and dug radiating galleries which followed the seams of flint. Today visitors can descend 9 metres (30 ft) by ladder into one excavated shaft – an unforgettable experience.

Grime's Graves flint was prized for its distinctive colour and easily 'knapped' qualities. Rough-outs of axes and other tools were made on site, but then traded on and finished elsewhere.

Set amid the distinctive Breckland heath landscape, Grime's Graves is also a Site of Special Scientific Interest: the habitat of a variety of rare and distinctive plants and animals. The Breckland flora are especially attractive from April to July.

A small introductory exhibition in the visitor centre includes information about Neolithic mining, a virtual tour of the mines and landscape, and touchable reproduction Neolithic tools. A trail leaflet guides visitors round the multi-period site, explaining features from the earliest times until today.

The family explorer kit will enable you to read vital clues about the site.

See the Neolithic mine, and the plants and creatures which thrive in this unique landscape.

NON-MEMBERS

Adult	£3.40
Concession	£3.10
Child	£2.00
Family	£8.80

No entry to the mines for children under 5 years of age

OPENING TIMES

1 Apr-30 Sep, daily	10am-5pm
1 Oct-4 Nov, Thu-Mon	10am-5pm
5 Nov-28 Mar	Closed

HOW TO FIND US

Direction: Located 7 miles NW of Thetford off A134

Train: Brandon 3½ miles

Bus: Coach Services Thetford service 40 to Lynford

Tel: 01842 810656

Disabled access (exhibition area only; access track rough).

Dogs on leads (restricted areas).

Visitors intending to descend the shaft should wear flat shoes.

MAP Page 317 (3G)
OS Map 144, 229: TL817899

St Mary's Church, East Bradenham
Norfolk – IP25 7QL

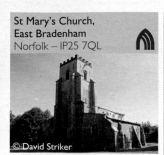
© David Striker

This simple church has a powerful tower and stands at the end of an avenue of lime trees. The bold, buttressed exterior in its grassy graveyard setting is striking. Inside, it is plainly furnished and gloriously lit, with several lovely memorials to local people.

Owned and managed by The Churches Conservation Trust.

OPENING TIMES
Open during daylight hours summer Sat & Sun

At other times keyholder nearby

HOW TO FIND US
Train: Nearest 🚉 Attleborough 11¼ miles

Bus: Route number 17 (occasional)

20 mins from Castle Acre Priory and Castle Acre

MAP Page 317 (2H)
OS Map 144, 237: TF931084

St Nicholas' Chapel, King's Lynn
Norfolk – PE30 1NH

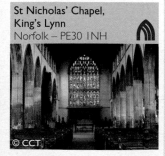
© CCT

Nine centuries of dazzling treasures can be found in England's largest chapel. Startlingly life-like painted figures celebrate Kings Lynn's seamen, merchants,

---

mayors and shopkeepers, and stunning carved woodwork adorns the interior, including the earliest known portrayal of an instrument in a church carving.

Owned and managed by The Churches Conservation Trust.

OPENING TIMES
Mid Jun-end Sep,
Tue & Sat   10.30am-4.30pm

HOW TO FIND US
Train: Nearest 🚉 King's Lynn 10 mins walk

Bus: Route numbers 2/4/35/44/C1/CH from bus station. Bus station in Vancouver Centre by Sainsbury's 10 mins walk

30 mins from Castle Rising Castle

MAP Page 317 (2G)
OS Map 132, 236/249/250: TF618204

St Olave's Priory
Norfolk

The wonderfully complete, 14th-century, brick-vaulted refectory undercroft – later a cottage occupied until 1902 – of a small Augustinian priory.

OPENING TIMES
Any reasonable time

HOW TO FIND US
Direction: Located 5½ miles SW of the town of Great Yarmouth on A143

Train: Haddiscoe 1¼ miles

Bus: Anglian 577, 581

Dogs on leads (restricted areas only).

MAP Page 317 (3K)
OS Map 134, OL40: TM459996

Thetford, Church of the Holy Sepulchre
Norfolk

The only surviving remains in England of a priory of Canons of the Holy Sepulchre, who aided pilgrims to Christ's tomb, the

---

ruined nave of their 14th-century church, later used as a barn.

Managed by Thetford Town Council.

OPENING TIMES
All year, daily   10am-5pm
(or dusk whichever is earlier)

25 Dec   Closed

HOW TO FIND US
Direction: Located on the W side of Thetford on A134

Bus: Coach Services of Thetford 40, 84, 86, 190, T1, T1A

Train: Thetford ¾ mile

🐕

MAP Page 317 (3H)
OS Map 144, 229: TL865831

Thetford Priory
Norfolk

The extensive remains of one of the most important East Anglian monasteries, the Cluniac Priory of Our Lady of Thetford, burial place of the earls and dukes of Norfolk for 400 years. Founded in the early 12th century, it owed much of its prosperity to a miraculous appearance of the Virgin Mary, whose statue here was discovered to conceal relics of saints, and became a magnet for pilgrims. Two of the greatest men in early Tudor England, Thomas Howard, victor of Flodden, and Henry Fitzroy, illegitimate son of Henry VIII, were buried near her shrine. Survivals include the lower walls of the church and cloister, along with the impressive shell of the priors' lodging and, reached by a pathway from the main site, an almost complete 14th-century gatehouse.

Managed by Thetford Town Council.

Thetford Priory

OPENING TIMES

1 Apr-30 Sep, daily	8am-6pm
1 Oct-28 Mar, daily	8am-4pm
25 Dec	Closed

HOW TO FIND US

Direction: Near Thetford station

Train: Thetford ¼ mile

Bus: See Church of the Holy Sepulchre

MAP Page 317 (3G)
OS Map 144, 229: TL865831

Thetford Warren Lodge
Norfolk

Probably built c. 1400 by the Prior of Thetford, this defensible lodge protected gamekeepers and hunting parties against armed poachers. Much later used by the local 'warreners' who harvested rabbits here.

OPENING TIMES
Any reasonable time

HOW TO FIND US

Direction: Located 2 miles W of Thetford off B1107

Train: Thetford 2½ miles

Bus: See above

MAP Page 317 (3G)
OS Map 144, 229: TL839984

Weeting Castle
Norfolk

The ruins of a substantial early, medieval moated manor house, built in local flint.

OPENING TIMES
Any reasonable time

HOW TO FIND US

Direction: Located 2 miles N of Brandon off B1106

Train: Brandon 1¼ miles

Bus: Coach Services 25, 28, 40 & 193

MAP Page 317 (3G)
OS Map 144, 229: TL778891

SUFFOLK

Bury St Edmunds Abbey
Suffolk

The extensive remains of the wealthiest and most powerful Benedictine monastery in England, shrine of St Edmund. They include the complete 14th-century Great Gate and Norman Tower, and the impressive ruins and altered west front of the immense church.

Managed by St Edmundsbury Borough Council.

OPENING TIMES
Any reasonable time

HOW TO FIND US

Direction: E end of town centre

Train: Bury St Edmunds 1 mile

Bus: From surrounding areas

Tel: 01284 764667

MAP Page 317 (4G)
OS Map 155, 211: TL857642

Don't forget to check opening times online before you visit
www.english-heritage.org.uk/daysout/properties

Church of St Mary the Virgin, Stonham Parva
Suffolk – IP14 5JL

© CCT

Spectacular and airy, this medieval flint-work church lies behind the village and beside the Old Hall. The nave and chancel are impressively high, and the double hammerbeam roof is a splendid example of medieval craftsmanship.

Owned and managed by The Churches Conservation Trust.

OPENING TIMES
Open daily during daylight hours

HOW TO FIND US

Train: Nearest 🚆 Needham Market 3½ miles

Bus: Route numbers 110/460

30 mins from Framlingham Castle

MAP Page 317 (4H)
OS Map 155, 211: TM115601

Framlingham Castle
See feature – Page 166

Landguard Fort Suffolk – IP11 3TX

The site of the last opposed seaborne invasion of England in 1667 and the first land battle of the Royal Marines. The current fort was built in the 18th century and modified in the 19th century with substantial additional 19th/20th-century outside batteries.

Guided tours and audio tours of the fort are supplemented by an audio-visual presentation of the site's history, and by guided tours of the outside batteries.

The nearby submarine mining building houses Felixstowe Museum's Collections of local interest.

Managed by Landguard Fort Trust.

NON-MEMBERS

Adult	£3.50
Concession	£2.50
Child	£1.50

Free entry for children under 5 and wheelchair users

OPENING TIMES

1 Apr-31 May, daily	10am-5pm
1 Jun-30 Sep, daily	10am-6pm
1 Oct-4 Nov, daily	10am-5pm

Last admission 1 hour before closing

There may be a premium payable by all visitors, including members, on event days – please check our website for details

Tel: 07749 695523

HOW TO FIND US

Direction: 1 mile S of Felixstowe town centre – follow signs to Landguard Point

Train: Felixstowe 2½ miles

Bus: First service 77 to Felixstowe Dock

Tel: 07749 6955523

MAP Page 317 (5J)
OS Map 169, 197: TM284319

Leiston Abbey
Suffolk

The mainly 14th-century remains of an abbey of Premonstratensian canons. Among Suffolk's most impressive monastic ruins, with some spectacular architectural features.

Managed by Pro Corda Music School.

OPENING TIMES

Any reasonable time

HOW TO FIND US

Direction: N of Leiston off B1069

Bus: Nightingale 196 and Simonds 626 (Tue) pass the site. First services 64; Anglian service 165 & 197 all serve Leiston (1½ mile walk)

Train: Saxmundham 5 miles

MAP Page 317 (4K)
OS Map 156, 212: TM445642

Lindsey St James's Chapel
Suffolk

A pretty, thatched, 13th-century chapel with lancet windows.

OPENING TIMES

All year, daily	10am-4pm

HOW TO FIND US

Direction: Located on an unclassified road ½ mile E of Rose Green and 8 miles E of Sudbury

Train: Sudbury 8 miles

Bus: Hadleigh Community Transport 'Suffolk Links Cosford' demand responsive bus service telephone 01473 828202 to book

Disabled access (single step).

MAP Page 317 (5H)
OS Map 155, 196: TL9784444

Framlingham Castle Suffolk – IP13 9BP

Framlingham is a magnificent example of a late 12th-century castle. Built by Roger Bigod, Earl of Norfolk, one of the most influential people at the court of the Plantagenet kings, the castle, together with Framlingham Mere, was designed both as a stronghold and a proclamation of power and status. Architecturally, the fortress is notable for its curtain wall with regular mural towers, being an early example of this style.

NON-MEMBERS

Adult	£6.50
Concession	£5.90
Child	£3.90
Family	£16.90

OPENING TIMES

1 Apr–4 Nov, daily	10am-5pm
5 Nov–17 Feb, Sat-Sun	10am-4pm
18-22 Feb, daily	10am-4pm
23 Feb-28 Mar, Sat-Sun	10am-4pm
24-26 Dec and 1 Jan	Closed

The property may close early if an event is booked, please ring in advance for details

HOW TO FIND US

Direction: In Framlingham on B1116

Train: Wickham Market 6½ miles; Saxmundham 7 miles

Bus: First service 63; Far East Travel 118, 119; Nightingale 482

Tel: 01728 724189

Local Tourist Information
Woodbridge: 01394 382240

Disabled access (grounds and ground floor only).

Parking charge, refundable to EH members and paying visitors on admission.

New refreshment kiosk in castle grounds

MAP Page 317 (4J)
OS Map 156, 212: TM287637

The castle fulfilled a number of roles. It was at the centre of the struggle between the Bigod barons and the Crown, and Mary Tudor mustered her supporters here in 1553, before being crowned Queen. At the end of the 16th century it was a prison; later still a Poorhouse was built within the walls. Today the imposing stone walls and crenellated towers with their ornate Tudor chimneys dominate, while the grassy earthworks around the castle are subdued reminders of its outer defences. To the west, the Mere provides a stunning setting.

Visitors can explore over 800 years of life at Framlingham Castle in an introductory exhibition in the Poorhouse, which tells the story of the people who lived in the castle during its long and varied history. The displays illustrate the struggle for power between monarchs and the lords of Framlingham;

the tragic stories of family members Anne Boleyn and Catherine Howard, both married to and beheaded by Henry VIII; the accession of Queen Mary Tudor; and the Poorhouse, still in use until 1839.

The Poorhouse Kitchen provides an area where visitors can enjoy a selection of factual and fictional books relating to Framlingham Castle. Entry also includes access to the Lanman Trust's Museum of local history.

Embark on a self-guided journey of discovery around the site with our themed trails and lively audio tour, and explore the Mere, the castle's outer courts and the wall-walk with its spectacular views over the surrounding landscape. Younger visitors can discover more about life in the castle with a variety of themed games and interactives.

www.english-heritage.org.uk/ framlinghamcastle

Moulton Packhorse Bridge
Suffolk

A pretty, four-arched, late medieval bridge spanning the River Kennett on the old route from Cambridge to Bury St Edmunds.

OPENING TIMES
Any reasonable time

HOW TO FIND US
Direction: In Moulton off B1085, 4 miles E of Newmarket

Train: Kennett 2 miles

Bus: Stephensons 312, 400 & 401; Suffolk CC service 310, 311A & 311B

MAP Page 317 (4G)
OS Map 154, 210/226: TL698645

St Peter's Church, Claydon
Suffolk – IP6 0EQ

© CCT

This originally Saxon church has wonderful views over the Gipping Valley, and is full of stunning, vibrant stained glass and extravagant carvings. A rector was responsible for the design of some of the stained glass, and it is possible he carved some of the stonework too.

Owned and managed by The Churches Conservation Trust.

OPENING TIMES
Open daily during daylight hours

HOW TO FIND US
Train: Nearest ⊠ Westerfield 2¾ miles, Ipswich 4 miles

Bus: Routes 18A/414/988/87/110

35 mins from Framlingham Castle

MAP Page 317 (4J)
OS Map 169, 197: TM137499

Saxtead Green Post Mill
Suffolk – IP13 9QQ

This fine four-sailed com-grinding 'post mill', whose whole body – turned by a secondary windmill or 'fantail' – revolves on its three-storey roundhouse base, is of a type characteristic of Suffolk since around the 13th century. It originates in about 1796, but has been three times rebuilt and raised: in 1854 it was given a full set of new cast-iron machinery. Though commercial milling ceased when the last miller died in 1947, the mill is still in full working order. Guided by our audio tour, climb the stairs to the various floors, which are full of fascinating mill machinery. Framlingham Castle is nearby.

NON-MEMBERS

Adult	£3.50
Concession	£3.20
Child	£2.10

OPENING TIMES
1 Apr-30 Sep,
Fri-Sat &
Bank Hols   12pm-5pm

HOW TO FIND US
Direction: 2½ miles NW of Framlingham on A1120

Train: Wickham Market 9 miles

Bus: Far East Travel 119

Tel: 01728 685789

MAP Page 317 (4J)
OS Map 156, 212: TM253644

Orford Castle Suffolk – IP12 2ND

© Skyscan Balloon Photography

The unique polygonal tower keep of Orford Castle stands beside the pretty town and former port, which Henry II also developed here in the 1160s. His aim was to counterbalance the power of turbulent East Anglian barons like Hugh Bigod of Framlingham, and to guard the coast against foreign mercenaries called to their aid.

An 18-sided drum with three square turrets and a forebuilding reinforcing its entrance, the keep

was built to a highly innovative design. The progress of its construction between 1165 and 1173 is extensively recorded in royal documents. Both exterior and interior survive almost intact, allowing visitors to explore the basement, with its vital well, and the lower and upper halls – the latter the principal room of the castle. Around these polygonal rooms is a maze of passages leading to the chapel, kitchen and other chambers in the turrets. From the roof there are magnificent views seaward to Orford Ness.

Recent archaeological work has provided a clearer understanding of how the castle worked and a painting by Frank Gardiner shows how the keep and its vanished outer defences looked in their heyday. The upper hall now houses a display by the Orford Museum Trust, including local finds of Roman brooches, medieval seals and

coins and some of the borough regalia. Graphic panels display maps, documents, pictures and photographs, illustrating Orford's history up to the 20th century.

NON-MEMBERS

Adult	£5.80
Concession	£5.20
Child	£3.50
Family	£15.10

OPENING TIMES

1 Apr-4 Nov, daily	10am-5pm
5 Nov-28 Mar, Sat-Sun	10am-4pm
24-26 Dec and 1 Jan	Closed

HOW TO FIND US

Direction: In Orford on B1084, 20 miles NE of Ipswich

Train: Wickham Market 8 miles

Bus: M&R Travel service 71

Tel: 01394 450472

🎧 ♿ 🖥 P 📷 ⚠ OVP

MAP Page 317 (4J)
OS Map 169, 212: TM419499

Associated attractions in the East of England

These visitor attractions, all independent of EH, offer discounts to our members. Please call before you visit to confirm details. A valid EH membership card must be produced for each member.

Felixstowe Museum
Suffolk IP11 3TW

Fourteen display rooms of local social, military and aviation history, housed within the 1878-built Submarine Mining Establishment. Large photograph archive, shop and tearoom. New exhibitions, including *The Queen's Jubilee*.

Next to Landguard Fort
Tel: 01394 674355
www.felixstowe-museum.co.uk

20% discount on entry

Holkham Hall
Norfolk NR23 1AB

Surrounded by acres of rolling parkland, this grand Palladian Hall is full of stunning architecture and art, original furniture and classical statuary. Visit the 18th-century walled gardens to see restoration work in progress.

2 miles West of Wells-next-the-Sea
Tel: 01328 710227
www.holkham.co.uk

20% discount on entry (Not valid on event days)

Give the gift of membership

English Heritage Gift of Membership makes the ideal present – a whole year of fantastic days out at over 400 properties including historic houses, castles and gardens.

Call 0870 333 1182 or visit **www.english-heritage.org.uk/gift** for more details.

Sample delicious refreshments at many of our properties

Check property listings for details of cafés.

IWM Duxford
Cambridgeshire CB22 4QR

Discover the history of aviation in times of war and peace in one of the world's finest aviation heritage sites; explore over 200 aircraft including the legendary Spitfire and Concorde.

10 mins from Duxford Chapel
Tel: 01223 835 000
www.iwm.org.uk

2 for 1 adult entry (Not valid on air shows and some event days)

Layer Marney Tower
Essex CO5 9US

England's tallest Tudor gatehouse, built in 1523. Climb the tower to enjoy magnificent views. Children's play areas, gardens, parkland, wildlife walks, gift shop and tearoom serving light lunches and homemade cakes.

6 miles to A12 Kelvedon
Tel: 01206 330784
www.layermarneytower.co.uk

£1 off admission (Not valid on event days or bank hols)

EH Members   OVP Holders ⛨? Discounted Child Places Included

Somerleyton Hall & Gardens
Suffolk NR32 5QQ

Originally Jacobean, extensively re-modelled in 1844. 12 acres of fabulous landscaped gardens including original ancient yew hedge maze. Guided tours of Hall. Excellent tearoom and gift shop. Offer not valid on Bank Holiday weekends.

10 mins from centre of Lowestoft

Tel: 01502 734901

www.somerleyton.co.uk

3 for 2 on Hall
tour and garden ⛨ OVP

Time and Tide – Museum of Great Yarmouth Life
Norfolk NR30 3BX

A short walk from the South Quay and Seafront. Housed in a former Victorian herring curing factory which has been beautifully restored, this museum tells the story of Great Yarmouth's rich maritime heritage.

½ mile from Great Yarmouth Row Houses

Tel: 01493 743930

www.museums.norfolk.gov.uk

2 for 1
entry ⛨ OVP

Woburn Abbey
Bedfordshire MK17 9WA

Home to the Duke of Bedford and birthplace of Afternoon Tea. Enjoy priceless art and treasures and beautiful gardens, all set in 3000 acres of deer park.

10 mins from J13 of M1

Tel: 01525 290333

www.woburn.co.uk/abbey

20% discount on entry
(Not valid on event days) ⛨

171

Holiday Cottage at Audley End House

Enjoy the most delightful of English Heritage's treasures at Audley End House

Cambridge Lodge, Audley End House

See pages 148-150.

For details on availability and how to book visit
www.english-heritage.org.uk/book-and-buy/holiday-cottages

Discounts for members

Kirby Muxloe Castle

EAST MIDLANDS

PROPERTIES

East Midlands properties consist of:

25	English Heritage
6	The Churches Conservation Trust
11	Associated Attractions

Remember to check opening times before you visit any of our properties www.english-heritage. org.uk/daysout

Details of local public transport information in England are available from Traveline www.traveline.org.uk or call 0871 200 2233.

174

Bolsover Castle

DERBYSHIRE

Arbor Low Stone Circle and Gib Hill Barrow
Bolsover Castle
Bolsover Cundy House
Hardwick Old Hall
Hob Hurst's House
Nine Ladies Stone Circle
Peveril Castle
Sutton Scarsdale Hall
Wingfield Manor

LEICESTERSHIRE

Ashby de la Zouch Castle
Jewry Wall
Kirby Muxloe Castle

LINCOLNSHIRE

Bolingbroke Castle
Gainsborough Old Hall
Lincoln Medieval Bishops' Palace
Sibsey Trader Windmill
Tattershall College

NORTHAMPTONSHIRE

Apethorpe Hall
Chichele College
Eleanor Cross, Geddington
Kirby Hall
Rushton Triangular Lodge

NOTTINGHAMSHIRE

Mattersey Priory
Rufford Abbey

RUTLAND

Lyddington Bede House

EAST MIDLANDS

Glossop

Buxton

Chesterfield

Bakewell

Worksop

Mansfield

Derbyshire

Nottinghamshire

Derby

Nottingham

Loughborough

Leicestershire

Leicester

Market Harborough

Gainsborough

Market Rasen

Lincoln

Lincolnshire

Skegness

Boston

Grantham

Spalding

Oakham

Rutland

Corby

Kettering

Northamptonshire

Daventry

Northampton

Brackley

HIGHLIGHTS FOR 2012/13 IN THE EAST MIDLANDS

- **Kirby Hall:** one of England's greatest Elizabethan houses, with exceptional gardens.
- **Bolsover Castle:** a uniquely preserved survival from an age of extravagance.
- **Peveril Castle:** stunning views over the Peak District from this Norman fortress.

DERBYSHIRE

All Saints' Church, Kedleston
Derbyshire – DE22 5JH

© CCT

All Saints' church is all that remains of the medieval village of Kedleston. A dazzling marble tomb, with life-size figures, floats on a sea of green translucent quartz, in its own chapel with spectacular stained glass windows. Carved monsters surround the Norman doorway.

Owned and managed by The Churches Conservation Trust.

OPENING TIMES

26 Mar-30 Oct, Mon-Wed during daylight hours;
Sat-Sun   11am-5pm

HOW TO FIND US

Train: Nearest 🚉 Derby 5 miles

Bus: 109

30 mins from Wingfield Manor

MAP Page 318 (3E)
OS Map 119/128, 259: SK313404

Arbor Low Stone Circle and Gib Hill Barrow
Derbyshire

The region's most important prehistoric site, Arbor Low is a Neolithic henge monument atmospherically set amid high moorland. Within an earthen bank and ditch, a circle of some 50 white limestone slabs, all now fallen, surrounds a central stone 'cove' – a feature found only in major sacred sites. Nearby is enigmatic Gib Hill, a large burial mound.

Please note: The farmer who owns access to the property will levy a charge for entry.

Managed by Peak District National Park Authority.

OPENING TIMES

Any reasonable time

Access charge of £1 per person to cross private land to the monument

HOW TO FIND US

Direction: ½ mile E of A515, 2 miles S of Monyash

Train: Buxton 10 miles

Bus: TM Travel (Sun only) service 181 passes the site, but Bowers service 42/42A, Warringtons 449 and Clowes service 446 both serve Parsley Hay which is within a 1 mile walk to the two locations

Tel: 01629 816200

🐾

MAP Page 318 (2E)
OS Map 119, OL24: SK160636

Bolsover Castle
See feature – page 178

Bolsover Cundy House
Derbyshire

This charming cottage-like 17th-century conduit house, with vaulted stone-slab roof, once supplied water to Bolsover Castle.

Managed by Bolsover Civic Society.

OPENING TIMES

Any reasonable time

HOW TO FIND US

Direction: Off M1 at junction 29A, follow signs for Bolsover Castle. At junction of Craggs Rd and Houghton Rd, Bolsover, 6 miles E of Chesterfield on A362

Train: Chesterfield 6 miles or Langwith – Whaley Thorns 4½ miles

Bus: Stagecoach in Chesterfield service 82 & TM Travel Bolsover town services B2 & B3 actually pass the property. Stagecoach Chesterfield services 53, 53A serve Hilltop Avenue a short walk from the Cundy House

Tel: 01246 822844 (Bolsover Castle)

MAP Page 319 (2F)
OS Map 120, 269: SK471709

Hardwick Old Hall
Derbyshire – S44 5QJ

The imposing shell of the remodelled family home of Bess of Hardwick, one of the most remarkable and most formidable women of Elizabethan England. Born on this site the daughter of an impoverished country squire, she rose via four increasingly advantageous marriages and much social manoeuvring to become Countess of Shrewsbury, and perhaps the richest woman in England. A friend and then enemy of Mary Queen of Scots, she was treated with respect even by Queen Elizabeth.

To celebrate her success and proclaim her status, Bess transformed her birthplace from a modest medieval manor house into a luxurious Elizabethan mansion. Completed by 1591, perhaps largely to Bess's own designs, the Old Hall was almost immediately superseded by her grander New Hall which stands beside it, becoming a guest and service wing to the newer mansion.

Though the Old Hall is now roofless, you can still ascend through four storeys to admire surviving decorative plasterwork and overmantels in the former staterooms, and view the kitchen and service rooms. An exhibition describes Bess's adventures in architecture, and on the ground floor there is a virtual tour of the first floor rooms (which are only accessible via steps).

Managed by English Heritage and owned by the National Trust.

 Holiday cottage available to let – see opposite

NON-MEMBERS

Adult	£5.00
Concession	£4.50
Child	£3.00
Family	£13.00

National Trust members admitted free, but small charge at EH events. Tickets for the New Hall (the National Trust) and joint tickets for both properties available at extra cost

OPENING TIMES

1 Apr-4 Nov, Wed-Sun & Bank Hols	10am-5pm
5 Nov-28 Mar, Sat-Sun	10am-4pm

Free members' guided tours 28 Nov, 30 Jan, 27 Mar — 11am & 2pm

HOW TO FIND US

Direction: 9½ miles SE of Chesterfield, off A6175 (J29 of M1)

Train: Chesterfield 8 miles

Bus: Trent Barton/Stagecoach in Chesterfield 'Pronto' service or G&J Hallmark service 49 (alight Glapwell 'Young Vanish', then 2 mile walk) or Stagecoach/TM Travel serices 96/97/97A to Hardstoft and 2 mile walk

Tel: 01246 850431

MAP Page 319 (2F)
OS Map 120, 269: SK462637

Hob Hurst's House
Derbyshire

A square prehistoric burial mound with earthwork ditch and bank, amid remote moorland. Named after a local goblin.

Managed by the Peak District National Park Authority.

OPENING TIMES
Any reasonable time

HOW TO FIND US

Direction: On open moorland from unclassified road off B5057, 9 miles W of Chesterfield

Train: Chesterfield 9 miles

Bus: TM Travel services 214 & TM Travel/Trent-Barton 215 to Beeley then walk 2 mile

Tel: 01629 816200

MAP Page 318 (2E)
OS Map 119, OL24: SK287692

Nine Ladies Stone Circle
Derbyshire

A small, early Bronze Age stone circle traditionally believed to represent nine ladies turned to stone as a penalty for dancing on Sunday. Their fiddler became the nearby King Stone. Part of an extensive complex of prehistoric remains on Stanton Moor.

Managed by Peak District National Park Authority.

OPENING TIMES
Any reasonable time

HOW TO FIND US

Direction: From an unclassified road off A6, 5 miles SE of Bakewell

Train: Matlock 4½ miles

Bus: Stagecoach/Hulleys service 172 to Stanton in Peak (within 1 mile)

Tel: 01629 816200

MAP Page 318 (2E)
OS Map 119, OL24: SK249635

Check opening times at www.english-heritage.org.uk

Bolsover Castle Derbyshire – S44 6PR

There is nothing else in Britain quite like Bolsover Castle – a unique survival of a 17th-century fantasy mansion intended solely for pleasure and extravagant display.

Discovery Centre exhibition

The Star Chamber

Visit the fairytale Little Castle and our new discovery centre.

- 🍽 Available for corporate and private hire
- 🔔 Licensed for civil wedding ceremonies

NON-MEMBERS
Adult	£8.00
Concession	£7.20
Child	£4.80
Family	£20.80

OPENING TIMES
1 Apr-4 Nov, daily	10am-5pm
5 Nov-17 Feb, Sat-Sun	10am-4pm
18-22 Feb, daily	10am-4pm
23 Feb-28 Mar, Sat-Sun	10am-4pm
24-26 Dec and 1 Jan	Closed

Part of the castle may close for 1 hour if an event is booked. Please call to check

Free members' guided tours
14 Nov, 12 Dec, 16 Jan, 13 Feb, 13 Mar   11am & 2pm

HOW TO FIND US
Direction: In Bolsover, 6 miles E of Chesterfield on A632. Off M1 at junction 29A (signposted)

Train: Chesterfield 6 miles

Bus: G&J Holmes service 49; TM Travel 53A (Sun only), B2 & B3; Doyles 81; Stagecoach services 82 & 83 pass close to the castle entrance

Tel: 01246 822844

Local Tourist Information (Chesterfield): 01246 345777

Parking (in castle car park, off main gate. Charge payable, refundable to EH members and paying visitors on admission). The coach drop-off point is in the council car park opposite.

There is good access to the grounds, but please note that the Little Castle is not accessible to wheelchairs.

MAP Page 319 (2F)
OS Map 120, 269: SK470707

NEW FOR 2012
A new audio visual display will explore the links between horse menage and dressage.

Dominating the countryside from its hilltop like a great ship, Bolsover occupies the site of a medieval castle built by the Peverel family. Sir Charles Cavendish – who already owned several other mansions, including one only a few miles away – bought the old fortress in 1612 and began work on his Little Castle project. Though playfully battlemented and pinnacled, his creation was not designed for defence, but as a fashionable retreat into an imaginary golden age of chivalry, courtly love – and opulent wealth.

His son William – playboy, poet, courtier and later Royalist general and first Duke of Newcastle – inherited the Little Castle in 1617 and set about its completion, assisted by the architect John Smythson. The exquisitely carved fireplaces and richly-coloured murals and panelling of its interiors still take the visitor on an allegorical journey from earthly concerns to heavenly (and erotic) delights.

William also added the immense Terrace Range, now a dramatic roofless shell. To show off his achievement, in 1634 he invited King Charles I and his court to *Love's Welcome to Bolsover*, a masque specially written by Ben Jonson for performance in the Fountain Garden. Finally he constructed the cavernous Riding House, with its magnificent roof, among the finest surviving indoor riding schools in the country. Here he indulged his passion for training great horses in stately dressage.

Following years of restoration by English Heritage, it is easy to imagine Bolsover as the setting for Cavendish's lavish lifestyle, attended by armies of servants from well-born gentleman ushers to the 'necessary woman' who emptied the chamberpots.

A family-friendly interactive exhibition in the Riding House stables introduces the site and explores the legacy of William Cavendish, his passion for horses and his contribution to the modern art of dressage. Includes dressing-up clothes and a replica 17th-century saddle children can sit on. See the model and film of the Little Castle, and find out about a lavish banquet held there for the king and queen in 1634. Disabled access to some parts of the Riding House and Terrace Range is subject to seasonal changes, please call 01246 822844 in advance of your visit for further details.

www.english-heritage.org.uk/bolsovercastle

www.facebook.com/bolsovercastle

Peveril Castle Derbyshire – S33 8WQ

Perched high above the pretty village of Castleton, the castle offers breathtaking views of the Peak District. Founded soon after 1066 by William Peverel, one of William the Conqueror's most trusted knights, it played an important role in guarding the Peak Forest.

Henry II made a number of additions to 'Castle Peak' (as it was known in the Middle Ages). Most notable is the great square keep, with its round-headed windows, built in 1176. Thirteenth-century developments included the great hall, and though by 1400 the fortress had ceased to be strategically important, its impregnability guaranteed its continued use as a prison.

Displays in the visitor centre tell the story of Peveril as the focal point of the Royal Forest of the Peak, a royal hunting preserve since the 11th century.

Wheelchair access is available to the visitor centre only.

www.english-heritage.org.uk/peverilcastle

NON-MEMBERS

Adult	£4.50
Concession	£4.10
Child	£2.70
Family	£11.70

OPENING TIMES

1 Apr-4 Nov, daily	10am-5pm
5 Nov-17 Feb, Sat-Sun	10am-4pm
18-22 Feb, daily	10am-4pm
23 Feb-28 Mar, Sat-Sun	10am-4pm
24-26 Dec and 1 Jan	Closed

HOW TO FIND US

Direction: Via the market place in Castleton; 15 miles W of Sheffield on A6187

Train: Hope 2½ miles

Bus: Hulley's 68,173, 174, 272, 273, 274, 276; First 51A, 272; TM Travel service 242, 272, 273, 274 & 373 all to Castleton then short walk

Tel: 01433 620613

Parking (in town).

MAP Page 318 (2E)
OS Map 110, OL1: SK149826

Sutton Scarsdale Hall
Derbyshire

The imposing shell of a grandiose Georgian mansion built in 1724-9, with an immensely columned exterior. Roofless since 1919, when its interiors were dismantled and some exported to America: but there is still much to discover within, including traces of sumptuous plasterwork. Set amid contemporary garden remains, including a ha-ha ditch and parish church.

OPENING TIMES

Summer, daily	10am-6pm
Rest of year, daily	10am-4pm
24-26 Dec and 1 Jan	Closed

HOW TO FIND US

Direction: Between Chesterfield and Bolsover, 1½ miles S of Arkwright Town

Train: Chesterfield 5 miles

Bus: G&J Holmes 'Hallmark' service 48

P A &

MAP Page 319 (2F)
OS Map 120, 269: SK442689

Travel back in time at Bolsover Castle with Will and the Time Travellers Go Gang

For bookings visit www.english-heritage.org.uk/timetravellersgo or call 0870 333 1183

Wingfield Manor Derbyshire – DE55 7NH

The vast and immensely impressive ruins of a palatial medieval manor house arranged round a pair of courtyards, with a huge undercrofted Great Hall and a defensible High Tower 22 metres (72 feet) tall. This monument to late medieval 'conspicuous consumption' was built in the 1440s for the wealthy Ralph, Lord Cromwell, Treasurer of England. Later the home of Bess of Hardwick's husband, the Earl of Shrewsbury, who imprisoned Mary Queen of Scots here in 1569, 1584 and 1585.

Please note: Wingfield Manor is part of a working farm and the owner's privacy should be respected at all times.

No access to the public except by pre-booked guided tours.

NON-MEMBERS

Adult	£5.50
Concession	£5.00
Child	£3.30

OPENING TIMES

Entry by pre-booked guided tours only, on first Sat of the month Apr-Sep

Call for full details of opening times and other site facilities

HOW TO FIND US

Direction: 17 miles N of Derby; 11 miles S of Chesterfield on B5035; ½ mile S of South Wingfield. From M1 junction 28, W on A38, A615 (Matlock Road) at Alfreton, 1½ miles and turn onto B5035

Train: Alfreton 4 miles

Bus: Yourbus 140 & 142; TM Travel service 150

Tel: 0870 333 1183 to book (Customer Services)

[ ] [ ]
Parking (none on site or in gateway).

MAP Page 318 (3E)
OS Map 119, 269: SK374548

LEICESTERSHIRE

Ashby de la Zouch Castle Leicestershire – LE65 1BR

Ashby Castle forms the backdrop to the famous jousting scenes in Sir Walter Scott's classic novel of 1819, *Ivanhoe*. Now a ruin, the castle began as a manor house in the 12th century. It only achieved castle status in the 15th century, by which time the hall and buttery had been enlarged with a solar to the east and a large integral kitchen added to the west.

Between 1474 and his execution by Richard III in 1483, Edward IV's Chamberlain Lord Hastings added the chapel and the impressive keep-like Hastings Tower – a castle within a castle. Visitors can climb the 24 metre (78 feet) high tower, which offers fine views. Later the castle hosted many royal visitors, including Henry VII, Mary Queen of Scots, James I and Charles I.

A Royalist stronghold during the Civil War, the castle finally fell to Parliament in 1646, and was then made unusable. An underground passage from the kitchen to the tower, probably created during this war, can still be explored today. Archaeologists recently investigated the mysterious castle garden, famous for its elaborately shaped sunken features.

Interpretation boards include beautiful illustrations evoking the splendour of Lord Hastings' additions to the castle. The audio guide provides an amusing account of the castle's dramatic history, drawing upon a masque performed here for Alice Spencer, Countess of Derby, in the early 17th century.

www.english-heritage.org.uk/
ashbydelazouchcastle

NON-MEMBERS

Adult	£4.50
Concession	£4.10
Child	£2.70
Family	£11.70

OPENING TIMES

1 Apr-30 Jun, Thu-Mon	10am-5pm
1 Jul-31 Aug, daily	10am-5pm
1 Sep-4 Nov, Thu-Mon	10am-5pm
5 Nov-10 Feb, Sat-Sun	10am-4pm
11-15 Feb, Mon, Thu-Fri	10am-4pm
16 Feb-28 Mar, Sat-Sun	10am-4pm
24-26 Dec and 1 Jan	Closed

HOW TO FIND US

Direction: In Ashby de la Zouch, 12 miles S of Derby on A511. Restricted parking on site, please park in town car park

Train: Burton on Trent 9 miles

Bus: Macpherson Coaches 2; Arriva 4, 9A; Cresswells 7 & 129; Arriva/Midland Classic 9

Local Tourist Information:
01530 411767

Tel: 01530 413343

Disabled access (grounds only).

Parking (restricted on site, please park in town car park – charge applies).

MAP Page 318 (4E)
OS Map 128, 245: SK361166

Jewry Wall
Leicestershire – LE1 4LB

A length of Roman bath-house wall over 9 metres (30 feet) high, near a museum displaying the archaeology of Leicester and its region. Graphic panels describe the Roman baths.

Managed by Leicester City Council Parks and Gardens.

OPENING TIMES
Any reasonable time

HOW TO FIND US
Direction: In St Nicholas St, W of Church of St Nicholas

Train: Leicester ¾ mile

Bus: Various services operated by First, Stagecoach, Thurmaston Bus, Arriva, NJ Travel, Kinch Bus, Robinson's and Coachcare

Tel: 01162 254971 (Jewry Wall Museum)

Parking (by museum, within St Nicholas Circle).

MAP Page 319 (4F)
OS Map 140, 233: SK582045

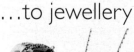

Kirby Muxloe Castle
Leicestershire – LE9 2DH

The picturesque moated remains – including the fine gatehouse and a complete corner tower – of this brick-built fortified mansion have recently been extensively conserved by English Heritage. Begun in 1480 by Lord Hastings, the castle was left unfinished after his execution by Richard III in 1483.

NON-MEMBERS
Adult	£3.50
Concession	£3.20
Child	£2.10

OPENING TIMES
5 May-31 Aug,
Sat, Sun & Bank Hols   10am-5pm

HOW TO FIND US
Direction: 4 miles W of Leicester off B5380; close to M1 junction 21A, northbound exit only

Train: Leicester 5 miles

Bus: NJ Travel service 13A

Tel: 01162 386886

MAP Page 319 (4F)
OS Map 140, 233: SK524046

LINCOLNSHIRE

Bolingbroke Castle
Lincolnshire

The remains of a 13th-century hexagonal castle, birthplace in 1366 of the future King Henry IV, with adjacent earthworks. Besieged and taken by Cromwell's Parliamentarians in 1643.

Managed by Heritage Lincolnshire.

OPENING TIMES
Any reasonable time

HOW TO FIND US
Direction: In Old Bolingbroke, 16 miles N of Boston off A16

Train: Thorpe Culvert 10 miles

Bus: Translinc Spilsby Call Connect (TC Minicoaches) service 6S will operate to Old Bolebrooke on request. To book telephone 0845 234 3344

Tel: 01529 461499

MAP Page 319 (2J)
OS Map 122, 273: TF349650

Gainsborough Old Hall
Lincolnshire – DN21 2NB

Gainsborough Old Hall is among the biggest and best-preserved medieval manor houses in England, part timber-framed but mostly brick-built. Later 15th-century with Elizabethan additions, it has an impressive kitchen with an enormous fireplace, a noble

Gainsborough Old Hall

great hall, and an imposing lodgings tower. Many rooms are furnished as they may have appeared in the 15th century, and there is an exhibition tracing the Hall's later links with the Pilgrim Fathers.

Managed by Lincolnshire County Council.

NON-MEMBERS

Adult	£6.00
Child	£4.00
Family	£16.00
Free entry for children under 5	

OPENING TIMES

6 Apr-31 Oct,	
Mon-Fri	10am-5pm
Sat-Sun	11am-5pm
1 Nov-29 Feb,	
Mon-Fri	10am-4pm
Sat	11am-4pm
Sun	Closed
19 Dec-2 Jan	Closed

HOW TO FIND US

Direction: In Gainsborough, opposite the library

Train: Gainsborough Central ½ mile, Gainsborough Lea Road 1 mile

Bus: Stagecoach, Yourbus and Wilfreda Beehive all operate services to Gainsborough bus station from surrounding areas. It is a short walk from there to the Old Hall

Tel: 01522 782040 or 01427 612669

Disabled access (most of ground floor).

MAP Page 319 (1G)
OS Map 112/121, 280: SK813900

Don't forget to check opening times online before you visit

www.english-heritage.org.uk/ daysout/properties

Lincoln Medieval Bishops' Palace

Lincolnshire – LN2 1PU

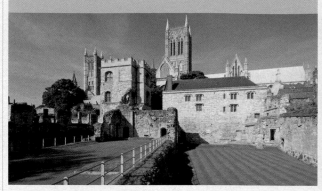

Standing almost in the shadow of Lincoln cathedral, with sweeping views over the ancient city and the countryside beyond, the medieval bishops' palace was once among the most important buildings in the country. The administrative centre of the largest diocese in medieval England, stretching from the Humber to the Thames, its architecture reflected the enormous power and wealth of the bishops as princes of the church.

Begun in the late 12th century, the palace's most impressive feature is the undercrofted West Hall, initiated by Bishop St Hugh and completed in the 1230s. The chapel range and entrance tower were built by Bishop William Alnwick, who modernised the palace in the 1430s. Having hosted visits from Henry VIII and James I, the palace was sacked by Royalist troops during the Civil War.

Built on hillside terraces, the palace also boasts a Contemporary Heritage Garden, designed by Mark Anthony Walker. Its form was inspired by the cathedral's medieval vaulting, with trees shaped to echo spires. Award-winning audio tour.

www.english-heritage.org.uk/ lincolnbishops

NON-MEMBERS

Adult	£4.50
Concession	£4.10
Child	£2.70
Family	£11.40

OPENING TIMES

1 Apr-4 Nov, Thu-Mon	10am-5pm
5 Nov-28 Mar, Sat-Sun	10am-4pm
24-26 Dec and 1 Jan	Closed

HOW TO FIND US

Direction: On the south side of Lincoln Cathedral. From the cathedral precinct gate, follow wall to your right to the gateway directly opposite cathedral south porch, then take tunnelled walkway (Chesney Gate). Entrance to the left down the pathway

Train: Lincoln 1 mile

Bus: From surrounding areas

Tel: 01522 527468

OVP

Parking (limited disabled parking on site).

MAP Page 319 (2H)
OS Map 121, 272: SK978717

Sibsey Trader Windmill
Lincolnshire — PE22 0SY

Built in 1877, this restored six-storey mill, with complete gear, sails and fantail, still works today. The award-winning tearoom sells produce made from the mill's organic, stone-ground flour.

Managed by Ian Ansell.
Tel: 07718 320449.

NON-MEMBERS

Adult	£2.50
Concession	£2.00
Child	£1.00

OPENING TIMES

3 Mar–30 Apr,	
Sat & Bank Hols	10am-6pm
Sun	11am-6pm
1 May–30 Sep,	
Sat & Bank Hols	10am-6pm
Sun	11am-6pm
Tue	10am-6pm
1 Oct–30 Nov	
Sat	10am-6pm
Sun	11am-6pm
1 Dec-28 Feb	
Sat	11am-5pm
31 Dec	Closed

Group and education visits outside these hours by arrangement

HOW TO FIND US

Direction: ½ mile W of Sibsey off A16, 5 miles N of Boston

Train: Boston 5 miles

Bus: Brylaine 113 and Grayscroft 8 (Wed) to Sibsey, then ½ mile walk

Tel: 01205 460647/07718 320449

Disabled access (exterior only).

MAP Page 319 (3J)
OS Map 122, 261: TF345510

St George's Church, Goltho
Lincolnshire — LN8 5JD

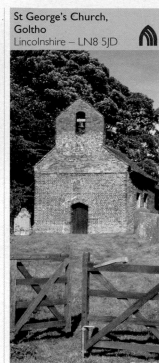

© CCT

The charming red-brick chapel of St George is situated beside one of Lincolnshire's lost Saxon villages. The name 'Goltho' is said to be Saxon for 'where the marigolds grow'. Inside, this tranquil atmospheric church contains rustic painted wooden pews and a sense of time stood still.

Owned and managed by The Churches Conservation Trust.

OPENING TIMES

Please phone 01904 709090 in advance of your visit to arrange collection of the key

HOW TO FIND US

Train: Nearest Market Rasen 7½ miles

Bus: Routes A2/T19

25 mins from Lincoln Medieval Bishops' Palace

MAP Page 319 (2H)
OS Map 121, 273: TF116775

Tattershall College
Lincolnshire

Remains of a grammar school for church choristers, founded in the mid-15th century by Ralph, Lord Cromwell, the builder of Wingfield Manor and nearby Tattershall Castle (National Trust).

The college is managed by Heritage Lincolnshire.

OPENING TIMES

Any reasonable time

HOW TO FIND US

Direction: In Tattershall, 14 miles NE of Sleaford on A153

Train: Ruskington 10 miles

Bus: Brylaine Interconnect service 5 and Translinc Call Connect service 6K

Tel: 01529 461499

MAP Page 319 (2H)
OS Map 122, 261: TF213578

Kirby Hall Northamptonshire – NN17 3EN

Kirby Hall is one of England's greatest Elizabethan and 17th-century houses. Begun by Sir Humphrey Stafford, it was purchased by Sir Christopher Hatton, one of Queen Elizabeth I's 'comely young men' and later her Lord Chancellor. Hatton hoped in vain to receive the Queen here during one of her annual 'progresses' around the country. Although this vast mansion is partly roofless, most of its walls survive to their full impressive height; as does the prodigious three-tier inner porch, begun following French pattern books and later embellished in the Classical style by the sculptor Nicholas Stone.

Kirby Hall's exceptionally rich decoration proclaims that its successive owners were always in the forefront of new ideas about architecture and design. The Great Hall and state rooms remain roofed and intact, their interiors refitted and redecorated to authentic 17th- and 18th-century specifications.

Sir Christopher Hatton the Fourth added the great gardens (described as 'the finest garden in England') in the late 17th century. They have been recreated as they may have appeared at that time, with elaborate period style 'cutwork', statues, urns, seating, topiary and other features.

The gardens and ground floor of the mansion are easily accessible by wheelchair users.

An audio tour guides visitors through the house and gardens, accompanied by commentaries from experts in garden history, conservation and country houses.

www.english-heritage.org.uk/kirbyhall

Owned by the Earl of Winchilsea and managed by English Heritage.

🏠 Holiday cottage available to let

NON-MEMBERS

Adult	£5.80
Concession	£5.20
Child	£3.50
Family	£15.10

OPENING TIMES

1 Apr-4 Nov, Thu-Mon	10am-5pm
5 Nov-28 Mar, Sat-Sun	10am-4pm
24-26 Dec and 1 Jan	Closed

May close early for private events. Please call to check

Free members' guided tours
14 Nov, 12 Dec, 16 Jan,
13 Feb, 13 Mar   11am & 2pm

HOW TO FIND US

Direction: On an unclassified road off A43, 4 miles NE of Corby

Train: Corby 4 miles

Bus: There are no bus services to the property. The closest is demand responsive service 4S operated by Translinc. Must be pre-booked by ringing 0845 263 8153. Alight at Deene Old School House then 1 mile walk

Tel: 01536 203230

Disabled access (grounds, gardens and ground floor only).

Dogs on leads (restricted areas).

MAP Page 319 (5G)
OS Map 141, 224: SP926927

Apethorpe Hall
Northamptonshire – PE8 5AQ

Among England's finest country houses, big and stately Apethorpe Hall was begun in the late 15th century. It contains one of the country's most complete Jacobean interiors, and hosted thirteen royal visits between 1565 and 1636.

While restoration work continues, English Heritage is pleased to offer access to visitors during 2012 on a limited, pre-booked and guided-tour basis only. For further details please visit our website or phone 0870 333 1181.

Please note: Apethorpe is still classed as a building site, and suitable footwear must be worn. There are lots of stairs, and no resting/seating points available. Children under 16 must be accompanied by an adult, and we are unable to admit children under 5.

NON-MEMBERS
Please call for details

OPENING TIMES
By pre-booked tour only – please call for details

Apethorpe Hall

HOW TO FIND US
Direction: Located off the A43 towards King's Cliffe. If entering Apethorpe via King's Cliffe Road, advance to Laundry Lane, not the High Street. If entering via Bridge St, pass the stone cross and turn left into Laundry Lane

Train: Stamford 11 miles or Peterborough 14 miles

Bus: Stagecoach 23 Peterborough – Oundle (not Sun); Mark Bland Travel 180 Oundle – Stamford (weekdays)

Tel: 0870 333 1181

Access via narrow residential lane – please observe 10mph speed limit at all times.

MAP Page 319 (5H)
OS Map 141, 224/234: TL023954

Chichele College
Northamptonshire

The gatehouse, chapel and other remains of a communal residence for priests serving the parish church, founded by locally-born Archbishop Chichele before 1425. Regularly used to display works of art. Managed by Higham Ferrers Tourism, Business and Community Partnership.

OPENING TIMES
Quadrangle – any reasonable time. Contact the keykeeper for the chapel: Mrs D Holyoak, 12 Lancaster St, Higham Ferrers
Tel: 01933 314157

HOW TO FIND US
Direction: In Higham Ferrers

Train: Wellingborough 5 miles

Bus: Stagecoach 49, 50, 51, X46, X47; Expresslines 'Rushden Higham Link'

Tel: 01933 314006

Dogs on leads (restricted areas only).

MAP Page 319 (6G)
OS Map 153, 224: SP960687

Eleanor Cross, Geddington
Northamptonshire

In 1290 Eleanor of Castile, the beloved wife of Edward I and mother of his 14 children, died at Harby in Nottinghamshire. The places where her body rested on the journey south to its tomb in Westminster Abbey were marked by stone crosses. The stately triangular Geddington cross, with its canopied statues surmounted by a slender hexagonal pinnacle, is the best-preserved of only three intact survivors. Other crosses stand at Hardingstone near Northampton and Waltham Cross, Hertfordshire.

OPENING TIMES
Any reasonable time

HOW TO FIND US
Direction: Located in the village of Geddington, off A43 between Kettering and Corby

Train: Kettering 4 miles

Bus: There are no bus services to the property. The closest are Stagecoach services X1 & X4 to Storefield Cottages on the A6003 then 3 mile walk

MAP Page 319 (5G)
OS Map 141, 224: SP894830

Rushton Triangular Lodge Northamptonshire – NN14 1RP

This delightful triangular building was designed by Sir Thomas Tresham (father of one of the Gunpowder Plotters) and constructed between 1593 and 1597. It is a testament to Tresham's Roman Catholicism: the number three, symbolising the Holy Trinity, is apparent everywhere. There are three floors, trefoil windows and three triangular gables on each side. On the entrance front is the inscription 'Tres Testimonium Dant' ('there are three that give witness'), a Biblical quotation from St John's Gospel referring to the Trinity. It is also a pun on Tresham's name: his wife called him 'Good Tres' in her letters.

NON-MEMBERS

Adult	£3.20
Concession	£2.90
Child	£1.90

OPENING TIMES

1 Apr-4 Nov, Thu-Mon 11am-4pm

HOW TO FIND US

Direction: 1 mile W of Rushton, on unclassified road; 3 miles from Desborough on A6

Train: Kettering 5 miles

Bus: Stagecoach in Northants service 18 & 19, alight Desborough Cemetery, then 1 mile walk

Tel: 01536 710761

Dogs on leads (restricted areas only).

Parking (limited parking in nearby lay-by).

MAP Page 319 (5G)
OS Map 141, 224: SP830831

St Andrew's Church, Cranford
Northamptonshire
NN14 4AD

© CCT

Sumptuous memorials to 300 years of the Robinson family fill medieval St Andrew's, which lies next to the Robinson seat of Cranford Hall. Structural additions, stained glass and furnishings from across the centuries give this church a rich and varied history.

Owned and managed by The Churches Conservation Trust.

OPENING TIMES
Keyholder nearby

HOW TO FIND US
Train: Nearest ≷ Kettering 4 miles

Bus: Routes 16/406

10 mins from Eleanor Cross, 30 mins from Kirby Hall

MAP Page 319 (5G)
OS Map 141, 224: SP925773

St Peter's Church, Deene
Northamptonshire
NN17 3EJ

© Steven Cole

Set in the estate of Deene Park, St Peter's is the family church of the Brudenells, who bought the estate in 1514. The church is a large building of local stone and Collyweston slate, with a tall west tower, a broach spire, and a number of family memorials.

Owned and managed by The Churches Conservation Trust.

OPENING TIMES
Keyholder nearby

HOW TO FIND US
Train: Nearest ≷ Kettering 10½ miles

Bus: No bus route nearby

4 mins from Kirby Hall

MAP Page 319 (5G)
OS Map 141, 224: SP952928

St Peter's Church, Northampton
Northamptonshire
NN1 1SR

© CCT

One of the most outstanding Norman churches in the county, this 900-year-old church in Northampton city centre is filled with glorious carved treasures. Inside, great stone arches rise and flow with zigzag waves of banded and plain stone, supported by carved capitals overflowing with foliage, scrollwork, birds and beasts.

Owned and managed by The Churches Conservation Trust.

OPENING TIMES
Nov-Feb, Wed-Sat	11am-3pm
Mar-Oct, Wed-Sat	10am-4pm

HOW TO FIND US
Train: Nearest ≷ Northampton ¼ mile

Bus: Multiple bus routes from town centre

30 mins from Chichele College

MAP Page 319 (6G)
OS Map 152, 207/223: SP7497160377

NOTTINGHAMSHIRE

Mattersey Priory
Nottinghamshire

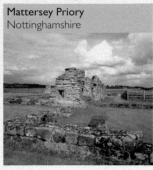

The remains, mainly the 13th-century refectory and kitchen, of a small monastery for just six Gilbertine canons – the only wholly English monastic order.

OPENING TIMES

Any reasonable time

HOW TO FIND US

Direction: ¾ mile down rough drive, 1 mile E of Mattersey off B6045

Train: Retford 7 miles

Bus: Stagecoach East Midlands service 27, 27A, Yourbus 83 to village centre then ½ mile walk

MAP Page 319 (1G)
OS Map 112/120, 280: SK703896

Create your own special moments at Bolsover Castle

Visit our website for more information at www.english-heritage.org.uk/hospitality

Milton Mausoleum, Markham Clinton
Nottinghamshire
NG22 0PJ

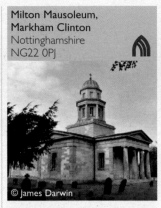

© James Darwin

This lovely Classical building with its domed tower was designed for the 4th Duke of Newcastle as a mausoleum for his wife. Inside there is an elegant Ionic reredos screen and some stunning marble effigies.

Owned and managed by The Churches Conservation Trust.

OPENING TIMES

May-Sep on
2nd and 4th Sun
of each month   2.30pm-4.30pm

At other times key holder nearby

HOW TO FIND US

Train: Nearest ⊠ Retford 4¼ miles

Bus: Route 38

20 mins from Rufford Abbey

MAP Page 319 (2G)
OS Map 120, 271: SK715730

Rufford Abbey
Nottinghamshire

Rufford Abbey

The best-preserved remains of a Cistercian abbey west cloister range in England, dating mainly from c. 1170. Incorporated into part of a 17th-century and later mansion, set in Rufford Country Park. Graphic panels show how the abbey was transformed into a great house.

Managed by Nottinghamshire County Council.

OPENING TIMES

1 Apr-31 Oct, daily   10am-5pm

1 Nov-28 Mar, daily   10am-4.30pm

25 Dec   Closed

See www.nottinghamshire.gov.uk/rufffordcp for full details

HOW TO FIND US

Direction: 2 miles S of Ollerton off A614

Train: Mansfield 8 miles

Bus: 'The Sherwood Arrow' (Stagecoach) Nottingham – Worksop; Travelwright 227 (Wed, Fri)

Tel: 01623 821338

Occasional charge for members on event days.

Parking (charge applies – not managed by EH).

Shop – craft centre.

MAP Page 319 (2F)
OS Map 120, 270: SK646648

Lyddington Bede House   Rutland – LE15 9LZ

NEW FOR 2012

New interpretation will include new graphic panels; a case displaying a Bible and prayer book used at the Bedehouse; and audio boxes where you can hear letters read by the 'bedesmen'. One of the bedeswomen's rooms will also be recreated as it may have appeared in late Victorian times.

NON-MEMBERS

Adult	£4.30
Concession	£3.90
Child	£2.60
Family	£11.20

OPENING TIMES

1 Apr-4 Nov,
Thu-Mon   10am-5pm

HOW TO FIND US

Direction: In Lyddington, 6 miles N of Corby; 1 mile E of A6003, next to the church

Train: Oakham 7 miles

Bus: Centrebus 'Rutland Flyer' service 1 Corby-Oakham (passes close to ≥ Oakham)

Tel: 01572 822438

Disabled access (ground floor only).

MAP Page 319 (5G)
OS Map 141, 234: SP876970

Set beside the church of a picturesque ironstone village, Lyddington Bede House originated as the medieval wing of a palace belonging to the Bishops of Lincoln. By 1600 it had passed to Sir Thomas Cecil, son of Queen Elizabeth I's chief minister, who converted it into an almshouse for twelve poor 'bedesmen' over 30 years old and two women (over 45), all free of lunacy, leprosy or the French pox. Visitors can wander through the bedesmen's rooms, with their tiny windows and fireplaces, and view the bishops' Great Chamber with its beautifully carved ceiling cornice. There is a small herb garden.

Associated attractions in the East Midlands

These visitor attractions, all independent of EH, offer discounts to our members. Please call before you visit to confirm details. A valid EH membership card must be produced for each member.

Althorp
Northamptonshire NN7 4HQ

Enjoy an insight into the personalities of the people who lived here. Plus a fascinating collection of pictures, ceramics and furniture, the result of one family's uninterrupted occupation for 500 years.

30 mins from Rushton Triangular Lodge

Tel: 01604 770107

www.althorp.com

Free entry
upstairs rooms   OVP 6

Ashby de la Zouch Museum
Leicestershire LE65 1HU

2010 and 2007 Leicestershire Museum of the Year. Models of Ashby Castle and Ivanhoe Baths. Temporary exhibitions, research facilities, archives, talks, workshops and guided walks. Education and Family Historian officers.

5 mins from Ashby de la Zouch Castle

Tel: 01530 560090

www.ashbydelazouchmuseum.org.uk

Free
admission   2

Bosworth Battlefield
Leicestershire CV13 0AD

Re-live the drama and excitement of the Battle of Bosworth, 1485, at the award-winning Bosworth Battlefield Visitor Centre. Facilities include interactive exhibition, reclaimed medieval Tithe Barn restaurant, gift shop and country park trail.

10 miles from J11 of M42/A444

Tel: 01455 290429

www.bosworthbattlefield.com

20% discount on entry
(Not valid on event days)   2

Burghley House
Lincolnshire PE9 3JY

England's greatest Elizabethan House. Burghley was built and designed by William Cecil, Lord High Treasurer to Queen Elizabeth I.

30 mins from Kirby Hall

Tel: 01780 752451

www.burghley.co.uk

20% discount House
& Garden Adult Ticket

Creswell Crags
Nottinghamshire and Derbyshire Border S80 3LH

Creswell Crags is internationally recognised as home to Britain's only known cave art. Featuring some of the most remarkable Ice Age artefacts, the visitor attraction provides a glimpse of life during the Ice Age.

30 mins from Hardwick Hall

Tel: 01909 720378

www.creswell-crags.org.uk

25% off
Ice Age Tour

Crich Tramway Village
Derbyshire DE4 5DP

Travel through time on vintage trams along the period street and out into the open countryside. Watch trams being restored and enjoy the woodland walk, with captivating sculptures around every corner.

8 miles from J28 of M1

Tel: 01773 854321

www.tramway.co.uk

Group discount rate
(Not valid on premier events)   OVP

78 Derngate: The Charles Rennie Mackintosh House & Galleries
Northamptonshire NN1 1UH

The house at 78 Derngate was remodelled by the world-famous architect, Charles Rennie Mackintosh, in his iconic Modernist style in 1916. Restaurant, gift and craft shop and changing gallery exhibitions. Winner of the Enjoy England small visitor attraction of the year 2009.

Tel: 01604 603407

www.78derngate.org.uk

2 for 1
entry   ■

The Heights of Abraham
Derbyshire DE4 3PT

Derbyshire's oldest tourist attraction, first opened to visitors in 1870, now with modern cable car ride to the top. Enjoy cavern tours, a Victorian prospect tower, exhibition, a thatched summer house built in 1801 and take in views across the Peak District.

15 miles from Bolsover Castle, Hardwick Old Hall & Peveril Castle

Tel: 01629 582365

www.heightsofabraham.com

£2 off adult   ■ OVP
£1 off child/snr   ♛2

Kelmarsh Hall & Gardens
Northamptonshire NN6 9LY

18th-century James Gibbs house set in beautiful gardens. Once home of Nancy Lancaster, acclaimed for creating the 'English Country House Style'. Plus Croome Court exhibition, showcasing furniture and paintings commissioned by the 6th Earl of Coventry.

15 mins from M1/M6

Tel: 01604 686543

www.kelmarsh.com

2 for 1
entry   ■

Papplewick Pumping Station
Nottinghamshire NG15 9AJ

Britain's finest working Victorian water pumping station, with ornate engine house, cooling pond, landscaped grounds, original twin beam engines and six boilers, woodland play area and miniature railway.

Close to J27 of the M1

Tel: 0115 9632938

www.papplewickpumpingstation.org.uk

25% discount   ■ OVP
on entry   ♛2

Peak Rail
Derbyshire DE4 3NA

Take a nostalgic steam train journey back in time through the Derbyshire dales between Matlock and Rowsley. Enjoy a cream or afternoon tea, or even Sunday lunch, on the train. Stations at Matlock, Darley Dale and Rowsley South.

Tel: 01629 580381

www.peakrail.co.uk

£2 off adult/snr, £1 off child   ■
Train ticket only   ♛3

Rockingham Castle
Leicestershire LE16 8TH

Begun by William the Conqueror. A royal fortress for 450 years, and a much-loved family home for another 450 years. Surrounded by 18 acres of gardens. Eye spy and quiz for children.

8 miles from A14

Tel: 01536 770240

www.rockinghamcastle.com

2 for 1
entry   ■

Kenilworth Castle & Elizabethan Garden

WEST MIDLANDS

PROPERTIES

West Midlands properties consist of:

30	English Heritage
6	The Churches Conservation Trust
10	Associated Attractions

Remember to check opening times before you visit any of our properties www.english-heritage. org.uk/daysout

Details of local public transport information in England are available from Traveline www.traveline.org.uk or call 0871 200 2233.

Kenilworth Castle and Elizabethan Garden

Make the most of your membership and keep up to date with upcoming events, the latest news and special offers by subscribing to our e-newsletter. Register online now at **www.english-heritage.org.uk/ newsletter**

HEREFORDSHIRE
Arthur's Stone
Edvin Loach Old Church
Goodrich Castle
Longtown Castle
Mortimer's Cross Water Mill
Rotherwas Chapel
Wigmore Castle

SHROPSHIRE
Acton Burnell Castle
Boscobel House and The Royal Oak
Buildwas Abbey
Cantlop Bridge
Clun Castle
Haughmond Abbey
Iron Bridge
Langley Chapel
Lilleshall Abbey
Mitchell's Fold Stone Circle
Moreton Corbet Castle
Old Oswestry Hill Fort
Stokesay Castle
Wenlock Priory
White Ladies Priory
Wroxeter Roman City

STAFFORDSHIRE
Croxden Abbey
Wall Roman Site

WEST MIDLANDS
Halesowen Abbey
J.W. Evans Silver Factory

WARWICKSHIRE
Kenilworth Castle and Elizabethan Garden

WORCESTERSHIRE
Leigh Court Barn
Witley Court and Gardens

WEST MIDLANDS

Stoke-on-Trent

Staffordshire

Oswestry

Burton upon Trent

Stafford

Shrewsbury Telford

Tamworth

Shropshire

Wolverhampton

Nuneaton

Bishop's Castle

Birmingham

West Midlands Coventry

Ludlow

Kidderminster

Rugby

Warwick

Worcestershire

Warwickshire

Leominster

Worcester

Stratford-upon-Avon

Herefordshire

Great Malvern

Evesham

Hereford

Ross-on-Wye

HIGHLIGHTS FOR 2012/13 IN THE WEST MIDLANDS

- **Kenilworth Castle & Elizabethan Garden:** one of Britain's most impressive historic sites.
- **Wroxeter Roman City:** glimpse life 2000 years ago in the recreated Roman Town House.
- **Witley Court & Gardens:** romantic ruins, beautiful fountains & perfect picnic spots.

HEREFORDSHIRE

Arthur's Stone
Herefordshire

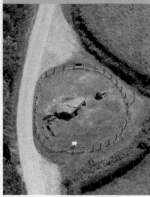

An atmospheric Neolithic burial chamber made of great stone slabs, in the hills above Herefordshire's Golden Valley.

OPENING TIMES
Any reasonable time

HOW TO FIND US
Direction: 7 miles E of Hay-on-Wye off B4348 near Dorstone

Bus: Stagecoach in South Wales service 39; Yeomans Canyon service 39A (Sun) ≥ Hereford – Brecon to within ¾ mile

MAP Page 318 (7B)
OS Map 148/161, OL13/201: SO319431

Church of St John the Baptist, Llanrothal
Herefordshire – NP25 5QJ

© Nicholas Kaye

Church of St John the Baptist, Llanrothal

This remote whitewashed church, right on the Welsh border, sits in an idyllic valley by the River Monnow. The church is said to have been founded by a Celtic saint, St Ridol, and has a beautiful medieval interior.

Owned and managed by The Churches Conservation Trust.

OPENING TIMES
Open daily during daylight hours

HOW TO FIND US
Train: Nearest ≥ Abergavenny 10¾ miles

Bus: Routes 54/416

20 mins from Goodrich Castle

MAP Page 318 (7B)
OS Map 161, OL14: SO489169

Edvin Loach Old Church
Herefordshire

The ruins of an 11th-century and later church built within the earthworks of a Norman motte and bailey castle, with a Victorian church nearby.

OPENING TIMES
Any reasonable time

HOW TO FIND US
Direction: Located 4 miles N of Bromyard on an unclassified road off B4203

Bus: The closest town is Bromyard (3½ miles). Bus services operated by Veolia Astons 405, First/DRM 420, DRM 469, 476, 482, 672, 673

MAP Page 318 (6C)
OS Map 149, 202: SO663584

Goodrich Castle
See feature – Page 200

Longtown Castle
Herefordshire

Built within an earlier square earthwork, Longtown Castle is a powerful, thick-walled round keep of c. 1200, characteristic of the Welsh Borders, on a large earthen mound within a stone-walled bailey. Set in the beautiful Olchon valley, with magnificent views of the Black Mountains.

OPENING TIMES
Any reasonable time

HOW TO FIND US
Direction: Located 4 miles WSW of Abbey Dore, off B4347

Bus: Abbey Cars service 441 (Wed) & 442 (Tue); Roy Brown Coaches (summer service) B17

MAP Page 318 (7B)
OS Map 161, OL13: SO321291

Mortimer's Cross Water Mill
Herefordshire – HR6 9PE

Owned and managed by Mr C Partington, this water mill is remarkable for being so complete and in such good condition. Milling days are held on Bank Holiday Mondays, and special day and evening tours are available by arrangement with the owner. Please call for details.

Mortimer's Cross Water Mill

NON-MEMBERS

Adult	£4.00
Concession	£3.50
Child	£2.50

OPENING TIMES

1 Apr-30 Sep, Sun & Bank Hol Mons	10am-4pm

Other times by arrangement

Access to the mill is by guided tour only:	11am, 1pm & 3pm

Free flow on milling days

HOW TO FIND US

Direction: Located 7 miles NW of Leominster on B4362

Train: Leominster 7½ miles

Bus: Lugg Valley 489 (Tue, Fri only), 491 (1st, 3rd & 5th Wed only), 494 (Sat only), 498 (2nd & 4th Wed only), 802 (Sun only)

Tel: 01568 708820

Disabled access (exterior and ground floor only).

Warning: there are steep river banks and sluice channels which are hazardous at all times.

MAP Page 318 (6B)
OS Map 137/148/149, 203: SO426637

Rotherwas Chapel
Herefordshire

The family chapel of the Roman Catholic Bodenham family. The originally simple medieval building has a fine Elizabethan timber roof, a rebuilt 18th-century tower, and striking Victorian interior decoration and furnishings by the Pugins.

OPENING TIMES

Any reasonable time. Key keeper located at nearby filling station

HOW TO FIND US

Direction: 1½ miles SE of Hereford on B4399, left into Chapel Road

Train: Hereford 3½ miles

Rotherwas Chapel

Bus: First service 78, 78A; Yeoman 82 then ½ mile walk

Disabled access via kissing gate only.

MAP Page 318 (7B)
OS Map 149, 189: SO536383

St Michael's Church, Michaelchurch
Herefordshire – HR2 8LD

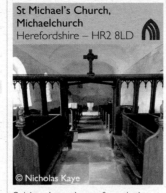
© Nicholas Kaye

Said to have been founded by Bishop Herwald of Llandaff in 1056, this lovely church hugs the side of a remote valley. A Roman altar is built into a blocked doorway, and 13th-century paintings decorate the walls.

Owned and managed by The Churches Conservation Trust.

OPENING TIMES

Open daily during daylight hours

HOW TO FIND US

Train: Nearest ⮕ Hereford 9¼ miles

Bus: Routes 38/411

60 mins from Goodrich Castle

MAP Page 318 (7B)
OS Map 162, 189: SO522255

Don't forget to check opening times online before you visit

www.english-heritage.org.uk/daysout/properties

Wigmore Castle
Herefordshire

Once the stronghold of the turbulent Mortimer family, Wigmore Castle was later dismantled to prevent its use during the Civil War. Now it is among the most remarkable ruins in England. Largely buried up to first floor level by earth and fallen masonry, yet many of its fortifications survive to full height, including parts of the keep on its towering mound. Graphic panels tell the story of this important medieval castle, now conserved for its wildlife habitats as well as its historic interest.

OPENING TIMES

Any reasonable time

HOW TO FIND US

Direction: Located 8 miles W of Ludlow on A4110. Accessible via footpath ¾ mile from the village on Mortimer Way

Train: Bucknell 6 miles, Ludlow 10 miles

Bus: Lugg Valley 489 (Tue, Fri only), 491 (1st, 3rd & 5th Wed only), 498 (2nd & 4th Wed only), 802 (Sun only); Veolia Cymru X11 (Mon only)

Toilets (including disabled) at the Village Hall.

There are steep steps to the summit, which are hazardous in icy conditions. Children must stay under close control and should not climb the walls or banks. Strong footwear is recommended. There is no staff presence.

MAP Page 318 (6B)
OS Map 137/148, 203: SO408693

Goodrich Castle Herefordshire – HR9 6HY

Goodrich stands majestically on a wooded hill commanding the passage of the River Wye into the picturesque valley of Symonds Yat.

Goodrich's delightful tearoom serves a fine selection of light refreshments made from locally-sourced Herefordshire ingredients.

NON-MEMBERS

Adult	£6.00
Concession	£5.40
Child	£3.60
Family	£15.60

OPENING TIMES

1 Apr-30 Jun, daily	10am-5pm
1 Jul-31 Aug, daily	10am-6pm
1 Sep-4 Nov, daily	10am-5pm
5 Nov-17 Feb, Sat-Sun	10am-4pm
18-22 Feb, daily	10am-4pm
23 Feb-28 Mar, Sat-Sun	10am-4pm
24-26 Dec and 1 Jan	Closed

Free members's guided tours
9 Nov, 7 Dec, 18 Jan,
15 Feb, 8 Mar
11am-12.30pm/2pm-3.30pm

HOW TO FIND US

Direction: 5 miles S of Ross-on-Wye off A40

Bus: H&H Coaches service 34 and 411 (Wed) to within ½ mile

Tel: 01600 890538

A car parking charge of £2 applies to ensure that EH members and paying visitors have priority. The charge will be refunded on admission.

Dogs on leads.

Disabled access (limited, please call for details or ask the visitor centre on arrival).

The tearoom will close one hour before the site closes.

MAP Page 318 (7C)
OS Map 162, OL14: SO577200

The castle was begun in the late 11th century by the English landowner Godric, who gave it his name. A generation later the splendidly preserved square keep that still forms its core was added, probably in the time of Richard 'Strongbow' de Clare, Earl of Pembroke and Lord of Goodrich 1148-76.

Under King Richard the Lionheart, Goodrich was granted along with the earldom of Pembroke to the famous William Marshal, a great castle builder who may have initiated work on the inner ward. Each of Marshal's four sons inherited the fortress in turn, the last dying childless at Goodrich in 1245.

Thereafter the fortress and earldom passed to Henry III's half-brother, William de Valence, who rebuilt its defences and living quarters in the most up-to-date style.

Goodrich still boasts one of the most complete sets of medieval domestic buildings surviving in any English castle. William's widow Countess Joan frequently stayed here with an entourage of up to 200, entertaining her relations and friends in the most lavish style.

During the Civil War, Goodrich was held successively by both sides. Sir Henry Lingen's Royalists eventually surrendered in 1646 under threats of undermining and a deadly Parliamentarian mortar. Visitors can see the famous 'Roaring Meg', the only surviving Civil War mortar, which has returned to the castle after over 350 years, and a cache of Civil War cannonballs, found at Goodrich in the 1920s. The visitor centre features an exhibition exploring life at the castle from its late 11th-century origins until its dramatic fall in 1646, including Civil War artefacts.

www.english-heritage.org.uk/goodrich

SHROPSHIRE

Acton Burnell Castle
Shropshire

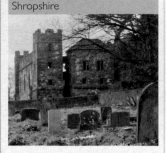

The impressive red sandstone shell of a battlemented tower house mansion, built c. 1283-92 by Bishop Robert Burnell, Edward I's Lord Chancellor. Parliament was held nearby in 1283, when the king ratified a law for the protection of merchants, known as the Statute of Acton Burnell.

OPENING TIMES
Open in daylight hours only

HOW TO FIND US
Direction: Located in Acton Burnell, signposted from A49, 8 miles S of Shrewsbury

Train: Shrewsbury or Church Stretton, both 8 miles

Bus: Boultons 540

MAP Page 318 (4B)
OS Map 126, 241: SJ534019

Boscobel House and The Royal Oak
See feature opposite

Buildwas Abbey
Shropshire – TF8 7BW

Impressive ruins of a Cistercian abbey, including its unusually unaltered 12th-century church, beautiful vaulted and tile-floored chapter house and recently re-opened crypt chapel.

In a wooded Severn-side setting, not far from the Iron Bridge (p.205) and Wenlock Priory (p.207) – once the home of Dr William Penny Brookes, originator of the still-continuing Olympian Wenlock Games, a major inspiration for the modern International Olympics.

www.english-heritage.org.uk/buildwas

NON-MEMBERS

Adult	£3.50
Concession	£3.20
Child	£2.10

OPENING TIMES
1 Apr-30 Sep, Wed-Sun & Bank Hols   10am-5pm

HOW TO FIND US
Direction: On S bank of River Severn on A4169, 2 miles W of Ironbridge

Train: Telford Central 6 miles

Bus: Arriva Midlands service 96

Tel: 01952 433274

Buildwas Abbey

Disabled access is limited.

Nature trail (not managed by EH) including site of abbey fishponds.

MAP Page 318 (4C)
OS Map 127, 242: SJ643043

Cantlop Bridge
Shropshire

A single-span, cast-iron road bridge over the Cound Brook. Possibly designed and certainly approved by the great engineer Thomas Telford, who was instrumental in shaping industrial Shropshire and the West Midlands.

OPENING TIMES
Any reasonable time

HOW TO FIND US
Direction: ¾ mile SW of Berrington on an unclassified road off A458

Train: Shrewsbury 5 miles

Bus: Boultons (of Cardington) service 540

MAP Page 318 (4B)
OS Map 126, 241: SJ517062

Boscobel House and The Royal Oak

Shropshire – ST19 9AR

A pretty timber-framed house that played a brief but important role in English history, Boscobel was converted into a lodge by John Giffard in about 1624. The Giffards were Roman Catholics, and tradition holds that its real purpose was to serve as a secret refuge for persecuted Catholics at times of need.

Boscobel was destined for greater fame. Following the execution of King Charles I in 1649, his son made a brave though misguided attempt to regain the throne. Defeated in 1651 at Worcester, the final battle of the Civil War, young Charles fled for his life.

Initially Charles intended to cross the River Severn into

Wales, but found his way blocked by Cromwell's patrols. He sought refuge instead at Boscobel, hiding first in a tree, known afterwards as 'The Royal Oak', and then in a priest-hole in the house's attic. The future King Charles II then travelled on in disguise via other safe houses before escaping to France.

Boscobel became a much-visited place, although it remained a working farm. Today's visitors can enjoy our audio and visual displays; take a guided tour of the lodge; see the garden and a descendant of the Royal Oak; and find out about Boscobel's past as a working Victorian farm.

There is a permissive path from Boscobel House to White Ladies Priory, another of Charles's hiding places.

www.english-heritage.org.uk/boscobel

NON-MEMBERS

Adult	£6.00
Concession	£5.40
Child	£3.60
Family	£15.60

OPENING TIMES

1 Apr-4 Nov, Wed-Sun & Bank Hols	10am-5pm

House will be closed for 1 hour at 11am and 2pm for guided tours. Guided tours are subject to availability and booking is advisable

5 Nov-28 Mar, Sat-Sun	10am-4pm

Guided tours only

24-26 Dec and 1 Jan	Closed

Last entry 1 hour before closing

HOW TO FIND US

Direction: On minor road from A41 to A5, 8 miles NW of Wolverhampton. 5 mins drive from M54 J3

Train: Cosford 3 miles

Bus: Arriva/Midland service 3, 12, 76; Coastal Liner 17 (Wed only); Midland service 878, 880. (Services 17 and 878 pass the house, the others pass within ¾ mile)

Tel: 01902 850244

Dogs on leads (grounds only).

Parking (coaches welcome).

Disabled access limited. Call for details.

MAP Page 318 (4C)
OS Map 127, 242: SJ838082

Church of St Mary the Virgin, Shrewsbury
Shropshire – SY1 1EF

© CCT

St Mary's is a gem on a grand scale. It has the tallest spire in England; glorious stained glass including a world-famous 14th century 'Jesse window' and a Medieval cartoon strip featuring St Bernard; a stunning 15th century carved oak ceiling and a wealth of rich colours and fascinating treasures.

Owned and managed by The Churches Conservation Trust.

OPENING TIMES
1 Apr-31 Oct, Mon-Sat   10am-5pm
1 Nov-31 Mar, Mon-Sat 10am-4pm
Sometimes open on Sundays

HOW TO FIND US
Train: Nearest ⇥ Shrewsbury 15 mins walk
Bus: Routes 33/435/492
10 mins from Haughmond Abbey

MAP Page 318 (4B)
OS Map 126, 241: SJ494126

Don't forget your membership card when visiting any of our properties

---

Clun Castle
Shropshire

The dramatic riverside ruins and extensive earthworks of a Welsh Border castle, its tall 13th-century keep unusually set on the side of its mound.

Information panels tell the story of the castle and the nearby town.

OPENING TIMES
Any reasonable time

HOW TO FIND US
Direction: In Clun, off A488, 18 miles W of Ludlow
Train: Hopton Heath 6½ miles; Knighton 6½ miles
Bus: Minsterley 745 (Mon & Fri only); M&J service 773 & 860 (Tue only)

MAP Page 318 (5B)
OS Map 137, 201: SO299809

Haughmond Abbey
Shropshire – SY4 4RW

The extensive remains of an Augustinian abbey, including its abbots' quarters, refectory and cloister. The substantially surviving chapter house has a frontage richly bedecked with 12th and 14th-century carving and statuary and a fine timber roof of c. 1500. Pictorial interpretation boards guide the visitor and an introductory exhibition displays archaeological finds. Picnic area and light refreshments available.

Haughmond Abbey
www.english-heritage.org.uk/haughmond

NON-MEMBERS
Adult	£3.50
Concession	£3.20
Child	£2.10

Members can also get a Passport discount at Ironbridge Gorge Museums. See p.218 for details.

OPENING TIMES
1 Apr-30 Sep, Wed-Sun & Bank Hols   10am-5pm

HOW TO FIND US
Direction: Located 3 miles NE of Shrewsbury off B5062
Train: Shrewsbury 3½ miles
Bus: Arriva 519 Shrewsbury – Newport
Tel: 01743 709661

Disabled access (not easy).

MAP Page 318 (4B)
OS Map 126, 241: SJ542152

Iron Bridge
See feature opposite

Langley Chapel
Shropshire

A small chapel tranquilly set all alone in charming countryside. Its atmospheric interior contains a perfect set of 17th-century timber furnishings, including a musicians' pew.

OPENING TIMES
1 Mar-4 Nov, daily	10am-5pm
5 Nov-28 Feb, daily	10am-4pm
24-26 Dec and 1 Jan	Closed

HOW TO FIND US
Direction: 1½ miles S of Acton Burnell, on an unclassified road off A49; 9½ miles S of Shrewsbury
Train: Shrewsbury 9½ miles
Bus: Boultons 540 (then 1¼ mile walk)

MAP Page 318 (5B)
OS Map 126/127/138, 217/241: SJ538001

Iron Bridge Shropshire

The world's first iron bridge was erected over the River Severn here in 1779. Britain's best-known industrial monument, the bridge gave its name to the spectacular wooded gorge which, though now tranquil, was once an industrial powerhouse and the cradle of the Industrial Revolution. Ironbridge Gorge is now a World Heritage Site.

At the beginning of the 18th century, Abraham Darby I pioneered the process of using coke made from local coal to smelt local iron ore, but industrial expansion was hampered by the lack of a bridge over the Severn, which had to be a single span to allow for barge traffic. An iron bridge was first suggested by the Shrewsbury architect Thomas Pritchard: he designed a single span-bridge 30 metres long, but died as work began. The project was then taken over by Abraham Darby III, who cast the bridge in his Coalbrookdale foundry, using 378 tons of iron. Recent research shows that most parts were individually cast to fit, each being slightly different from the next: and that traditional woodworking-style joints were adapted to assemble them.

Costing over £6000, this proclamation of the achievements of Shropshire ironmasters was formally opened on New Year's Day 1781. It continued in full use by ever-increasing traffic until closed and designated an Ancient Monument in 1934. Massive strengthening works were later undertaken, and in 1999-2000 English Heritage assisted with a full survey of this revolutionary and iconic structure.

The Iron Bridge is the perfect place to begin a tour of the Gorge's many museums and the many other English Heritage sites nearby, including Buildwas Abbey, Wenlock Priory and Wroxeter Roman City.

OPENING TIMES

Any reasonable time

HOW TO FIND US

Direction: Adjacent to A4169

Bus: Arriva 77, 88, 88A 96, 99, 99A Gorge Connect service WH1 (summer Sat & Sun only)

MAP Page 318 (4C)
OS Map 127, 242: SJ672034

Lilleshall Abbey
Shropshire

Extensive ruins of an Augustinian abbey, later a Civil War stronghold, in a deeply rural setting. Much of the church survives, unusually viewable from gallery level, along with the lavishly sculpted processional door and other cloister buildings. Graphic panels show how the abbey appeared in medieval times.

OPENING TIMES

1 Apr-30 Sep, daily	10am-5pm
1 Oct-31 Mar	Closed

HOW TO FIND US

Direction: On an unclassified road off A518, 4 miles N of Oakengates

Train: Oakengates 4½ miles

Bus: Arriva service 481 Telford-Stafford (passes close to ⊠ Telford Central and Stafford) or Arriva 115/116 (Sat only passes close to Shinall station) to within 1 mile – alight between Sheriffhales and Heath Hill

MAP Page 318 (4C)
OS Map 127, 242: SJ738142

Mitchell's Fold Stone Circle
Shropshire

A Bronze Age stone circle, the focus of many legends, set in dramatic moorland on Stapeley Hill. It once consisted of some 30 stones, 15 of which are still visible.

OPENING TIMES

Any reasonable time

HOW TO FIND US

Direction: 16 miles SW of Shrewsbury

Train: Welshpool 10 miles

Bus: Minsterley Motors service 553 Shrewsbury – Bishop's Castle (passes close to ⊠ Shrewsbury) to within 1 mile

MAP Page 318 (5B)
OS Map 137, 216: SO304984

Moreton Corbet Castle
Shropshire

The ruins of the medieval castle and Tudor manor house of the Corbets are dominated by the theatrical shell of an ambitious Elizabethan mansion wing in Italianate style, which was devastated during the Civil War. Fine Corbet monuments fill the adjacent church.

OPENING TIMES

Open in daylight hours only

HOW TO FIND US

Direction: In Moreton Corbet off B5063 (a turning off A49), 7 miles NE of Shrewsbury

Train: Yorton 4 miles

Bus: Arriva service 64 to Shawbury then ¾ mile walk

Disabled access is limited.

MAP Page 318 (4C)
OS Map 126, 241: SJ561231

Old Oswestry Hill Fort
Shropshire

Among the most hugely impressive Iron Age hillforts on the Welsh Borders, covering 40 acres, with formidable multiple ramparts.

Information panels tell you about the hillfort and its inhabitants.

OPENING TIMES

Any reasonable time

HOW TO FIND US

Direction: 1 mile N of Oswestry, off an unclassified road off A483

Train: Gobowen 2 miles

Old Oswestry Hill Fort

Bus: Arriva service 2, 2A, 53 to Gobowen Road or Arriva Oswestry town service 402 or 404 to Old Fort Way and then short walk

MAP Page 318 (3B)
OS Map 126, 240/258: SJ295310

St Andrew's Church, Wroxeter
Shropshire – SY5 6PH

© Martin Peters

St Andrew's is built on the site of Viroconium, the fourth largest town of Roman Britain, and evidence of its past can be found in and around the church. Parts of the building date from before the Domesday Book (1086) but the interior mostly dates from the 17th and 18th centuries and contains some wonderful monuments.

Owned and managed by The Churches Conservation Trust.

OPENING TIMES

Open daily during daylight hours

HOW TO FIND US

Train: Nearest ⊠ Shrewsbury 4 miles

Bus: Route 96 via Ironbridge to Telford

Next to Wroxeter Roman City

MAP Page 318 (4C)
OS Map 126, 241: SJ564083

Stokesay Castle
See feature – Page 208

Wenlock Priory
Shropshire – TF13 6HS

The tranquil ruins of Wenlock Priory stand in a picturesque setting on the fringe of beautiful Much Wenlock. An Anglo-Saxon monastery was founded here in about 680 by King Merewalh of Mercia, whose abbess daughter Milburge was hailed as a saint. Her relics were miraculously re-discovered here in 1101, attracting both pilgrims and prosperity.

By then Wenlock had been re-founded by the Normans as a priory of Cluniac monks. The impressive remains of this medieval priory survive today, everywhere reflecting the Cluniac love of elaborate decoration. Parts of the great 13th-century church still stand high; and in the adjoining cloister garth is an unusual monks' washing fountain with 12th-century carvings. Once enclosed in an octagonal building, 16 monks could wash here at once before eating in the nearby refectory.

Perhaps the greatest glory is the extravagantly decorated chapter house of about 1140, its walls bedecked with blind arcading on multiple carved columns.

All this is enhanced by the topiary-filled cloister garden, and set against the backdrop of the complete infirmary wing, converted into a mansion after the priory's dissolution and still a private residence.

www.english-heritage.org.uk/
wenlockpriory

NON-MEMBERS

Adult	£4.00
Concession	£3.60
Child	£2.40

OPENING TIMES

1-30 Apr, Wed-Sun & Bank Hols	10am-5pm
1 May-31 Aug, daily	10am-5pm
1 Sep-4 Nov, Wed-Sun	10am-5pm
5 Nov-17 Feb, Sat-Sun	10am-4pm
18-22 Feb, daily	10am-4pm
23 Feb-28 Mar, Sat-Sun	10am-4pm
24-26 Dec and 1 Jan	Closed

HOW TO FIND US

Direction: In Much Wenlock

Train: Telford Central 9 miles

Bus: Arriva service 88, 88A & 436

Tel: 01952 727466

A car parking charge of £2 applies to ensure EH members and paying visitors have priority. The charge will be refunded on admission.

MAP Page 318 (5C)
OS Map 127/138, 217/242: SJ625001

OLYMPICS 2012

Much Wenlock was the home of Dr William Penny Brookes, originator of the Wenlock Olympian Games first held here in 1850, a major inspiration for the modern International Olympics. July 2012 will see the 126th Olympian Games, five days of sporting competition in and around Wenlock. The town's connection with the Olympics is the inspiration for 'Wenlock', a London 2012 Olympic mascot.

White Ladies Priory
Shropshire

Ruins of the late 12th-century church of a small nunnery of 'white ladies' or Augustinian canonesses. Charles II came here in 1651 before seeking refuge at nearby Boscobel House.

Permissive path from Boscobel House to White Ladies Priory.

OPENING TIMES

Open in daylight hours only

HOW TO FIND US

Direction: Located 1 mile SW of Boscobel House off an unclassified road between A41 and A5; 8 miles NW of Wolverhampton

Train: Cosford 2½ miles

Bus: Arriva/Midland service 3; Coastal Liner 17 (Wed only); Midland service 880 then 1 mile walk

MAP Page 318 (4C)
OS Map 217, 242: SJ826076

Wroxeter Roman City
See feature – Page 210

Stokesay Castle Shropshire – SY7 9AH

Stokesay Castle is the finest and best preserved fortified medieval manor house in England. Set in peaceful countryside near the Welsh border, the castle, timber-framed gatehouse and parish church form an unforgettably picturesque group.

An audio tour will help you to imagine Stokesay as the centre of medieval life. Its grounds include cottage-style gardens, a tearoom open from April to October, and a gift shop.

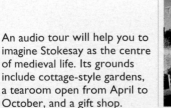

include beautiful cottage-style gardens, a moat, a tearoom open from April to October, and a gift shop.

www.english-heritage.org.uk/ stokesaycastle

NON-MEMBERS

Adult	£6.00
Concession	£5.40
Child	£3.60
Family	£15.60

OPENING TIMES

1 Apr-30 Sep, daily	10am-5pm
1 Oct-4 Nov, Wed-Sun	10am-5pm
5 Nov-17 Feb, Sat-Sun	10am-4pm
18-22 Feb, daily	10am-4pm
23 Feb-28 Mar, Sat-Sun	10am-4pm
24-26 Dec and 1 Jan	Closed

HOW TO FIND US

Direction: 7 miles NW of Ludlow off A49

Train: Craven Arms 1 mile

Bus: Minsterley Motors (of Stiperstones) 435 to Stokesay turning on the A49 then ½ mile walk

Tel: 01588 672544

Local Tourist Information
Ludlow: 01584 875053

A car parking charge of £2 applies to ensure EH members and paying visitors have priority. The charge will be refunded on admission.

Disabled access (call site for details).

Entrance to the courtyard is through a historic gate. Unsuitable for motorised scooters and unassisted wheelchair users.

Tearoom (Seasonal: 1 Apr-31 Oct).

MAP Page 318 (5B)
OS Map 137/148, 203: SO436815

Lawrence of Ludlow, a wealthy local wool-merchant wishing to set up as a country gentleman, bought the property in 1281, when the long Anglo-Welsh wars were ending. So it was safe to raise here one of the first fortified manor houses in England, 'builded like a castle' for effect but lit by large domestic-style windows.

Extensive recent tree-ring dating confirms that Lawrence had completed virtually the whole of the still-surviving house by 1291, using the same team of carpenters throughout. More remarkably, the dating also revealed that it has scarcely been altered since.

Stokesay's magnificent open-hearthed great hall displays a fine timber roof, shuttered gable windows and a precipitous staircase, its treads cut from whole tree-trunks. It is flanked by the north tower, with an original medieval tiled floor and remains of a wall painting, and a 'solar' or private apartment block and the tall south tower – the most castle-like part of the house, self-

contained and reached by a defensible stairway.

The solar block contains one of the few post-medieval alterations to the house, a fine panelled chamber. Its dominating feature is a fireplace with a richly carved overmantel, still bearing clear traces of original painting in five colours. This was added in about 1641, at the same time as the truly delightful gatehouse: an outstanding and recently-conserved example of the Marches style of lavishly showy timber-framing, bedecked with charming carvings of Adam and Eve.

A few years later, in 1645, Stokesay experienced its only known military encounter, surrendering without fighting to a Parliamentarian force. So the house remained undamaged, and sensitive conservation by Victorian owners and English Heritage have left it the medieval jewel which survives today.

An audio tour helps you to imagine Stokesay as a centre of medieval life. Its attractions

Wroxeter Roman City Shropshire – SY5 6PH

Wroxeter (or 'Viroconium') was the fourth largest city in Roman Britain. It began as a legionary fortress and later developed into a thriving civilian city, populated by retired soldiers and traders. Today the most impressive features are the remains of the 2nd-century municipal baths and the huge wall dividing them from the exercise hall, in the heart of the city. The site museum and audio tour reveal how Wroxeter worked in its heyday and the health and beauty practices of its 5000 citizens. Dramatic archaeological discoveries provide a glimpse of the last years of the Roman city and its possible conversion into the headquarters of a 5th century British or Irish warlord.

The latest addition to the site is a two-thirds scale recreation of a Roman town house excavated here: it was built using traditional methods as interpreted by six modern building-trade workers, for the Channel 4 series 'Rome Wasn't Built in a Day'.

www.english-heritage.org.uk/ wroxeter

NEW FOR 2012

Visit Wroxeter Roman City during 2012 and see how the Roman Town House has been brought to life with new interpretation and furnishings.

NON-MEMBERS

Adult	£5.00
Concession	£4.50
Child	£3.00
Family	£13.00

OPENING TIMES

1 Apr-4 Nov, daily	10am-5pm
5 Nov-28 Mar, Sat-Sun	10am-4pm
24-26 Dec and 1 Jan	Closed

HOW TO FIND US

Direction: Located at Wroxeter, 5 miles E of Shrewsbury on B4380

Train: Shrewsbury 5½ miles; Wellington Telford West 6 miles

Bus: Arriva 96 Telford – Shrewsbury (passes close to ⭾ Telford Central)

Tel: 01743 761330

OVP

A car parking charge of £2 applies to ensure EH members and paying visitors have priority. The charge will be refunded on admission.

MAP Page 318 (4B)
OS Map 126, 241: SJ565087

Croxden Abbey
Staffordshire

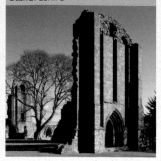

The impressive remains of an abbey of Cistercian 'white monks', including towering fragments of its 13th-century church, infirmary and 14th-century abbot's lodging. Information panels tell the story of the abbey's spectacular architecture.

OPENING TIMES
Daily	10am-5pm
24-26 Dec and 1 Jan	Closed

HOW TO FIND US
Direction: 5 miles NW of Uttoxeter off A522

Train: Uttoxeter 6 miles

Bus: Closest service is Phil Smith 184 to Hollington. Otherwise First 32/32A or Alton Towers Transport 30 to Alton then 2½ mile walk

MAP Page 318 (3D)
OS Map 128, 259: SK066397

Wall Roman Site (Letocetum)
Staffordshire — WS14 0AW

Wall Roman Site (Letocetum)

Wall was an important staging post on Watling Street, the Roman military road to North Wales. It provided overnight accommodation for travelling Roman officials and imperial messengers. The foundations of an inn and bathhouse can be seen, and many of the excavated finds are displayed in the on-site museum.

Managed by English Heritage on behalf of the National Trust, with thanks to the Friends of Letocetum.

www.english-heritage.org.uk/wall

OPENING TIMES
Site
1 Mar-4 Nov, daily	10am-5pm
5 Nov-28 Feb, daily	10am-4pm
24-26 Dec and 1 Jan	Closed

Museum
24-25 Mar, 7-9, 28-29 Apr, 5-7, 26-27 May, 2-4, 23-24 June, 15, 22, 28-29 Jul, 5, 12, 19, 25-27 Aug, 2, 29-30 Sep, 27-28 Oct 11am-4pm

11am-4pm or dusk, whichever comes sooner

HOW TO FIND US
Direction: Off A5 at Wall, near Lichfield

Train: Shenstone 1½ miles

Bus: Midland service 81

MAP Page 318 (4D)
OS Map 139, 244: SK098066

All Saints' Church, Billesley
Warwickshire — B49 6NF

© Sarah McCarthy

Tradition has it that William Shakespeare married Anne Hathaway here. His granddaughter's wedding's also said to have taken place in this church that dates back 1,000 years. Some remains of the early church survive, in particular two spectacular 12th century stone carvings.

Owned and managed by The Churches Conservation Trust.

OPENING TIMES
Open daily during daylight hours

HOW TO FIND US
Train: Nearest Wilmcote 2½ miles and Stratford-upon-Avon 4 miles

Bus: Routes 26/29/299

30 mins to Kenilworth Castle and Elizabethan Garden

MAP Page 318 (6E)
OS Map 151, 205: SP148568

Kenilworth Castle
and Elizabethan Garden

Warwickshire – CV8 1NE

A vast medieval fortress which became an Elizabethan palace, Kenilworth Castle is one of Britain's largest and most impressive historic sites. Extensive developments here highlight Kenilworth's famous associations with Queen Elizabeth I and her favourite, Robert Dudley; most spectacularly the re-creation of the fabulous garden, which Dudley commissioned to astound visitors – especially Queen Elizabeth!

Check opening times at www.english-heritage.org.uk

Visit the website for details of special events held here throughout the year.

Spanning more than five centuries, Kenilworth's varied buildings and architectural styles reflect its long connection with successive English monarchs. Geoffrey de Clinton, Henry I's treasurer, began the massive Norman keep at the core of the fortress in the 1120s, and under Henry II Kenilworth became a royal castle. King John greatly strengthened it between 1210 and 1215, enlarging the surrounding watery 'mere' which effectively made it an island stronghold. Thus it could withstand an epic siege in 1266, when rebellious barons held out against Henry III's siege engines for six months, succumbing only to starvation. In the impressively-timbered Tudor stables, which now house the castle's tearoom, trebuchet balls from the siege can be seen in the fascinating interactive display on the castle's history.

During the late 14th century John of Gaunt, Duke of Lancaster, rebuilt the splendid great hall and staterooms of Kenilworth's inner court, beginning the castle's transition into a palace and favourite residence of the Lancastrian and early Tudor kings. Here Henry V

received the insulting French 'gift' of tennis-balls which sparked off the Agincourt campaign, and by Henry VIII's time the castle was already renowned for its 'many fair chambers'. The scene was set for Kenilworth's greatest period of fame.

This began when Queen Elizabeth's favourite, Robert Dudley, Earl of Leicester, took possession of the castle in 1563. He then lavished fortunes on converting it into a great showpiece mansion, designed to receive the Queen and her court on their ceremonial 'progresses' around her realm. Striking evidence of Dudley's transformation can still be seen everywhere at Kenilworth exhibition. Not content with remodelling its existing structures, he added the tall, mansion-sized 'Leicester's Building' – complete with a 'dancing chamber' on its top floor – specifically for the Queen's use as well as an imposing new entrance to his quasi-royal palace, 'Leicester's Gatehouse'.

As part of a multi-million pound English Heritage investment in Kenilworth Castle, Leicester's

Gatehouse is displayed with the chambers on its lower floors re-created as they might have appeared when the gatehouse was last inhabited in the 1930s, while the top floor houses 'The Queen and the Castle: Robert Dudley's Kenilworth'. Featuring items both from museums and private collections, this exhibition tells the story of Elizabeth I's relationship with Dudley and her four visits to Kenilworth.

On the last and most famous of these visits, in July 1575, Elizabeth stayed here for 19 days – her longest sojourn in a courtier's house during any of her progresses. Dudley not only entertained her lavishly throughout with music, dancing, hunting and plays; he also created specially for her visit a fabulous garden, the re-creation of which is English Heritage's latest contribution to Kenilworth's long history.

A bejewelled Renaissance aviary; magnificent carved arbours; a planting scheme abundant in colour, perfume and fruit and an 18-foot-high fountain carved from dazzling Carrara marble. These are just some of the glories of Robert Dudley's garden at Kenilworth Castle. In an age famous for its extravagance, it was designed to score off rival aristocratic garden-creators, but principally to astound visitors, including Elizabeth I.

This garden, lost for centuries, has been brought back to life by a pioneering team of historians, archaeologists, plantsmen and plantswomen, designers, craftspeople and gardeners. It presents the most complete evocation of an Elizabethan

Kenilworth Castle and Elizabethan Garden | continued

The impressively-timbered Tudor stables now house the castle's tearoom and a fascinating interactive display on the castle's history.

garden anywhere in the world – a garden to seduce and beguile visitors today, just as it did in 1575.

Such an outstandingly comprehensive re-creation of Elizabethan garden architecture, design, statuary and planting has never been attempted on this scale before. It has been made possible by important advances in garden archaeology and the survival of an extraordinary eye-witness description of the Kenilworth garden, written by Robert Langham in 1575. Thus a garden that was once the 'glory of England' can once again be admired at this most romantic of castles. It opens a window on the period's most enduring love story – that of Elizabeth I and her favourite, Robert Dudley.

Though largely unscathed during the Civil War, Kenilworth was afterwards rendered indefensible and gradually fell into dilapidation. Made famous by Walter Scott's romantic novel, *Kenilworth* (1821), it came into state guardianship in 1938.

www.english-heritage.org.uk/ kenilworth

 www.facebook.com/ kenilworthcastle

⊤ Available for corporate and private hire

▲ Licensed for civil wedding ceremonies

NON-MEMBERS

Adult	£8.20
Concession	£7.40
Child	£4.90
Family	£21.30

Additional charges for members and non-members may apply on event days

OPENING TIMES

1 Apr-4 Nov, daily	10am-5pm
5 Nov-17 Feb, Sat-Sun	10am-4pm
18-22 Feb, daily	10am-4pm
23 Feb-28 Mar, Sat-Sun	10am-4pm
24-26 Dec and 1 Jan	Closed

Note: the gatehouse may close early for private events, please call or check the website before you visit

Free members' guided tours
9-19 Nov, 7 Dec, 11 Jan, 15 Feb, 8-25 Mar
11am-12.30pm/2pm-3.30pm

HOW TO FIND US

Direction: In Kenilworth off A46. Clearly signposted from the town centre, off B4103

Train: Warwick or Coventry 5 miles

Bus: Johnsons of Henley 539 passes the castle site; Travel West Midlands 12; Stagecoach U2, U12, 16, U17 & X17 all serve Kenilworth from surrounding area

Tel: 01926 852078

Local Tourist Information
Kenilworth: 01926 748900

Audio tours available (English, French, German and a children's version). Audio tours not available on Bank Holiday weekends or special event days.

Apr-Oct – tearoom only daily, Nov-Mar – tearoom open Sat & Sun, Feb half term – tearoom open daily.

A car parking charge applies to ensure that EH members and paying visitors have priority. The charge will be refunded on admission, except on Bank Holiday weekends and at selected special events.

MAP Page 318 (5E)
OS Map 140, 221: SP278723

Halesowen Abbey
West Midlands – B62 8RJ

Remains of an abbey founded by King John in the 13th century.

OPENING TIMES

Open to view from the public footpath only, due to construction works taking place on the site during 2012. Will re-open for visits in 2013

HOW TO FIND US

Directions: Off A456, ½ mile W of J3, M5

Train: Old Hill 2½ miles

Bus: Diamond services 002, 007; National Express West Midlands services 9 & 241 (then ½ mile walk)

Please note there are no toilets on site.

MAP Page 318 (5D)
OS Map 139, 219: SO975828

J. W. Evans Silver Factory
Birmingham – B1 3EA

Established in 1881, J. W. Evans is one of the most complete surviving historic factories in Birmingham's Jewellery Quarter. Behind the frontage of four terraced houses, the workshops retain their original drop stamps and fly presses. They are packed with thousands of dies for the manufacture of silverware, as well as the whole of the working equipment, stock and records of the business. English Heritage stepped in to rescue the factory in 2008. The site is now open for pre-booked guided tours only.

www.english-heritage.org.uk/ jwevans

J. W. Evans Silver Factory

OPENING TIMES
4, 14, 18, 28 Apr
2, 12, 16, 26 May
6, 16, 20, 30 Jun
4, 14, 18, 28 Jul
1, 11, 15, 18 Aug
5, 15, 19, 29 Sep
3, 13, 17, 27 Oct
Pre-booked tours only, max 10 persons per tour

HOW TO FIND US

Direction: Located ½ mile from Birmingham City Centre. 54-57 Albion Street

Train: Jewellery Quarter 5 minutes, New Street ½ mile

Bus: From surrounding areas
Tel: 0870 333 1181

MAP Page 318 (5D)
OS Map 139, 220: SP062870

WORCESTERSHIRE

Church of St Mary Magdalene, Croome D'Abitot
Worcestershire – WR8 9DW

© CCT

A masterpiece of architectural fantasy. The original church at Croome was demolished,

Church of St Mary Magdalene, Croome D'Abitot

and replaced by this 'Georgian Gothic' church in Croome Park. Built by some of the finest craftsmen in England, every detail has been considered, from pretty plaster mouldings to handsome carved pews and elegant Gothic windows.

Owned and managed by The Churches Conservation Trust.

OPENING TIMES
Open when Croome Park is open. For further details see National Trust website

HOW TO FIND US
Train: Nearest 🚉 Pershore 7 miles

Bus: Route 362

MAP Page 318 (6D)
OS Map 150, 190: SO886450

Leigh Court Barn
Worcestershire

An outstanding display of English medieval carpentry, this mighty timber-framed barn is the largest cruck framed structure in Britain. Built for Pershore Abbey in 1344, it is 46 metres (150 feet) long, with 18 cruck blades each made from a single oak tree.

OPENING TIMES
1 Apr-30 Sep,
Thu-Sun & Bank Hols   10am-5pm

HOW TO FIND US
Direction: 5 miles W of Worcester on an unclassified road off A4103

Train: Worcester Foregate Street 5 miles

Bus: Veolia-Astons service 417 or First 423 & LMS 425 (Fri only) to within 1 mile

MAP Page 318 (6C)
OS Map 150, 204: SO783535

Witley Court and Gardens

Worcestershire – WR6 6JT

A hundred years ago, Witley Court was one of England's great country houses, hosting many extravagant parties. Today it is a spectacular ruin, the result of a disastrous fire in 1937. Restoration work to the West Wing has made several new rooms accessible to the public.

The substantial Pool House holiday cottage can sleep up to 8 people, and has its own well-screened garden with sheltered dining terrace.

Great Witley Church

The vast and rambling remains of the palatial 19th-century mansion are surrounded by magnificent landscaped gardens, which still contain huge stone fountains. The largest, representing Perseus and Andromeda – now restored – was described in its day as making the 'noise of an express train' when fired.

Before 1846, when William Humble Ward (later first Earl of Dudley) inherited Witley Court, the land surrounding the house was laid out in the 18th-century English landscape style. As part of Ward's transformation of the estate, he called in the leading landscape designer of the time, William Andrews Nesfield, whose skills in designing intricate and elegant parterres were complemented by his great ability as an artist and engineer.

Nesfield started work in 1854, creating the South Parterre with its great Perseus and Andromeda fountain. His scheme involved elegantly designed plantings and parterres of clipped evergreens and shrubs. The East Parterre garden, with its Flora Fountain, was designed in the Parterre de Broderie style, resembling embroidery.

Following the disastrous fire in 1937 the Witley Estate,

including its gardens, fell into long decline. English Heritage has now restored the south garden. In addition, Wolfson Foundation funding has assisted with recently-completed major restoration works in the East Parterre garden, based on two years of archaeological investigation and old photographs of the garden in its prime. A scrollwork pattern of box hedges has been planted, interspersed with areas of coloured gravels and colourful bedding plant displays. The showpiece Woodland Walks in the North Park pass many different species of tree and shrub from all over the world.

Close to Witley Court is Great Witley Church (not managed by English Heritage), with its amazing Italianate Baroque interior. The church has a tearoom and Witley Court has a gift shop. The restored Perseus and Andromeda fountain, with the original high cascades operating, will be firing between April and October. (Weekdays: 11am, 12pm, 2pm, 3pm and 4pm. Weekends: on the hour every hour from 11am to 4pm.)

www.english-heritage.org.uk/witleycourt

NEW FOR 2012

Discover some of Witley's wildlife with a stroll around the newly opened lakeside walk.

 www.facebook.com/witleycourt

⌂ Holiday cottage available to let

NON-MEMBERS

Adult	£6.50
Concession	£5.90
Child	£3.90
Family	£16.90

OPENING TIMES

1 Apr-30 Jun, daily	10am-5pm
1 Jul-31 Aug, daily	10am-6pm
1 Sep-4 Nov, daily	10am-5pm
5 Nov-28 Mar, Sat-Sun	10am-4pm
24-26 Dec and 1 Jan	Closed

HOW TO FIND US

Direction: 10 miles NW of Worcester on A443

Train: Worcester Foregate St 9½ miles

Bus: Yarranton service 758 Worcester – Tenbury Wells (passes close to Worcester Foregate Street ⊠ Worcester); CC 359 (Fri only); R&B 760 (Thu only)

Tel: 01299 896636

Local Tourist Information
Worcester: 01905 726311

Disabled access (exterior and grounds only). A terrain guide is available on the website.

Tearoom open daily, Apr-Sep, Sat and Sun in Oct (not managed by EH).

MAP Page 318 (6C)
OS Map 138/150, 204: SO769649

Associated attractions in the West Midlands

These visitor attractions, all independent of EH, offer discounts to our members. Please call before you visit to confirm details. A valid EH membership card must be produced for each member.

Anne Hathaway's Cottage
Warwickswhire CV37 9HH

Visit Anne Hathaway's Cottage, the most romantic of the five Shakespeare Houses, and see the family home of Shakespeare's wife.

Shottery, Stratford-upon-Avon
Tel: 01789 204016
www.shakespeare.org.uk

2 for 1
entry

Compton Verney
Warwickswhire CV35 9HZ

Visitors of all ages are warmly welcomed to this award-winning art gallery. Explore art from around the world and relax and play in 'Capability' Brown landscaped parkland.

12½ miles from Kenilworth Castle
Tel: 01926 645500
www.comptonverney.org.uk

2 for 1
entry OVP

Eastnor Castle
Herefordshire HR8 1RL

Eastnor is a dramatic, fairytale castle situated in a 5000-acre estate in the Malvern Hills, within an Area of Outstanding Natural Beauty. The castle is surrounded by a lake, deer park and arboretum, with magnificent views of the rolling Herefordshire countryside.

10 mins from J2 of M50
Tel: 01531 633160
www.eastnorcastle.com

50% discount OVP
on entry 1

Heritage Motor Centre
Warwickshire CV35 0BJ

The Centre is home to the world's largest collection of historic British cars. Fun for all the family; Museum, 4x4 Experience, Electric Go-Karts, Café and Shop. Check website for holiday activities and special events.

30 mins to Kenilworth Castle
Tel: 01926 641188
www.heritage-motor-centre.co.uk

£2 off entry (up to 5 people)
(Not valid on special event days) 1

Ironbridge Gorge Museums
Shropshire TF8 7DQ

The ten Ironbridge Gorge Museums offer a remarkable insight into the industrial heritage of the area. Walk around the recreated streets and meet the Victorians at Blists Hill Victorian Town.

2 miles from the Iron Bridge
Tel: 01952 433424
www.ironbridge.org.uk

20% passport
discount 6

Mary Arden's Farm
Warwickswhire CV37 9UN

Visit the real working Tudor Farm, the home of Shakespeare's mother Mary Arden, and experience life as it would have been when he was a boy. (Closed in winter).

Wilmcote, Stratford-upon-Avon
Tel: 01789 204016
www.shakespeare.org.uk

2 for 1
entry

Shakespeare's Birthplace
Warwickswhire CV37 6QW

Discover the fascinating story of William Shakespeare's early years. Explore the *Life, Love & Legacy* exhibition, enter the beautiful historic house and enjoy its outstanding gardens.

Stratford-upon-Avon Town Centre
Tel: 01789 204016
www.shakespeare.org.uk

2 for 1
entry   ⊞

Stoneleigh Abbey
Warwickshire CV8 2LF

From medieval monks to Victorian gentry, Stoneleigh Abbey covers 800 years of history and events that have transformed a Cistercian Abbey into a stately home. Stroll the pleasure grounds or take a guided tour of a site that inspired Jane Austen.

5 mins from Kenilworth Castle
Tel: 01926 858535
www.stoneleighabbey.org

15% discount on entry
to house and gardens   ⊞

Warwick Castle
Warwickshire CV34 4QU

Immerse yourself in a thousand years of history – come rain or shine. See lavishly decorated state rooms, walk the towers and ramparts, or explore the 60 acres of glorious landscaped grounds and gardens. It could only be Warwick Castle.

Close to Kenilworth Castle
www.warwick-castle.com

50% discount   ⊞
on entry   👪2

219

The Wedgwood Museum
Staffordshire ST12 9ER

Home of one of the world's most interesting ceramic collections, the Wedgwood Museum's galleries tell the story of Josiah Wedgwood, his family, and the company he founded two-and-a-half centuries ago.

10 mins from J15 of M6
Tel: 01782 371919
www.wedgwoodmuseum.org.uk

25% discount
on entry   ⊞

Rievaulx Abbey

YORKSHIRE & THE HUMBER

PROPERTIES

**Yorkshire & The Humber
properties consist of:**

32	English Heritage
9	The Churches Conservation Trust
12	Associated Attractions

**Remember to check
opening times before you
visit any of our properties
www.english-heritage.
org.uk/daysout**

Details of local public transport
information in England are
available from Traveline
www.traveline.org.uk
or call 0871 200 2233.

Byland Abbey

Make the most of your
membership and keep up to
date with upcoming events, the
latest news and special offers by
subscribing to our e-newsletter.
Register online now at
**www.english-heritage.org.uk/
newsletter**

EAST RIDING OF YORKSHIRE

Burton Agnes Manor House
Howden Minster
Skipsea Castle

NORTH LINCOLNSHIRE

Gainsthorpe Medieval Village
St Peter's Church,
   Barton-upon-Humber
Thornton Abbey and Gatehouse

NORTH YORKSHIRE

Aldborough Roman Site
Byland Abbey
Clifford's Tower
Easby Abbey
Helmsley Castle
Kirkham Priory
Marmion Tower
Middleham Castle
Mount Grace Priory
Pickering Castle
Piercebridge Roman Bridge
Richmond Castle
Rievaulx Abbey
St Mary's Church, Studley Royal
Scarborough Castle
Spofforth Castle
Stanwick Iron Age Fortifications
Steeton Hall Gateway
Wharram Percy Deserted
   Medieval Village
Wheeldale Roman Road
Whitby Abbey
York Cold War Bunker

SOUTH YORKSHIRE

Brodsworth Hall and Gardens
Conisbrough Castle
Monk Bretton Priory
Roche Abbey

YORKSHIRE & THE HUMBER

Whitby

Richmond

Northallerton

Scarborough

North Yorkshire

Ripon

Settle

Bridlington

Harrogate

York

Skipton

East Riding

Hornsea

Beverley

West Yorkshire

Bradford • Leeds

Selby

Kingston upon Hull

Halifax

Goole

Huddersfield

North Lincolnshire

Barnsley

Scunthorpe

Grimsby

Doncaster

South Yorkshire

Rotherham

Sheffield

North East Lincolnshire

HIGHLIGHTS FOR 2012/13 IN YORKSHIRE & THE HUMBER

▪ **Brodsworth Hall & Gardens:** explore evocative interiors & acres of restored gardens.

▪ **Clifford's Tower:** fabulous views over the City of York.

▪ **Whitby Abbey:** discover the abbey's link to Dracula.

EAST RIDING OF YORKSHIRE

Burton Agnes Manor House
East Riding of Yorkshire

A medieval manor house interior, with a rare and well-preserved Norman undercroft and a 15th-century roof, all encased in brick during the 17th and 18th centuries.

OPENING TIMES

1 Apr–4 Nov, daily	11am–5pm
5 Nov–28 Mar	Closed

The nearby Burton Agnes Hall and Gardens are privately owned and are not managed by English Heritage

HOW TO FIND US

Direction: In Burton Agnes village, 5 miles SW of Bridlington on A166

Train: Nafferton 5 miles

Bus: East Yorkshire service 121 & 744

Parking (in Hall and Gardens car park, subject to charge).

MAP Page 321 (3J)
OS Map 101, 295: TA102632

Howden Minster
East Yorkshire – DN14 7BL

Howden Minster

The elaborately decorated ruins of a 14th-century chancel and chapter house (viewable only from the outside), attached to the still operational cathedral-like minster church.

OPENING TIMES

Any reasonable time

24–26 Dec and 1 Jan	Closed

HOW TO FIND US

Direction: In Howden; 23 miles W of Kingston Upon Hull, 25 miles SE of York, near the junction of A63 and A614

Train: Howden 1½ miles

Bus: East Yorkshire services 156, 160 (Wed, Sun only), 358 (Tue only)

🐕 🅿

Parking (on-street parking nearby – pay and display).

MAP Page 321 (4H)
OS Map 105/106, 291: SE748283

Skipsea Castle
East Riding of Yorkshire

An impressive Norman motte and bailey castle, dating from before 1086 and among the first raised in Yorkshire, with the earthworks of an attendant fortified 'borough'.

OPENING TIMES

Any reasonable time

HOW TO FIND US

Direction: Located 8 miles S of Bridlington; W of Skipsea village

Train: Bridlington 9 miles

Bus: East Yorkshire services 130

🐕

Dogs on leads (restricted areas only).

Waterproof footwear recommended.

MAP Page 321 (3J)
OS Map 107, 295: TA162551

NORTH LINCOLNSHIRE

Gainsthorpe Medieval Village
North Lincolnshire

A deserted medieval village, one of the best-preserved examples in England, clearly visible as a complex of grassy humps and bumps. According to legend demolished as a den of thieves, the real reason for its abandonment remains uncertain.

OPENING TIMES

Any reasonable time

HOW TO FIND US

Direction: Located on minor road W of A15 – towards Cleatham; S of Hibaldstow; 5 miles SW of Brigg

Train: Kirton Lindsey 3 miles

Bus: Hornsby Travel service 94

🐕

MAP Page 321 (5J)
OS Map 112, 281: SE954011

St Peter's Church, Barton-upon-Humber
See feature – Page 226

Thornton Abbey & Gatehouse

The enormous and ornate fortified gatehouse of Thornton Abbey is the largest and among the finest of all English monastic gatehouses. An early example of brick building in England, it proclaimed the wool trade-based prosperity of one of the wealthiest English Augustinian monasteries, for centuries a focus of spiritual and economic influence. Begun in the 1360s, the gatehouse was enlarged and fortified with battlements after the Peasants' Revolt of 1381, presumably as insurance against further trouble. Standing some 21 metres (69 feet) high and resembling a castle keep gatehouse, it may have protected the abbey's treasures as well as providing spacious lodgings for the abbot and his guests.

Within the grounds stand the ruins of the monastic buildings, notably the elegantly decorated octagonal chapter house of 1282-1308. These buildings were plundered for stone to build a 'most stately' Jacobean manor house which, mysteriously, 'fell quite down to the bare ground without any visible cause' (Abraham de la Pryme). The remains of its formal gardens have recently been rediscovered.

An exterior oak staircase gives visitors access to the restored gatehouse's atmospheric interior. The gatehouse includes features revealed following restoration work. An exhibition and graphic panels offer an insight into the abbey's history, including its role as the meeting place for huge Victorian Temperance rallies.

St Peter's Church, Barton-upon-Humber (see p.226) is nearby.

NON-MEMBERS

Adult	£4.40
Concession	£4.00
Child	£2.60

OPENING TIMES

1 Apr-30 Jun, Wed-Sun & Bank Hols	10am-5pm
1 Jul-31 Aug, daily	10am-5pm
1 Sep-4 Nov, Fri-Sun	10am-4pm
5 Nov-28 Mar, Sat-Sun	10am-4pm
24-26 Dec and 1 Jan	Closed

HOW TO FIND US

Direction: 18 miles NE of Scunthorpe, on a road N of A160; 7 miles SE of the Humber Bridge, on a road E of A1077

Train: Thornton Abbey ¼ mile

Bus: Stagecoach 'The Villager' service 260 passes the site, but rail is definitely the best way to reach this site

Tel: 01469 541445

⛴ 🦅 🎞 E ♨ P 🚃 ♿ 📷 OVP

Disabled access (except gatehouse interior and part of chapter ruins).

Dogs on leads (restricted areas only).

MAP Page 321 (5J)
OS Map 113, 284: TA118189

St Peter's Church, Barton-upon-Humber
North Lincolnshire – DN18 5EX

This famous Anglo-Saxon and medieval church is an archaeological as well as an architectural treasure-trove, and Britain's largest resource for historic bone analysis. The *Buried Lives* exhibition offers greater understanding of the church begun in c. 970, and the archaeological revelations it has produced. The analysis of 2800 burials here, ranging from Anglo-Saxon to Victorian times, has yielded unprecedented insights into medieval disease and diet, and medical and burial practices. Thornton Abbey and Gatehouse (see p.225) is nearby.

NON-MEMBERS

Adult	£3.60
Concession	£3.20
Child	£2.20

OPENING TIMES

1 Apr-30 Sep, Sat-Sun & Bank Hols	11am-3pm
1 Oct-28 Mar	Closed

HOW TO FIND US

Direction: In Barton-upon-Humber

Train: Barton-upon-Humber ½ mile

Bus: Stagecoach in Lincolnshire services 2, 250, 260, 350, 450 and Humber Flyer 2; Stagecoach/East Yorkshire Humber Fast Cat service 350 also passes close by

Tel: 01652 632516/01302 722598

MAP Page 321 (5J)
OS Map 107, 112, 281: TA035219

NORTH YORKSHIRE

Aldborough Roman Site
N. Yorkshire – YO51 9ES

Among the northernmost urban centres in the Roman Empire, Aldborough was the 'capital' of the Romanised Brigantes, the largest tribe in Britain. One corner of the defences is laid out amid a Victorian arboretum, and two mosaic pavements can be viewed in their original positions. The site museum has an outstanding collection of Roman finds.

NON-MEMBERS

Adult	£3.40
Concession	£3.10
Child	£2.00

OPENING TIMES

1 Apr-30 Sep, Sat-Sun & Bank Hols	11am-5pm
1 Oct-28 Mar	Closed

HOW TO FIND US

Direction: Located in Aldborough, ¾ mile SE of Boroughbridge on a minor road off B6265; within 1 mile of junction of A1 and A6055

Train: Cattal 7½ miles

Bus: Eddie Brown 56, 56A, 57, 57A, 58; Eddie Brown/Harrogate Coach Travel services 142, 143; Abbotts 55 (Wed only)

Tel: 01423 322768

Dogs on leads (restricted areas only).

MAP Page 321 (3G)
OS Map 299, 99: SE405662

Byland Abbey
See feature opposite

Church of Christ the Consoler, Skelton-cum-Newby
N. Yorkshire – HG4 5AE

© CCT

A grieving mother built this impressive church in the grounds of Newby Hall as a memorial for her murdered son. The interior is wonderfully rich, with pattern and colour everywhere, and a little carved stone dog provides a sweetly domestic touch amid the magnificent splendour. The same patroness and architect built St Mary's, Studley Royal (see p.234)

Owned and managed by The Churches Conservation Trust.

OPENING TIMES
Open daily during daylight hours

HOW TO FIND US

Train: Nearest Knaresborough 6½ miles

Bus: Routes 142/143

15 mins from Aldborough Roman Site, 40 mins from Rievaulx Abbey

MAP Page 321 (3G)
OS Map 99, 299: SE360679

Don't forget your membership card

Byland Abbey

North Yorkshire – YO61 4BD

Byland was one of the great Yorkshire Cistercian abbeys, housing at its zenith well over 200 monks and lay brothers. Much of its huge cathedral-sized church survives, including the whole north side and the greater part of the 13th-century west

front. The mixture of rounded Romanesque and pointed Gothic arches shows how architectural styles changed, and reveals that Byland was one of the earliest Gothic buildings in the north. Its great circular rose window, now surviving only in part, was probably the model for the rose window of York Minster. New archaeological research by English Heritage is beginning to throw light on the abbey's wider landscape setting, and revealing how the monks tamed a very boggy and inhospitable site when building work started in the mid-12th century. The compact museum is full of archaeological site finds, intermingled with colourful interpretation panels giving and insight into monastic life.

Rievaulx Abbey and Helmsley Castle are within reasonable travelling distance.

NON-MEMBERS

Adult	£4.40
Concession	£4.00
Child	£2.60

OPENING TIMES

1 Apr-30 Jun, Thu-Mon	10am-6pm
1 Jul-31 Aug, daily	10am-6pm
1-30 Sep, Thu-Mon	10am-6pm
1 Oct-28 Mar, Sat-Sun	10am-4pm
24-26 Dec and 1 Jan	Closed

HOW TO FIND US

Direction: 2 miles S of A170, between Thirsk and Helmsley; near Coxwold village

Train: Thirsk 10 miles

Bus: Hutchinsons 12; Stephensons service 31/31X; Moorsbus services M11 & M15 (seasonal); Smiths HB1, HB2, HB3 (seasonal)

Tel: 01347 868614 (Byland Abbey) 01347 868204 (Abbey Inn)

Local Tourist Information 01439 770173

Parking (adjacent to Abbey Inn). Toilets at Abbey Inn.

MAP Page 321 (2G)
OS Map 100, OL26/299: SE549789

Church of St John the Baptist, Stanwick
N. Yorkshire – DL11 7RT

© CCT

Surrounded by the high ramparts and impressive earthworks of Stanwick Camp, an important settlement in pre-Roman Britain, this Early English church is in an area of great natural beauty. St John's has the best collection of Anglo-Saxon grave markers in North Yorkshire. A 9th-century cross-shaft found in the churchyard and carved stones set into the walls suggest an even earlier building than Early English occupied this site.

Owned and managed by The Churches Conservation Trust.

OPENING TIMES
Open daily during daylight hours

HOW TO FIND US
Train: Nearest 🚋 Darlington 7 miles

1 mile Stanwick Iron Age Fortification

MAP Page 321 (1F)
OS Map 92, 304: NZ185120

Clifford's Tower, York
See feature opposite

Easby Abbey
N. Yorkshire

The substantial remains of an abbey of Premonstratensian 'white canons', probably most notable for its lavish roof-height refectory of c. 1300 and other monastic buildings. Within the precinct is the still-active parish church, displaying fine 13th-century wall-paintings. In a beautiful setting by the River Swale, Easby can be reached via a pleasant walk from Richmond Castle.

OPENING TIMES

1 Apr–30 Sep, daily	10am–6pm
1 Oct–4 Nov, daily	10am–5pm
5 Nov–28 Mar, daily	10am–4pm
24–26 Dec and 1 Jan	Closed

HOW TO FIND US
Direction: 1 mile SE of Richmond, off B6271

Bus: Dales & District 32, 32A, X34, 55

🐕 🏠 Ⓟ 🏞 ⚠

Guidebook (from Richmond Castle).

MAP Page 321 (2F)
OS Map 92, 304: NZ185003

Helmsley Castle
See feature – Page 230

Holy Trinity Church, Wensley
N. Yorkshire – DL8 4HX

© Graham Moore

Built on 8th-century Saxon foundations, this church stands on the bank of the River Ure in picturesque Wensleydale. Inside, there are interesting medieval wall paintings and a fine Flemish brass, and visitors can sit and marvel at the sumptuous richness of the local landowners' family pew, said to have come from Easby Abbey.

Owned and managed by The Churches Conservation Trust.

OPENING TIMES
Open daily during daylight hours

HOW TO FIND US
Train: Nearest 🚋 Northallerton 17 miles

Bus: Routes 59/156

10 mins from Middleham Castle

MAP Page 321 (2F)
OS Map 99, OL30: SE092895

Clifford's Tower, York

North Yorkshire – YO1 9SA

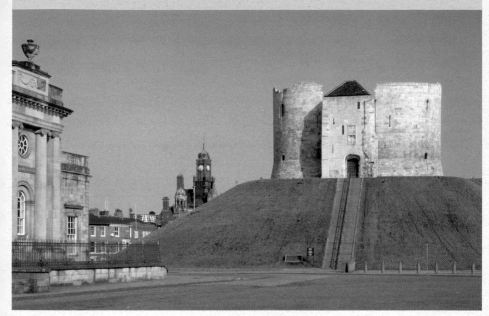

Perched on the summit of the mighty fortress mound raised by William the Conqueror in 1068, Clifford's Tower was the keep and chief strongpoint of York Castle, the greatest royal stronghold in medieval northern England. Built during the 1250s for Henry III, its four-lobed shape – giving it the old local nickname 'the Minced Pie' – is unique in England.

Like the city it once overawed, the tower has a rich history. A timber predecessor was burnt when York's Jews committed mass suicide there to avoid massacre by a mob in 1190. The present tower saw the hanging in chains in 1537 of Robert Aske, tragic leader of the Pilgrimage of Grace. Following plots to sell off

its stonework by a crooked Elizabethan custodian, the tower was used as a Civil War gun-platform.

Today it remains the principal surviving remnant of the medieval castle, still commanding amazing 360 degree panoramas from its lofty rampart walk. There are unrivalled views of the Minster, the towers and spires of York's medieval and later churches; and the fine Georgian buildings in the old castle bailey. In the distance the Yorkshire Wolds and – on a clear day – even the North York Moors can be seen.

Family events bring the history of the tower to life during the summer holidays.

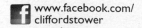 www.facebook.com/
cliffordstower

NON-MEMBERS

Adult	£4.00
Concession	£3.60
Child	£2.40
Family	£10.40

OPENING TIMES

1 Apr–4 Nov, daily	10am-6pm
5 Nov–17 Feb, Sat-Sun	10am-4pm
18–22 Feb, daily	10am-4pm
23 Feb–28 Mar, Sat-Sun	10am-4pm
24–26 Dec and 1 Jan	Closed

HOW TO FIND US

Direction: Tower St, York

Train: York 1 mile

Bus: From surrounding areas

Tel: 01904 646940

Local Tourist Information
York: 01904 550099

Parking (local charge).
Access (via steep steps).

MAP Page 321 (3G)
OS Map 105, 290: SE605515

Check opening times at www.english-heritage.org.uk

Helmsley Castle North Yorkshire – YO62 5AB

Surrounded by spectacular banks and ditches, this great medieval castle's impressive ruins stand beside the attractive market town of Helmsley.

Rievaulx and Byland Abbeys are both nearby. Rievaulx can be reached on foot via the Cleveland Way National Trail. Approx. 1½ hours (3½ miles/ 5.6 km) each way. Strong footwear is required.

NON-MEMBERS

Adult	£4.90
Concession	£4.40
Child	£2.90
Family	£12.70

OPENING TIMES

1 Apr-30 Sep, daily	10am-6pm
1-28 Oct, Thu-Mon	10am-5pm
29 Oct-2 Nov, daily	10am-4pm
3 Nov-17 Feb, Sat-Sun	10am-4pm
18-22 Feb, daily	10am-4pm
23 Feb-28 Mar, Sat-Sun	10am-4pm
24-26 Dec and 1 Jan	Closed

Helmsley Archaeology store tours
23 Apr, 29 May, 27 Jun, 19 Jul, 28 Sep, 15 Oct   11am & 2pm
Booking essential on 01439 770173.
Tours are free to members and non-members and are led by the Collections Curators

HOW TO FIND US

Direction: Near the town centre

Bus: Hutchinsons 15; Stephenson's 31, 31X, 194, 195 (Tue, Thu, Sat only), 196 (Mon, Wed & Fri only); Scarborough & District 128, Hodgson 199 (Fri only), Moorsbus HB1, HB2, HB3, M2, M3, M9, M13, M15

Tourist Information Centre
Tel: 01439 770173
Email: helmsley.tic@english-heritage.org.uk

Tel: 01439 770442

Audio tours.

Parking (large car park adjacent to castle; charge payable).

Toilets (in car park and town centre).

MAP Page 321 (2G)
OS Map 100, OL26: SE611836

The fortress was probably begun after 1120 by Walter Espec – 'Walter the Woodpecker'. Renowned for piety as well as soldiering, this Norman baron of 'gigantic stature' also founded nearby Rievaulx Abbey and Kirkham Priory, both English Heritage properties.

Most of Helmsley's surviving stonework defences were raised during the late 12th and 13th centuries by the crusader Robert de Roos and his descendants. They include a pair of immensely strong 'barbican' entrances and the high, keep-like east tower, unusually D-shaped in plan, which still dominates the town.

But Helmsley is not only a medieval fortress. During the Elizabethan period the Manners family remodelled the castle's chamber block into a luxurious mansion, whose fine plasterwork and panelling still partly survive. The castle's first and last military trial came during the Civil War. Held for King Charles, it endured a three-month siege before being starved into submission in November 1644 by Parliamentarians under Sir Thomas Fairfax, who was seriously wounded in the fighting. Fairfax then dismantled the defences but spared the mansion, subsequently the home of his daughter and her husband, the profligate Duke of Buckingham.

Demoted to a romantic backdrop when later owners moved to nearby Duncombe Park, Helmsley Castle has undergone a thorough makeover by English Heritage, making it more accessible to a wide range of visitors. This includes a visitor centre building with shop and information point, an audio tour and an imaginative hands-on exhibition in the mansion range. Displaying a fascinating array of finds from Civil War cannon balls to early tableware, this exhibition explores the social and domestic, as well as the military, aspects of the fortress. Facilities for disabled visitors include full ground-level ramping, a virtual tour of less accessible areas, and a tactile model with braille text. Enhanced learning resources include family-friendly books and activities.

www.english-heritage.org.uk/helmsleycastle

Holy Trinity Church, York
N. Yorkshire – YO1 7LF

© Graham White

Holy Trinity has the air of a hidden treasure, standing in a secluded churchyard behind York's busiest shopping street. On sunny days, gems of coloured light are scattered on the walls. The box pews and medieval stained glass are exceptionally fine, and monuments paint a picture of city life.

Owned and managed by The Churches Conservation Trust.

OPENING TIMES

Tue-Sat	10am-4pm
Sun-Mon	12-4pm

HOW TO FIND US

Train: Nearest ⬛ York ½ mile

Bus: Route 14A

10 min walk from Clifford's Tower

MAP Page 321 (3G)
OS Map 105, 290: SE605522

A charming stone built holiday cottage is available at Mount Grace Priory – see opposite

www.english-heritage.org.uk/holidaycottages

Kirkham Priory
N. Yorkshire – YO60 7JS

The riverside ruins of an Augustinian priory, picturesquely set in the beautiful Derwent valley. Features include a gatehouse bedecked with heraldry, including that of the De Roos family, Barons of Helmsley Castle; handsome monastic washbasins; and a small display of monastic artefacts.

NON-MEMBERS

Adult	£3.40
Concession	£3.10
Child	£2.00

OPENING TIMES

1 Apr-31 Jul, Thu-Mon	10am-5pm
1-31 Aug, daily	10am-5pm
1-30 Sep, Thu-Mon	10am-5pm
1 Oct-28 Mar, Sat-Sun	10am-4pm
24-26 Dec and 1 Jan	Closed

HOW TO FIND US

Direction: 5 miles SW of Malton, on a minor road off A64

Train: Malton 6 miles

Bus: Yorkshire Coastliner X40/840/3/5 (pass ⬛ York and ⬛ Malton) to Whitwell on the Hill and then ¾ mile walk; W.P.Hutchinson services 184 serves Kirkham village on (Tue, Fri, Sat only)

Tel: 01653 618768

Local Tourist Information
01653 600048

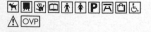

MAP Page 321 (3H)
OS Map 100, 300: SE736658

Marmion Tower
N. Yorkshire

The fine 15th-century gatehouse of a vanished riverside manor house, with a beautiful oriel window. The monuments of the manor's Marmion family owners grace the adjacent church.

OPENING TIMES

1 Apr-30 Sep, daily	10am-6pm
1 Oct-4 Nov, daily	10am-5pm
5 Nov-28 Mar, daily	10am-4pm
24-26 Dec and 1 Jan	Closed

HOW TO FIND US

Direction: On A6108 in West Tanfield

Train: Thirsk 10 miles

Bus: Dales & District service 159 also Vintage Omnibus Service 127 (summer only). Dales Bus 820 (summer Sun & Bank Hol Mon)

MAP Page 321 (3F)
OS Map 99, 298: SE268787

Middleham Castle
N. Yorkshire – DL8 4QG

The childhood and favourite home of Richard III, Middleham Castle was a fortress of the mighty Neville family, Earls of Westmoreland and of Warwick. Around the massive 12th-century central keep, they progressively constructed three ranges of luxurious chambers and lodgings, turning the castle into a fortified palace by the mid-15th century. Though roofless, many of these buildings survive, making Middleham a fascinating castle to explore. Here Richard spent part of his youth, in the guardianship of 'Warwick the Kingmaker'.

Middleham Castle

An exhibition about notable personalities from the castle's past includes a replica of the beautiful Middleham Jewel, a 15th-century pendant decorated with a large sapphire found near the castle.

NON-MEMBERS

Adult	£4.40
Concession	£4.00
Child	£2.60

OPENING TIMES

1 Apr-30 Sep, daily	10am-6pm
1 Oct-4 Nov, Sat-Wed	10am-4pm
5 Nov-28 Mar, Sat-Sun	10am-4pm
24-26 Dec and 1 Jan	Closed

Free members' guided tours
22 Nov, 17 Dec, 26 Jan,
13 Feb, 12 Mar   10.30am & 1.30pm

HOW TO FIND US

Direction: Located at Middleham; 2 miles S of Leyburn on A6108

Train: Leyburn (Wensleydale Railway) 2 miles

Bus: Dales & District service 159 also Vintage Omnibus Service 127 (summer only); Dales Bus York Pullman 820 (summer Sun & Bank Hol Mon)

Tel: 01969 623899

Local Tourist Information
Leyburn: 01969 623069

Disabled access (except keep).

MAP Page 321 (2F)
OS Map 99, OL30: SE127876

Mount Grace Priory
N. Yorkshire – DL6 3JG

Set amid North York Moors, Mount Grace was once the home of Carthusian monks, who lived as hermits in cottage-like cells.

Mount Grace Priory

A reconstructed and furnished monk's cell and a recently revamped herb plot offer a glimpse into the lives of the medieval residents. Two additional rooms in the guest house are now open following refurbishment. The gardens are a haven for wildlife, including the famous 'Priory Stoats'. There are also children's activities during school holidays.

Owned by the National Trust, maintained and managed by English Heritage.

⌂ Holiday cottage available to let

☂ Available for corporate and private hire

NON-MEMBERS

Adult	£5.20
Concession	£4.70
Child	£3.10
Family	£13.50

National Trust members admitted free, except on event days

OPENING TIMES

1 Apr-30 Sep, Thu-Mon	10am-6pm
1 Oct-4 Nov, Thu-Sun	10am-4pm
5 Nov-28 Mar, Sat-Sun	10am-4pm
24-26 Dec and 1 Jan	Closed

Please note: on days when there are summer evening theatre events, the site will open at 12 noon

HOW TO FIND US

Direction: 12 miles N of Thirsk; 6 miles NE of Northallerton, on A19

Train: Northallerton 6 miles

Bus: Arriva service 27 (Wed only); Abbott services 80, 89; Moorsbus M10 alight Priory Road End, ½ mile

Tel: 01609 883494

Local Tourist Information
Thirsk: 01845 522755

MAP Page 321 (2G)
OS Map 99, OL26: SE449985

Pickering Castle
N. Yorkshire – YO18 7AX

A fine early Norman castle set in an attractive moors-edge market town, with spectacular views from the motte-top. Pickering is a classic and well-preserved example of an early earthwork castle refortified in stone during the 13th and 14th centuries. There is an exhibition in the chapel and family-friendly books and activities.

NON-MEMBERS

Adult	£3.90
Concession	£3.50
Child	£2.30
Family	£10.10

OPENING TIMES

1 Apr-30 Jun, Thu-Mon	10am-5pm
1 Jul-31 Aug, daily	10am-5pm
1-30 Sep, Thu-Mon	10am-5pm
1 Oct-28 Mar	Closed

HOW TO FIND US

Direction: In Pickering; 15 miles SW of Scarborough

Train: Malton (9 miles) or Pickering (North Yorkshire Moors Rly) ¼ mile

Bus: Scarborough & District 128; W.P. Hutchinson 175; Yorkshire Coastliner 840 & X40; Moorsbus M5, M6, M8, M13 & M14

Tel: 01751 474989

Local Tourist Information
Pickering: 01751 473791

Disabled access (except motte).

MAP Page 321 (2H)
OS Map 100, OL27: SE799845

Piercebridge Roman Bridge
N. Yorkshire

Stonework foundations of a bridge, now marooned in a field, which once led to Piercebridge Roman Fort.

OPENING TIMES

Any reasonable time

HOW TO FIND US

Direction: At Piercebridge; 4 miles W of Darlington, on B6275

Train: Darlington 5 miles

Bus: Arriva 75, 76

MAP Page 321 (1F)
OS Map 93, 304: NZ214155

Richmond Castle
See feature opposite

Rievaulx Abbey
See feature – Page 236

Scarborough Castle
See feature – Page 238

St Mary's Church, Studley Royal
N. Yorkshire – HG4 3DY

This magnificent High Victorian Anglican church was designed in the 1870s by the flamboyant architect William Burges, and has been called his 'ecclesiastical masterpiece'. The extravagantly decorated interior displays coloured marble, stained glass, a splendid organ and painted and gilded figures in all their original glory.

Owned by English Heritage and managed by the National Trust as part of the Fountains Abbey and Studley Royal Estate (see p.248).

OPENING TIMES

1 Apr-30 Sep, daily	12pm-4pm
1 Oct-28 Mar	Closed

St Mary's Church, Studley Royal

HOW TO FIND US

Direction: Located 2½ miles W of Ripon, off B6265; in the grounds of the Studley Royal Estate

Bus: Dales & District 139

Tel: 01765 608888

Parking (at visitor centre or Studley Royal).

MAP Page 321 (3F)
OS Map 99, 298/299: SE275693

Spofforth Castle
N. Yorkshire

The ruined hall and chamber of a fortified manor house of the powerful Percy family, begun in the 13th and rebuilt in the 15th century. Its undercroft is cut into a rocky outcrop.

Managed by Spofforth-with-Stockeld Parish Council.

OPENING TIMES

1 Apr-30 Sep, daily	10am-6pm
1 Oct-28 Mar, daily (managed by a keykeeper)	10am-4pm
24-26 Dec and 1 Jan	Closed

HOW TO FIND US

Direction: 3½ miles SE of Harrogate; off A661 at Spofforth

Train: Pannal 4 miles

Bus: Transdev Harrogate & District services 77, 770; Connexions Buses X70

Dogs on leads (restricted areas only).

MAP Page 321 (4G)
OS Map 104, 289: SE360511

Stanwick Iron Age Fortifications
N. Yorkshire

An excavated section, part cut into rock, of the ramparts of the huge Iron Age trading and power-centre of the Brigantes, the most important tribe in pre-Roman northern Britain. Some 4 miles (6½ kilometres) long, the defences enclosed an area of 766 acres (310 hectares). Following Roman conquest, the Brigantian centre moved to Aldborough Roman Site (see p.226).

OPENING TIMES

Any reasonable time

HOW TO FIND US

Direction: Located on a minor road off A6274, at Forcett Village

Train: Darlington 10 miles

Bus: Dales & District service 29; Hodgsons 79A (Wed only)

Dogs on leads (restricted areas only).

MAP Page 321 (1F)
OS Map 92, 304: NZ179124

Richmond Castle

North Yorkshire – DL10 4QW

Impressive Richmond Castle is breathtakingly sited on a rocky promontory above the River Swale, overlooking an outstandingly picturesque market town at the foot of beautiful Swaledale. Among the oldest Norman stone fortresses in Britain, it was begun in about 1071 by William the Conqueror's Breton supporter Alan the Red. The towering keep, added a century later during the reign of Henry II, stands over 100 feet (30m) high, with walls up to 11 feet (3.35m)

thick. It is remarkably complete within, and visitors can climb to the top for panoramic views over the castle's great courtyard, the cobbled market place of Richmond and the Yorkshire Dales beyond.

According to legend, King Arthur and his knights lie sleeping in a cavern beneath the keep, and the drumbeats of a drummer-boy lost in a secret passage can still be heard.

More certainly, two medieval kings of Scotland were imprisoned here after defeat in battle, as more recently were conscientious objectors – including many Dales Quakers – who refused to fight in World War I. Their story is told in an interactive display exploring the castle's nine centuries of history, which is also woven into the contemporary Cockpit Garden overlooking the Swale. Family-friendly books and activities.

NON-MEMBERS

Adult	£4.70
Concession	£4.20
Child	£2.80

OPENING TIMES

1 Apr-30 Sep, daily	10am-6pm
1 Oct-4 Nov, Thu-Mon	10am-4pm
5 Nov-28 Mar, Sat-Sun	10am-4pm
24-26 Dec and 1 Jan	Closed

HOW TO FIND US

Direction: In Richmond just off the market place

Bus: Arriva X26, X27, X59; Dales & District 29, 30, 32, 32A, X34, 54, X54, 55, 73, 159; Hodgsons Coaches 79, 79A (Thu only), 79X; Also Dales Bus York Pullman 820 and Dales Bus Kirby Lonsdale Coach Hire 830 & 830 (seasonal Sun & Bank Hol Mon)

Tel: 01748 822493

Parking (2 hours free in market place – not managed by EH; disabled parking at Castle).

MAP Page 321 (2F)
OS Map 92, 304: NZ172007

Rievaulx Abbey North Yorkshire – YO62 5LB

'Everywhere peace, everywhere serenity, and a marvellous freedom from the tumult of the world.' Written over eight centuries ago by the monastery's third abbot, St Aelred, these words still describe Rievaulx today.

Set in a beautiful valley, Rievaulx is among the most atmospheric of all ruined abbeys in the North. Nestled into the breathtaking surroundings of this tranquil setting is a stunning detached holiday cottage which comfortably sleeps four people.

The tearoom has an indoor and outdoor seating area and serves a delicious variety of locally-sourced food, including ingredients grown in the Rievaulx Abbey garden.

🏠 Holiday cottage available to let

Words are not the only link to Rievaulx's medieval monks. Over the past few years, the site has become something of an archaeological treasure, with unexpected discoveries shedding new light on the lives of the monks and the extensive renewal and rebuilding of their abbey church in the Early English Gothic style. Archaeologists continue to study the landscape around Rievaulx, revealing the remarkable extent of the abbey's influence and industry. Their discoveries are showcased within the on-site museum.

The abbey was founded by St Bernard of Clairvaux, as part of the missionary effort to reform Christianity in western Europe. Twelve Clairvaux monks came to Rievaulx in 1132. From these modest beginnings grew one of the wealthiest monasteries of medieval England and the first northern Cistercian monastery. Rievaulx also enjoyed the protection of Walter Espec of nearby Helmsley Castle, who provided much of the abbey's land. The monks of neighbouring Byland Abbey initially disputed land ownership with Rievaulx, but subsequently moved to their present location and relinquished the disputed land, thus allowing the major expansion of Rievaulx Abbey. You can still see traces of the channels dug by the Rievaulx monks.

A steady flow of monks came to Rievaulx, attracted by the prestige of Abbot Aelred, author and preacher, who was regarded then and later as a wise and saintly man. Following his death in 1167, the monks of Rievaulx sought canonisation for their former leader, and in the 1220s they rebuilt the east part of their church in a much more elaborate style to house his tomb. Most of this 13th-century 'presbytery' still stands to virtually its full impressive height, a reminder of Rievaulx's original splendour.

Rievaulx was still a vibrant community when Henry VIII dissolved it in 1538. Its new owner, Thomas Manners, first Earl of Rutland, swiftly instigated the systematic destruction of the buildings, yet the substantial remains constitute one of the most eloquent of all monastic sites, free 'from the tumult of the world'. Schoolchildren from the local area have helped to create a Sensory Garden full of scented and flavoured herbs, amid tile motifs based on medieval designs.

Don't miss the exciting indoor exhibition, *The Work of God and Man*, which explores the agricultural, industrial, spiritual and commercial aspects of Rievaulx's history, employing a variety of lively and interactive displays. There are family-friendly events, books and activities during school holidays.

www.english-heritage.org.uk/ rievaulxabbey

NON-MEMBERS

Adult	£5.80
Concession	£5.20
Child	£3.50

OPENING TIMES

1 Apr-30 Sep, daily	10am-6pm
1-28 Oct, Thu-Mon	10am-5pm
29 Oct-2 Nov, daily	10am-4pm
3 Nov-17 Feb, Sat-Sun	10am-4pm
18-22 Feb, daily	10am-4pm
23 Feb-28 Mar, Sat-Sun	10am-4pm
24-26 Dec and 1 Jan	Closed

HOW TO FIND US

Direction: In Rievaulx; 2¼ miles N of Helmsley, on minor road off B1257

Bus: Moorsbus services M9 (Sun & Bank Holidays also Wed in high summer); Moorsbus HB3 (summer Sun) & Hutchinson service 199 (Fri only); Moorsbus service M2 passes within ½ mile (Sun & Bank Hols also Wed in high summer)

Tel: 01439 798228

Local Tourist Information Helmsley: 01439 770173

Audio tours (also available for the visually impaired, those with learning difficulties and in French and German).

Parking: Pay and display parking, refundable to EH members and paying visitors upon admission.

MAP Page 321 (2G)
OS Map 100, OL26: SE577850

Scarborough Castle North Yorkshire – YO11 1HY

Scarborough Castle defends a prominent headland between two bays, with sheer drops to the sea and only a narrow landward approach. Specially constructed viewing platforms on the battlements offer panoramic views. Long before the castle was built, this natural fortress was favoured by prehistoric settlers, and later housed a defended Roman signal station.

Henry II's towering 12th-century keep, dominating the approach, is the centrepiece of fortifications developed over later centuries in response to repeated sieges – notably by rebel barons in 1312 and twice during the Civil War. Though again strengthened with barracks and gun-batteries against Jacobite threats in 1745, the castle failed to defend the harbour against the American sea-raider John Paul Jones in 1779, and was itself damaged by German naval bombardment in 1914. During World War II it played the more covert role of hosting a secret listening post.

The site's 3000 year history is explored in interactive displays in the restored Master Gunner's House, accompanied by artefacts from each period of Scarborough's past. Less mobile visitors can enjoy a ground-floor, touch-screen virtual tour of the displays, as well as virtual views reproducing those from the raised platforms.

Timelined graphic panels around the castle focus on characters from the past and there are free activity sheets, an audio tour, and an investigative story box to help younger visitors visualise and understand the history of the castle.

www.english-heritage.org.uk/ scarboroughcastle

NON-MEMBERS

Adult	£4.90
Concession	£4.40
Child	£2.90
Family	£12.70

OPENING TIMES

1 Apr-30 Sep, daily	10am-6pm
1 Oct-4 Nov, Thu-Mon	10am-4pm
5 Nov-28 Mar, Sat-Sun	10am-4pm
24-26 Dec and 1 Jan	Closed

HOW TO FIND US

Direction: Castle Road, E of the town centre

Train: Scarborough 1 mile

Bus: From surrounding areas

Tel: 01723 372451

Local Tourist Information
Scarborough: 01723 383636

Parking (pre-booked parking only for disabled visitors, otherwise located in town centre).

MAP Page 321 (2J)
OS Map 101, 301: TA050892

Steeton Hall Gateway
N. Yorkshire – LS25 5PD

A fine example of a small, well-preserved manorial gatehouse dating from the 14th century.

OPENING TIMES

1 Apr-28 Mar, daily   10am-5pm
(exterior only)

HOW TO FIND US

Direction: Located 4 miles NE of Castleford, on a minor road off A162 at South Milford

Train: South Milford 1 mile

Bus: Arriva Yorkshire services 492 & 493

Dogs on leads (restricted areas only).

MAP Page 321 (4G)
OS Map 105, 290: SE484314

St Peter's Church, Wintringham
N. Yorkshire – YO17 8HU

© Cameron Newham

This beautiful and peaceful church, with an elegant spire, has Norman origins and is full of interesting furnishings including Jacobean bench pews, medieval carvings and stained glass. If you look carefully, you might even find some mythical beasts and ancient sword markings!

Owned and managed by The Churches Conservation Trust.

OPENING TIMES

Open daily during daylight hours

St Peter's Church, Wintringham

HOW TO FIND US

Train: Nearest ⊕ Malton 6 miles

Bus: Routes 199R/222R/239R

20 mins from Wharram Percy Deserted Medieval Village, 35 mins from Scarborough Castle

MAP Page 321 (3H)
OS Map 101, 300: SE887731

St Stephen's Church, Fylingdales
N. Yorkshire – YO22 4PN

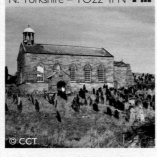

© CCT

St Stephen's, a fisherman's church, stands majestically on the hillside overlooking the sea. Resonating with a resilient North Sea fishing community there are memorials to the shipwrecked in both the church and churchyard. Outside, windswept gravestones huddle tightly round the church walls.

Owned and managed by The Churches Conservation Trust.

OPENING TIMES

Keyholder nearby

HOW TO FIND US

Train: Nearest ⊕ Whitby 5 miles

Bus: Arriva Bus 93 runs a regular service from Middlesborough bus station to Scarborough rail station going past the church

10 mins from Whitby Abbey

MAP Page 321 (2J)
OS Map 94, OL27: NZ942059

Wharram Percy Deserted Medieval Village
N. Yorkshire

The most famous and intensively studied of Britain's 3000 or so deserted medieval villages, Wharram Percy occupies a remote but attractive site in a beautiful Wolds valley. Above the substantial ruins of the church and a recreated fishpond, the outlines of many lost houses are traceable on a grassy plateau. First settled in prehistoric times, Wharram flourished as a village between the 12th and 14th centuries, before final abandonment in about 1500. Graphic interpretation panels tell its story and recreate the original appearance of the buildings. A free downloadable audio tour is available at www.english-heritage.org.uk/wharrampercy

OPENING TIMES

Any reasonable time

HOW TO FIND US

Direction: 6 miles SE of Malton, on minor road from B1248; ½ mile S of Wharram-le-Street. Park in car park, then ¾ mile walk via uneven track, steep in places. Site also accessible on foot via Wolds Way ramblers' path. Sturdy and waterproof footwear required. Parts of site slope steeply, and farm livestock likely to be present on site and access path

Train: Malton 8 miles

Bus: Busking Ltd service 133 (Sat, Sun and Bank Hols only); Royal Mail Malton–Foxholes post bus to Wharram Le Street on the B1248 then ½ mile walk

Please note: site is hazardous in snowy conditions.

MAP Page 321 (3H)
OS Map 100, 300: SE859644

Whitby Abbey North Yorkshire – YO22 4JT

Dominating the picturesque seaside town of Whitby, the dramatic ruins of the abbey stand on a headland rich in over thirteen centuries of history.

The mansion now houses the highly imaginative and award-winning visitor centre, displaying fascinating finds from the Anglo-Saxon, medieval and Cholmley periods.

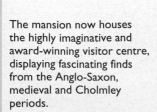

The first monastery here was founded in AD 657 by King Oswy of Northumbria. An Anglo-Saxon style 'double monastery' for men and women, its first ruler was the formidable royal princess Abbess Hild; here Caedmon the cowherd was miraculously transformed into an inspired poet; here the future of the English church was decided in 664; and here the relics of Northumbrian kings and saints were enshrined.

Though many intriguing excavated finds from it are displayed in the visitor centre, nothing survives above ground of this Anglo-Saxon monastery. The imposing ruins belong to the church of the Benedictine abbey refounded on its site by the Normans. Begun in about 1220 in the Early English style of Gothic, the pinnacled east end and north transept still stand high, richly carved with characteristic 'dog's tooth' embellishment. Time, war and nature have left their marks. Parts of the church collapsed during storms, its west front was hit by German naval shelling in 1914 and centuries of wind and rain have added their own etched and pitted decoration. These supremely romantic ruins enjoy panoramic views, and literary renown as the backdrop

to Bram Stoker's *Dracula*, the Victorian novel which has made Whitby the 'Goth' capital of Britain. More recently the site has inspired *Shadowmancer* and other best-selling children's novels by ex-vicar, ex-policeman and exorcist, GP Taylor.

The ruins share the headland with the Cholmley family mansion, begun after Henry VIII's suppression of the abbey. Its impressive Classical façade of 1672 is fronted by a restoration of the 'hard garden' courtyard rediscovered during English Heritage excavations. The courtyard's centrepiece is a specially-commissioned bronze copy of the famous 'Borghese Gladiator' statue. The Roman marble original of this spectacular life-sized statue, now in the Paris Louvre, dates from the 1st century BC: it was found in 1611 in Italy and bronze casts were made for King Charles I. Copies graced many great English houses and gardens including the Cholmleys' Whitby mansion, recalling the family's Civil War support for the Royalist cause.

The mansion now houses the highly imaginative and award-winning visitor centre. Displaying fascinating finds from the Anglo-Saxon, medieval and Cholmley periods, this is packed with

computer-generated images and entertaining interactives: touch-screens allow visitors to question Whitby personalities, from Abbess Hild via a medieval monk to Bram Stoker.

Please note: from the Whitby harbour area, the abbey can only be directly reached on foot via the 199 'abbey steps'. Alternatively, a well-signposted road leads from the town outskirts to the cliff-top abbey.

www.english-heritage.org.uk/ whitbyabbey

NON-MEMBERS

Adult	£6.20
Concession	£5.60
Child	£3.70
Family	£16.10

OPENING TIMES

1 Apr-30 Sep, daily	10am-6pm
1-28 Oct, Thu-Mon	10am-4pm
29 Oct-2 Nov, daily	10am-4pm
3 Nov-17 Feb, Sat-Sun	10am-4pm
18-22 Feb, daily	10am-4pm
23 Feb-28 Mar, Sat-Sun	10am-4pm
24-26 Dec and 1 Jan	Closed

HOW TO FIND US

Direction: On cliff top, E of Whitby

Train: Whitby ½ mile

Bus: Esk Valley service 8A, 96, 97, 98; Arriva 5, 5A, X5, X60 (seasonal), 91, 93, X93, 94, 95, 100; Coastal & Country 97A, 98 & Whitby Town Tour; M&D 99; Yorkshire Coastliner 840 & X40; Moorsbus Vintage bus service (summer Sun & Aug Bank Hol)

Tel: 01947 603568

Local Tourist Information Whitby: 01947 602674

Disabled access (south entrance parking, charged).

Dogs on leads (restricted areas only).

Parking not managed by English Heritage (charge payable).

Toilets situated in the car park are not operated by English Heritage.

MAP Page 321 (1J)
OS Map 94, OL27: NZ903112

Wheeldale Roman Road
N. Yorkshire

A mile-long stretch of enigmatic ancient road – probably Roman but possibly later or earlier – still with its hard core and drainage ditches. Amid wild and beautiful moorland.

OPENING TIMES
Any reasonable time

HOW TO FIND US
Direction: S of Goathland; W of A169; 7 miles S of Whitby

Train: Goathland (North Yorkshire Moors Rly) (4 miles) or Newtondale Halt (then 3 mile forest walk)

Bus: Yorkshire Coastliner service 840 to Goathland then 4 mile walk

Local Tourist Information
Pickering: 01751 473791

MAP Page 321 (2H)
OS Map 94/100, OL27: SE806977

Whitby Abbey
See feature – Page 240

Sample delicious homemade treats at Brodsworth Hall
Check property listings for details of cafés.

York Cold War Bunker
N. Yorkshire – YO24 4HT

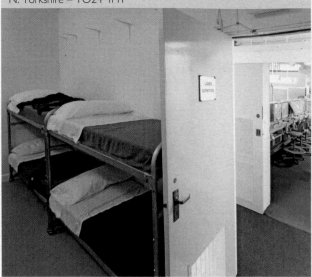

English Heritage's most modern, most unusual and perhaps most spine-chilling site, 'No. 20 Group Royal Observer Corps HQ' is the semi-subterranean bunker which would have monitored nuclear explosions and fallout in the Yorkshire region. In service between 1961 and 1991, the Bunker's control rooms display 'colour-psychology décor' together with original monitoring and communications equipment. Decontamination rooms with air filters and special sewage ejectors were intended to seal off the 60-strong workforce from the devastated outside world. A guided tour, enhanced by a striking 10-minute film (PG rated) and interpretation, tells the story of the Cold War's 'Mutually Assured Destruction.'

NON-MEMBERS

Adult	£6.20
Concession	£5.60
Child	£3.70

OPENING TIMES

1 Apr-28 Mar Sun & Bank Hols	10am-4pm

By tour only, tours every ½ hour

Tours last approx 1 hour. No need to book. Last tour 3pm

Weekdays: Admission for schools and groups only. Booking 14 days in advance, minimum fee applies

Free members' guided tours
19 Nov, 11 Dec, 24 Jan,
15 Feb, 20 Mar   10.30am & 1.30pm

HOW TO FIND US
Direction: Monument Close, off Acomb Road, near the Carlton Tavern, approx. 2 miles from York city centre

Train: York 2 miles

Bus: First in York service 1; Arriva 412 & 413

Tel: 01904 646940 (Clifford's Tower)

Local Tourist Information
York: 01904 550099

Parking (limited to 3 spaces).

MAP Page 321 (3G)
OS Map 105, 290: SE580515

Brodsworth Hall and Gardens
See feature – Page 244

Conisbrough Castle
S. Yorkshire – DN12 3BU

Conisbrough's spectacular magnesian limestone keep, nearly 100 feet high, is cylindrical with wedge-shaped turret-buttresses, a design unique in Britain. Now with reinstated roof and floors, it was built in the late 12th century for Hamelin Plantagenet, illegitimate half-brother of King Henry II, and subsequently reinforced by turreted curtain walls. Conisbrough was among the inspirations for Sir Walter Scott's classic novel, *Ivanhoe*.

NON-MEMBERS

Adult	£4.60
Concession	£4.10
Child	£2.80
Family	£12.00

OPENING TIMES

1 Apr-30 Jun, Sat-Wed	10am-5pm
1 Jul-31 Aug, daily	10am-5pm
1 Sep-4 Nov, Sat-Wed	10am-5pm
5 Nov-28 Mar, Sat-Sun	10am-4pm
24-26 Dec and 1 Jan	Closed
Open Mon-Fri all year for schools	

HOW TO FIND US

Direction: Located NE of Conisbrough town centre off A630; 4½ miles SW of Doncaster

Conisbrough Castle

Train: Conisbrough ½ mile or Rotherham 6 miles

Bus: Stagecoach services 220, 221 & 222; First X78

Tel: 01709 863329

🍽 🎫 🇪 😀 🚶 👫 🅿 📷 ♿ ⚠
OVP

Dogs on leads (in grounds only).

Parking (visitors with disabilities may be dropped off at the visitor centre).

Access (limited to some areas).

MAP Page 321 (5G)
OS Map 111, 279: SK515989

Holy Trinity Church, Wentworth
S. Yorkshire – S62 7TX

© CCT

Rooted in village history, this atmospheric, partly ruined building started life as a church but was converted to a mausoleum in 1877. Today, only the chancel and north chapel remain intact. Brass and stone memorials and effigies trace the fascinating history of the powerful Wentworth family.

Owned and managed by The Churches Conservation Trust.

OPENING TIMES

Open during daylight hours May-Sep, Sun & Bank Holidays

At other times keyholder nearby

Holy Trinity Church, Wentworth

HOW TO FIND US

Train: Nearest ⬛ Elsecar 1½ miles

Bus: Route 690

20 mins from Conisbrough Castle

MAP Page 321 (5G)
OS Map 110/111, 278: SK384983

Monk Bretton Priory
S. Yorkshire

The substantial ruins of a Cluniac monastery, with an unusually well-marked ground plan, an almost complete west range and a 15th-century gatehouse.

NON-MEMBERS

Charge may apply on event days

OPENING TIMES

1 Apr-28 Mar, daily	10am-3pm
(managed by a keykeeper)	
24-26 Dec and 1 Jan	Closed

HOW TO FIND US

Direction: Located 1 mile E of Barnsley town centre, off A633

Train: Barnsley 2½ miles

Bus: Stagecoach services 32, 33, 33A; Tates 34

🍽 🅿 🖼 ⚠

MAP Page 321 (5G)
OS Map 110/111, 278: SE373065

Brodsworth Hall and Gardens

South Yorkshire – DN5 7XJ

Brodsworth Hall is unique. This is no glossily restored showpiece, frozen in manicured grandeur. 'Conserved as found', it is a mansion which has grown comfortably old over 120 years, a country house as it really was: still reflecting its original opulence, but well-worn, gently conserved – and full of surprises.

In contrast to the house, the extensive gardens have been wonderfully restored to their original horticultural splendour as 'a collection of grand gardens in miniature'.

Built in the 1860s by the fabulously wealthy Charles Thellusson, Brodsworth Hall was occupied by his family for over 120 years. The 'grand rooms' on the ground floor recall the house's Victorian heyday, but elsewhere Brodsworth's gentle decline during the 20th century is much more apparent. The last resident, the indomitable Sylvia Grant-Dalton, fought a losing battle against subsidence and leaking roofs in her latter years. Following her death in 1988, English Heritage took the bold decision to conserve the interiors as they were found, rather than restoring them.

Thus the house appears as she used it, making do and mending as funds and servants dwindled. The Library's original wallpaper and carpets are faded, and Charles Thellusson's woodworking room is crowded with delightful clutter. Some bedrooms fell out of use, along with the spartan rooms of the redundant servants' wing. Others were partially modernised over the years, including objects from the 1900s to the 1980s which may be startlingly familiar to many visitors.

Downstairs, the cavernous Victorian kitchen with its stupendous cooking range was deserted for a cosier 'Aga kitchen' and scullery. These remain as they were at the end of Brodsworth's active life, with their Tupperware, Formica and Fanny Craddock cookbooks. Beside the Aga rests the once-grand but battered and mended armchair of the house's last cook-housekeeper.

For garden lovers

In contrast to the house, the extensive gardens have been wonderfully restored to their original splendour as 'a collection of grand gardens in miniature', with vistas last enjoyed before World War I.

The flower garden displays a fine selection of period bedding plants, while romantic views from the restored summerhouse take in both the formal gardens and the pleasure grounds. Stroll through the statue walks, the fern dell grotto and the beautiful wild rose dell.

Here are our suggestions for enjoying the best of the garden collections:

Spring
Snowdrops, Bluebells and Daffodils put on a fantastic show.

Summer
The Rose Garden with its hundred varieties. Two contrasting herbaceous borders. The fern dell with its architectural foliage. On summer Sunday afternoons, the best of Yorkshire's brass bands play in the gardens.

Autumn
Brilliant autumn colours in the acer dell and clipped evergreen foliage in the formal gardens.

Winter
The collection of Victorian hollies.

Brodsworth Hall and Gardens   continued

The Enchanted Garden event

A family-friendly property

Brodsworth Hall and Gardens are outstandingly user-friendly for visitors of all ages. For children, there is a playroom, a hands-on resources room, and an outdoor play area, featuring a real ex-naval training boat. The friendly volunteer room stewards are another unique Brodsworth attraction: many knew the property before English Heritage acquired it.

www.english-heritage.org.uk/brodsworthhall

NEW FOR 2012

Back by popular demand, the wonderful Enchanted Garden event. See the Victorian gardens in a whole new light at this autumn evening event.

NON-MEMBERS

House and gardens

Adult	£9.30
Concession	£8.40
Child	£5.60

Gardens only

Adult	£5.70
Concession	£5.10
Child	£3.40

OPENING TIMES

House

1 Apr-30 Sep, Tue-Sun & Bank Hols	1pm-5pm
1 Oct-4 Nov, Sat-Sun	12pm-4pm
5 Nov-28 Mar	Closed

Gardens and tearoom

1 Apr-4 Nov, Tue-Sun & Bank Hols	10am-5.30pm

Gardens, tearoom, shop and servants' wing

5 Nov-17 Feb, Sat-Sun	10am-4pm
18-22 Feb, daily	10am-4pm
23 Feb-28 Mar, Sat-Sun	10am-4pm
24-26 Dec and 1 Jan	Closed

Last admission is 30 mins before closing

Mobility around the site

Prams and back carriers for babies are not allowed in the hall, small padded pushchairs and slings are available instead. For visitors with mobility needs or young children, an electric buggy operates a shuttle service from the car park. Benches throughout the gardens, although steps and steep slopes limit access to some areas. The hall has ramps and seats, and a lift to the first floor.

HOW TO FIND US

Direction: In Brodsworth, 5 miles NW of Doncaster off A635 Barnsley Road; from junction 37 of A1(M)

Train: South Elmsall 4 miles; Moorthorpe 4½ miles; Doncaster 5½ miles; Adwick Le Street 3 miles

Bus: Wilfreda Beehive service 203 Doncaster – Mexborough, alight Pickburn Five Ways, then ⅔ mile

Local Tourist Information
Doncaster: 01302 734309

Tel: 01302 722598

Info-line: 01302 724969

No cameras (house).

MAP Page 321 (5G)
OS Map 111, 279: SE506070

Roche Abbey
S. Yorkshire – S66 8NW

Beautifully set in a valley landscaped by 'Capability' Brown in the 18th century, the most striking feature of this Cistercian abbey is the eastern end of its church, built in the new Gothic style in c.1170. It has one of the most complete ground plans of any English Cistercian monastery, laid out as excavated foundations. The story of the pillaging of Roche, recorded by the son of an eye-witness, is among the most vivid documents of the Dissolution of the Monasteries.

NON-MEMBERS

Adult	£3.40
Concession	£3.10
Child	£2.00

OPENING TIMES

1 Apr-30 Sep, Thu-Sun & Bank Hols	11am-4pm
1 Oct-28 Mar	Closed

HOW TO FIND US

Direction: 1½ miles S of Maltby, off A634

Train: Conisbrough 7 miles

Bus: First services 2 & 10; TM Travel services 10 & 10A to Maltby Outgang Lane then 1½ miles walk

Tel: 01709 812739

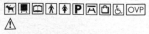

MAP Page 321 (6G)
OS Map 111/120, 279: SK544898

All Saints' Church, Harewood
W. Yorkshire – LS17 9LG

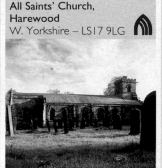
© CCT

All Saints', standing in the grounds of Harewood House, is remarkable for six pairs of alabaster effigies – virtually without rival in England – commemorating the owners of Harewood. They provide a fascinating insight into the armour, robes, jewellery and headdresses of the 15th century.

Owned and managed by The Churches Conservation Trust.

OPENING TIMES

Apr-Oct, daily	10am-6pm

Other times call Harewood House Trust Office on 0113 218 1010 in advance of your visit

HOW TO FIND US

Train: Nearest ☰ Weeton 3 miles

Bus: Routes 381/383/425/561/781

20 mins from Spofforth Castle

MAP Page 321 (4F)
OS Map 104, 289/297: SE314451

> ### Don't forget to check opening times online before you visit
>
> www.english-heritage.org.uk/daysout/properties

Church of St John the Evangelist, Leeds
W. Yorkshire – LS2 8JD

© CCT

The oldest church in Leeds. The glory of the church lies in its magnificent fittings, particularly the fabulously detailed wooden screen. Monuments commemorate the citizens of Leeds, while brightly painted angels play instruments in the roof, looking down to the wonderfully carved pews below.

Owned and managed by The Churches Conservation Trust.

OPENING TIMES

Tue-Sat	11am-3pm

HOW TO FIND US

Train: Nearest ☰ Leeds 1 mile

Bus: Routes 12/13/13A/781

30 mins from Steeton Hall Gateway

MAP Page 321 (4F)
OS Map 104, 289: SE302338

247

Associated attractions in Yorkshire

These visitor attractions, all independent of EH, offer discounts to our members. Please call before you visit to confirm details. A valid EH membership card must be produced for each member.

Barley Hall
North Yorkshire YO1 8AR

Discover the town house of a medieval Lord Mayor of York. Rediscovered under a relatively modern façade, this stunning building has beautiful exposed timber frames and high roofs.

10 mins from Clifford's Tower
Tel: 01904 615505
www.barleyhall.org.uk

| 15% discount on entry | |

Castle Howard
North Yorkshire YO60 7DA

Explore this fine historic house, featuring dramatic interiors; world-renowned collections; monumental landscape and gardens; exhibitions; events; adventure playground; shops and cafés.

15 miles north east of York
Tel: 01653 648333
www.castlehoward.co.uk

Discounted house & garden ticket

DIG
An Archaeological Adventure
North Yorkshire YO1 8NN

DIG offers you a unique adventure to get you on your way to becoming a real archaeologist. Come and dig in our Roman, Viking, medieval and Victorian pits.

10 mins from Clifford's Tower
Tel: 01904 615505
www.digyork.com

15% discount on entry

Duncombe Park
North Yorkshire YO62 5EB

A masterpiece of landscape gardening with long sweeping terraces, towering veteran trees, classical temples and breathtaking views over the Rye valley. Visitors will also discover woodland walks, ornamental parterres and a 'secret garden' at the Conservatory.

1 mile from Helmsley Castle
Tel: 01439 770213
www.duncombepark.com

10% off garden and parkland ticket

Fountains Abbey & Studley Royal Water Garden
North Yorkshire HG4 3DY

Spectacular World Heritage Site set in 800 acres of naturally beautiful countryside. Stunning 12th-century abbey ruins, Georgian water garden, deer park and monastic mill with interactive exhibition.

11 miles from Aldborough
Tel: 01765 608888
www.nationaltrust.org.uk fountainsabbey

FREE admission

Harewood House
North/West Yorkshire Border LS17 9LG

A great day out for all the family, with award-winning gardens, adventure playground and bird garden. The House boasts sumptuous state rooms with Adam interiors, Chippendale furniture and Renaissance art. Exciting events and exhibitions.

7 miles north of Leeds
Tel: 0113 218 1010
www.harewood.org

25% off adult Freedom tickets from 1 Apr-30 Oct

JORVIK Viking Centre
North Yorkshire YO1 9WT

Take hold of the past and explore the excavations which first unearthed the Viking-age city of Jorvik in our new exhibitions.

2 mins from Clifford's Tower
Tel: 01904 615505
www.jorvik-viking-centre.co.uk

15% discount on entry   ▦ OVP ▯▯6

Merchant Adventurers' Hall
North Yorkshire YO1 9XD

One of the world's finest medieval guild halls, dating from 1357, featuring the great hall, undercroft, chapel, gardens, unique collections and interactive exhibits. Fully accessible from Fossgate.

Close to Clifford's Tower
Tel: 01904 654818
www.theyorkcompany.co.uk

50% discount on entry   ▦ OVP ▯▯6

Micklegate Bar Museum
North Yorkshire YO1 6JX

Mickegate Bar has stood sentinel to the city for over 800 years. Visit the ancient gateway to explore the pageantry and barbaric history that has unfolded within these walls.

15 mins from Clifford's Tower
Tel: 01904 615505
www.micklegatebar.com

15% discount on entry   ▦ OVP ▯▯6

National Media Museum
Bradford BD1 1NQ

The National Media Museum boasts 8 floors of free galleries including national collections, an extensive research facility, exciting tours, talks, activities and 3 cinemas including the UK's first IMAX.

Tel: 0844 856 3797
www.nationalmediamuseum.org.uk

20% off IMAX tickets (Not IMAX DMR films)   ▦ OVP ▯▯6

North Yorkshire Moors Railway
North Yorkshire YO18 7JF

Enjoy fun days with the NYMR and be transported back to an era when magnificent steam engines ruled the railways. From Pickering to Whitby through the North York Moors.

¼ mile from Pickering Castle, 1 mile from Whitby Abbey
Tel: 01751 472508
www.nymr.co.uk

Adults travel at concessionary rate Mon-Fri (Not valid Bank Hols or event days) ▦

York Minster
North Yorkshire YO1 7JF

York Minster is one of the great cathedrals of the world. Enjoy its vast spaces and music and witness the human imagination at work on glass, stone and other fabrics.

10 mins from Clifford's Tower
Tel: 0844 939 0016
www.yorkminster.org

£1 off entry
(Separate charge for entry to the Central Tower and special events) ▦ ▯▯6

Brough Castle

NORTH WEST

PROPERTIES

North West properties consist of:

27	English Heritage
1	The Churches Conservation Trust
6	Associated Attractions

Remember to check opening times before you visit any of our properties www.english-heritage. org.uk/daysout

Details of local public transport information in England are available from Traveline www.traveline.org.uk or call 0871 200 2233.

Make the most of your membership and keep up to date with upcoming events, the latest news and special offers by subscribing to our e-newsletter. Register online now at **www.english-heritage.org.uk/ newsletter**

Carlisle Castle

CHESHIRE
Beeston Castle and Woodland Park
Chester Castle: Agricola Tower and Castle Walls
Chester Roman Amphitheatre
Sandbach Crosses

CUMBRIA
Ambleside Roman Fort
Bow Bridge
Brough Castle
Brougham Castle
Carlisle Castle
Castlerigg Stone Circle
Clifton Hall
Countess Pillar
Furness Abbey
Hadrian's Wall (see page 267)
Hardknott Roman Fort
King Arthur's Round Table
Lanercost Priory
Mayburgh Henge
Penrith Castle
Piel Castle
Ravenglass Roman Bath House
Shap Abbey
Stott Park Bobbin Mill
Wetheral Priory Gatehouse

LANCASHIRE
Goodshaw Chapel
Sawley Abbey
Warton Old Rectory
Whalley Abbey Gatehouse

NORTH WEST

Hadrian's Wall

Carlisle

Workington
Penrith
Keswick

Cumbria

Windermere

Ulverston

Barrow-
in-Furness

Lancaster

Lancashire

Blackpool
Burnley
Preston
Blackburn

Southport

Wigan • Bolton
Oldham

Merseyside
Greater Manchester
St Helens
Manchester
Liverpool
Birkenhead
Warrington

Macclesfield

Chester Cheshire

Crewe

HIGHLIGHTS FOR 2012/13 IN THE NORTH WEST

- **Beeston Castle & Woodland Park:** spectacular location enjoying stunning views over eight counties.
- **Carlisle Castle:** unlock the stories of this fortress in a new exhibition.
- **Hadrian's Wall:** visit Birdoswald Roman Fort and see one of the longest continuous stretches of the Wall.

Beeston Castle & Woodland Park

Cheshire – CW6 9TX

Spectacularly crowning a sandstone crag towering above the Cheshire Plain, Beeston Castle is among the most dramatically-sited fortresses in England. Its extensive wooded surroundings, rich in wildlife, are now even more fascinating to explore. Visitors can experience some of the best views in Cheshire from the top of the castle mound.

Beeston Castle is a paradise for walkers, nature-lovers and adventurous children.

Naturally defended by steep cliffs on three sides, Beeston's crag attracted prehistoric settlers. It became an important Bronze Age metal-working site and later an immense Iron Age hillfort, whose earthwork defences were adapted by medieval castle-builders.

The 'Castle of the Rock' – its medieval title – was begun in the 1220s by Ranulf, Earl of Chester, one of the greatest barons of Henry III's England. A defence against aristocratic rivals and a proclamation of Ranulf's power, his fortress is approached via a ruined gatehouse in a multi-towered outer wall, defining a huge outer bailey climbing steadily up the hill.

At its summit is the crowning glory of Beeston, the inner bailey, defended by a deep rock-cut ditch and a mighty double-towered gatehouse. The best-preserved part of the castle, the inner bailey commands astounding views

across eight counties, from the Welsh Mountains to the west, to the Pennines in the east. It also contains the famous castle well, over 100 metres deep and traditionally the hiding place of Richard II's treasure.

Beeston Castle experienced a final blaze of glory as an important English Civil War stronghold, which finally surrendered to Parliament in November 1645 after a long and eventful siege. Thereafter it became the romantic ruin which caught the attention of wealthy Victorian John Tollemache, who promoted Beeston as a tourist attraction, even stocking its grounds with kangaroos.

English Heritage's development of landscape helps visitors to explore more of the castle's surroundings – a paradise for walkers, nature-lovers and adventurous children. A circular Woodland Walk leads fairly gently downhill from near the outer bailey gate. Winding around the base of the crag

through wildlife-thronged woods, the path provides glimpses of the castle above, before reaching another of Beeston's attractions, the sandstone caves, one of which appeared as 'Robin Hood's Cave' in a 1992 film. The caves can also be reached via a shorter walk from the Visitor Centre, where the *Castle of the Rock* display vividly recounts Beeston's 4000 years of history.

Visit the website for details of special events.

NON-MEMBERS

Adult	£5.70
Concession	£5.10
Child	£3.40

OPENING TIMES

1 Apr-30 Sep, daily	10am-6pm
1 Oct-4 Nov, Thu-Mon	10am-4pm
5 Nov-17 Feb, Sat-Sun	10am-4pm
18-22 Feb, daily	10am-4pm
23 Feb-28 Mar, Sat-Sun	10am-4pm
24-26 Dec and 1 Jan	Closed

HOW TO FIND US

Direction: Located 11 miles SE of Chester, on minor road off A49

Train: Chester 10 miles

Bus: GHA service 83 (Tue) is the only bus service to Beeston; Otherwise Arriva service 84 to Tarporley (2½ miles)

Tel: 01829 260464

Local Tourist Information
Chester: 01244 402111

Please note: Steep climb (no disabled access to the top of the hill). Boots or stout footwear recommended for Woodland Walk.

Parking: charges apply, may vary on event days. Car park not managed by English Heritage.

MAP Page 320 (7D)
OS Map 117, 257/258: SJ537593

255

Check opening times at www.english-heritage.org.uk

Chester Castle: Agricola Tower and Castle Walls
Cheshire

The original gateway to Chester Castle, this 12th-century tower houses a chapel with exceptionally fine wall-paintings of c. 1220, rediscovered in the 1980s. An access stair to the castle's wall-walk is nearby.

OPENING TIMES
Castle only open for guided tours. Please call 01829 260464 for details

HOW TO FIND US
Direction: Access via Assizes Court car park on Grosvenor St

Train: Chester 1¼ miles

Bus: From surrounding areas

Disabled access (certain parts only).

MAP Page 320 (7C)
OS Map 117, 266: SJ405657

Chester Roman Amphitheatre
Cheshire

The largest Roman amphitheatre in Britain, used for entertainment and military training by the 20th Legion, based at the fortress of 'Deva' (Chester). Excavations by English Heritage and Chester City Council in 2004-5 revealed two successive stone-built amphitheatres with wooden seating. The first included access to the upper tiers of seats via stairs on the rear wall, as at Pompeii, and had a small shrine next to its north entrance. The second provided seat access via vaulted stairways. The two buildings differed both from each other and from all other British amphitheatres, underlining the importance of Roman Chester.

Managed by Cheshire West and Chester Council.

Chester Roman Amphitheatre

OPENING TIMES
Any reasonable time

HOW TO FIND US
Direction: On Vicars Lane, beyond Newgate, Chester

Train: Chester ¾ mile

Bus: From surrounding areas

Disabled access (no access to amphitheatre floor).

MAP Page 320 (7C)
OS Map 117, 266: SJ408662

Sandbach Crosses
Cheshire

The two massive Saxon stone crosses, elaborately carved with animals and Biblical scenes including the Nativity of Christ and the Crucifixion, dominate the cobbled market square of Sandbach. Probably dating from the 9th century and originally painted as well as carved, they are among the finest surviving examples of Anglo-Saxon high crosses.

OPENING TIMES
Any reasonable time

HOW TO FIND US
Direction: Market Sq, Sandbach

Train: Sandbach 1½ miles

Bus: From surrounding areas

MAP Page 320 (7D)
OS Map 118, 268: SJ759608

CUMBRIA

Ambleside Roman Fort
Cumbria

The well-marked remains of a 2nd-century fort with large granaries, probably built under Hadrian's rule to guard the Roman road from Brougham to Ravenglass and act as a supply base.

Managed by the National Trust.

OPENING TIMES
Any reasonable time

HOW TO FIND US
Direction: 182 metres W of Waterhead car park, Ambleside

Train: Windermere 5 miles

Bus: Stagecoach Cumbria 505, 516, 555, 599; Travellers Choice 618.

MAP Page 322 (6D)
OS Map 90, OL7: NY372034

Bow Bridge
Cumbria

This narrow 15th-century stone bridge across Mill Beck carried an old packhorse route to nearby Furness Abbey (see p.260).

OPENING TIMES
Any reasonable time

HOW TO FIND US
Direction: Located ½ mile N of Barrow-in-Furness, on minor road off A590; near Furness Abbey

Train: Barrow-in-Furness 1½ miles

Bus: Stagecoach in Cumbria service 6/6A, X35; Travellers Choice 618 to within ¾ mile

MAP Page 322 (7D)
OS Map 96, OL6: SD224715

Brough Castle
Cumbria

Starkly impressive Brough Castle stands on a ridge commanding strategic Stainmore Pass, on the site of a Roman fort. Frequently the target of Scots raids, its towering keep dates from c. 1200. More comfortable living quarters were later added by the Clifford family, only to be accidentally burnt following a 'great Christmas' party in 1521. Like so many other castles hereabouts, Brough was restored in the 17th century by Lady Anne Clifford, traces of whose additions can still be seen.

St Michael's Parish Church, in pretty Church Brough near the castle, displays an exhibition about the region. This living church is open 10am-4pm daily (not English Heritage).

OPENING TIMES

1 Apr-30 Sep, daily	10am-5pm
1 Oct-28 Mar, daily	10am-4pm
24-26 Dec and 1 Jan	Closed

HOW TO FIND US

Direction: 8 miles SE of Appleby S of A66.

Train: Kirkby Stephen 6 miles

Bus: Classic service 352; Grand Prix service 563; Cumbria Classic Bus 572; Kirby Lonsdale Coaches/ Woofs 564

Please note: approach may be muddy, stout footwear recommended.

Guidebook available at Brougham Castle.

MAP Page 323 (6F)
OS Map 91, OL19: NY791141

Brougham Castle
Cumbria – CA10 2AA

In a picturesque setting beside the crossing of the River Eamont, Brougham Castle was founded in the early 13th century by King John's agent Robert de Vieuxpont. His great keep largely survives amid many later buildings – including the unusual double gatehouse and impressive 'Tower of League' – added by the powerful Clifford family, Wardens of the Marches. Both a formidable barrier against Scots invaders and a prestigious residence, their castle welcomed Edward I in 1300.

A complex of passages and spiral stairways makes Brougham a fascinating castle to explore, as well as an ideal picnic setting: the keep top provides panoramic views over the Eden Valley and the earthworks of the adjacent Roman fort of Brocavum. Having fallen into decay after James I's visit in 1617, the castle was restored by the indomitable Lady Anne Clifford (see also Brough Castle and Countess Pillar). She often visited with her travelling 'court', and died here in 1676. An exhibition highlights her remarkable life and includes carvings from the Roman fort. There is good wheelchair access to most of the site (excluding the keep).

NON-MEMBERS

Adult	£3.90
Concession	£3.50
Child	£2.30
Family	£10.10

Brougham Castle

OPENING TIMES

1 Apr-30 Sep, daily	10am-5pm
1 Oct-28 Mar, Sat-Sun	10am-4pm
24-26 Dec and 1 Jan	Closed

HOW TO FIND US

Direction: 1½ miles SE of Penrith, off A66.

Train: Penrith 2 miles

Bus: Stagecoach service 104 and Grand Prix service 563 pass the castle on the A66, but the nearest official stop is at Whinfell Park (about 1 mile east). Fellrunner 562 (Tue only) serves Brougham village.

Local Tourist information
Penrith: 01768 867466;
Rheged: 01768 860034

Tel: 01768 862488

Please note: Car parking limited, in 'no through road' opposite castle entrance.

MAP Page 322 (5E)
OS Map 90, OL5: NY537290

Carlisle Castle
See feature – Page 258

Castlerigg Stone Circle
Cumbria

Dramatically sited with the mountains of Helvellyn and High Seat as a backdrop, Castlerigg is among the most dramatic stone circles in Britain, probably built in the later Neolithic period.

Managed by the National Trust.

OPENING TIMES
Any reasonable time

HOW TO FIND US

Direction: 1½ miles E of Keswick

Train: Penrith 16 miles

Bus: Stagecoach Caldbeck Rambler services 73/73A pass the site. Otherwise Stagecoach 555 passes within 1 mile of the site

MAP Page 322 (5D)
OS Map 89/90, OL4: NY291236

Check opening times at www.english-heritage.org.uk

Carlisle Castle Cumbria – CA3 8UR

A mighty presence in the city it has dominated for nine centuries, Carlisle Castle was a constantly updated working fortress until well within living memory. Now its rich and varied visitor attractions reflect its long and eventful history.

NEW FOR 2012

A new introductory exhibition highlights key moments and stories from the castle's history, including a reconstruction graphic of its original Norman Keep; its role in Anglo-Scottish border warfare; the Civil War and Jacobite Rising sieges and the fortress's long connection with the King's Own Royal Border Regiment. The Captain's Tower, one of the best preserved gatehouses in the UK, will also be opening to visitors.

The castle remained the headquarters of the Border Regiment until 1959.

Even before the medieval castle was begun, this site was an important Roman fortress. Today, the castle still plays a prominent role as one of Cumbria's best loved landmarks.

The commanding keep, begun during the 12th century by King Henry I of England and completed by King David I of Scotland, is both the oldest part of the castle and a reminder that Carlisle was a disputed frontier fortress, long commanding the especially turbulent western end of the Anglo-Scottish border.

The castle's violent history included medieval assaults, daring escapes by Elizabethan Border Reivers, a Civil War siege, and Bonnie Prince Charlie's Jacobite Rising of 1745-6.

Carlisle was then the very last English fortress ever to suffer a siege: overwhelmed by the Duke of Cumberland's Hanoverian army, its Jacobite garrison were imprisoned in the keep's dank basement, where visitors can see the legendary 'licking stones', which they supposedly licked for life-giving moisture. Equally famous are the strange and fantastic carvings on the keep's second floor, cut in about 1480. The Warden's Apartments in the castle's outer gatehouse have been furnished as they appeared at about this date.

By the time Mary Queen of Scots was imprisoned here in 1567-8, Henry VIII's updating for heavy artillery had left its mark on Carlisle, including the keep's rounded 'shot-deflecting' battlements and the Half Moon Battery defending the Captain's Tower gateway. The castle's military history did not end after the Jacobite Rising: fear of a radical revolution made it a permanently occupied garrison from the 1820s, when the barrack blocks lining the outer ward were begun. Indeed, the castle remained the headquarters of the Border Regiment until 1959, and the 300-year history of this famous local infantry regiment is vividly told here in Cumbria's Military Museum (entry included in the castle admission charge, tel 01228 532774).

www.english-heritage.org.uk/ carlislecastle

NON-MEMBERS

Adult	£5.50
Concession	£5.00
Child	£3.30

OPENING TIMES

1 Apr-30 Sep, daily	9.30am-5pm
1 Oct-4 Nov, daily	10am-4pm
5 Nov-28 Mar, Sat-Sun	10am-4pm
24-26 Dec and 1 Jan	Closed

Free members' guided tours
27 Nov, 13 Dec,
13 Feb, 11 Mar 10.30am & 1.30pm

HOW TO FIND US

Direction: In Carlisle city centre

Train: Carlisle ½ mile

Bus: Stagecoach 38, 60, 60A, 61, 61A, 67, 68, 93, 300, 553, 600. Also Reay's Coaches service 39 (Tue & Fri only) and Stacey's 71

Tel: 01228 591922

Local Tourist Information: 01228 625600

Disabled access (limited).

Dogs on leads (restricted areas only).

Guided tours (available at peak times at a small extra charge; groups please pre-book).

Parking (disabled only, but signposted city centre car parks nearby).

MAP Page 322 (4D)
OS Map 85, 315: NY396562

Clifton Hall
Cumbria

This fortified tower, built in about 1500, is the sole surviving and most important part of the manor house of the Wybergh family. It displays fascinating clues about the changing appearance of the house in the late medieval period.

OPENING TIMES

Any reasonable time

24-26 Dec and 1 Jan	Closed

HOW TO FIND US

Direction: Next to Clifton Hall Farm; 2 miles S of Penrith, on A6

Train: Penrith 2½ miles

MAP Page 322 (5E)
OS Map 90, OL5: NY530271

Countess Pillar, Brougham
Cumbria

A monument erected in 1656 by Lady Anne Clifford of nearby Brougham Castle, to commemorate her final parting here from her mother. On the low stone beside it, money was given to the poor each anniversary of their parting.

OPENING TIMES

Any reasonable time

HOW TO FIND US

Direction: ¼ mile E of Brougham. A new access route has also been created which runs from the B6262 (to Brougham) and starts near the junction with the A66

Countess Pillar, Brougham

Train: Penrith 2½ miles

Bus: Stagecoach service 104 and Grand Prix service 563 pass the castle on the A66, but the nearest official stop is at Whinfell Park (about 1 mile east). Fellrunner 562 (Tue only) serves Brougham village

Warning: site on a very busy main road. Parking on B6262, close to the junction with A66. Safe access by footpath.

MAP Page 322 (5E)
OS Map 90, OL5: NY546289

Furness Abbey
Cumbria – LA13 0PJ

The impressive remains of an abbey founded by Stephen, later King of England, including much of the east end and west tower of the church, the ornately decorated chapter house and the cloister buildings. Originally of the Savigniac order, it passed to the Cistercians in 1147, and despite damage by Scottish raiders became (after Fountains Abbey) the second most prosperous Cistercian abbey in all England. Set in the 'vale of nightshade', the romantic ruins were celebrated by Wordsworth in his *Prelude* of 1805.

www.facebook.com/
furnessabbey

Furness Abbey

An exhibition on the history of the abbey, with a display of elaborately carved stones, can be seen in the visitor centre. (See also Bow Bridge, p.256)

NON-MEMBERS

Adult	£3.90
Concession	£3.50
Child	£2.30

OPENING TIMES

1 Apr-30 Sep, Thu-Mon	10am-5pm
1 Oct-28 Mar, Sat-Sun	10am-4pm
24-26 Dec and 1 Jan	Closed

HOW TO FIND US

Direction: Located 1½ miles N of Barrow-in-Furness, off A590

Train: Dalton and Roose 1½ miles, Barrow-in-Furness 2 miles

Bus: Stagecoach in Cumbria service 6/6A, X35; Travellers Choice 618 to within ¾ mile

Tel: 01229 823420

Dogs on leads (restricted areas only).

MAP Page 322 (7D)
OS Map 96, OL6: SD218717

Hadrian's Wall
See page 267

Hardknott Roman Fort
Cumbria

This remote and dramatically-sited fort was founded under Hadrian's rule in the 2nd century. Well-marked remains include the headquarters building, commandant's house and bath house. The site of the parade ground survives beside the fort, and the road which

Hardknott Roman Fort

Hardknott guarded can be traced for some distance as an earthwork.

Managed by the National Trust.

OPENING TIMES
Any reasonable time

HOW TO FIND US
Direction: 9 miles NE of Ravenglass; at W end of Hardknott Pass

Train: Dalegarth (Ravenglass & Eskdale) 3 miles or Ravenglass 10 miles

Bus: Closest by bus is 3D Travel service 6 (Mon-Sat) or AA Travel service X6 (Sun only) to Ravenglass or Muncaster Mill then R&ER Dalegarth and then 3½ mile walk

Warning: access may be hazardous during the winter months.

MAP Page 322 (6C)
OS Map 89/90, OL6: NY218015

King Arthur's Round Table
Cumbria

A Neolithic earthwork henge, dating from c. 2500 BC, but much later believed to be King Arthur's jousting arena. Mayburgh Henge is adjacent.

OPENING TIMES
Any reasonable time

HOW TO FIND US
Direction: Located at Eamont Bridge, 1 mile S of Penrith. Mayburgh Henge is nearby

Train: Penrith 1½ miles

Bus: Stagecoach service 108; Appolo 8 Travel/Grand Prix/ Stagecoach/Services 106 & 107; NBM Hire service 111 (Tue only)

MAP Page 322 (5E)
OS Map 90, OL5: NY523284

Lanercost Priory
See feature – Page 262

Mayburgh Henge
Cumbria

A large and impressive Neolithic henge, much better preserved than neighbouring King Arthur's Round Table. Its banks stand up to 3 metres (10 feet) high and unusually are constructed of pebbles collected from the nearby river. Near the centre is a single standing stone: old drawings suggest that it was one of a group of four here, four more having been removed from the entranceway.

OPENING TIMES
Any reasonable time

HOW TO FIND US
Direction: 1 mile S of Penrith off A6

Train: Penrith 1½ miles

Bus: Stagecoach service 108; Appolo 8 Travel/Grand Prix/ Stagecoach/Services 106 & 107; NBM Hire service 111 (Tue only)

MAP Page 322 (5E)
OS Map 90, OL5: NY519284

Penrith Castle
Cumbria

Penrith Castle was begun at the end of the 14th century by Ralph Neville, who played a key role in defending this area against the Scots. It was later transformed into a luxurious residence by Richard, Duke of Gloucester (subsequently Richard III). Surviving to their full height, the castle walls stand in a public park. Graphic panels tell the story of the castle.

OPENING TIMES
Park:
Summer	7.30am-9pm
Winter	7.30am-4.30pm

HOW TO FIND US
Direction: Opposite Penrith railway station

Train: Penrith (adjacent)

Bus: From surrounding areas

MAP Page 322 (5E)
OS Map 90, OL5: NY513299

Lanercost Priory

Cumbria – CA8 2HQ

The beautiful and now tranquil setting of Augustinian Lanercost Priory belies an often troubled history. Standing close to Hadrian's Wall, it suffered frequent attacks during the long Anglo-Scottish wars, once by Robert Bruce in person. The mortally sick King Edward I rested here for five months in 1306-7, shortly before his death on his final campaign.

Yet there is still much to see in this best-preserved of Cumbrian monasteries. The east end of the noble 13th-century church survives to its full height, housing within its dramatic triple tier of arches some fine monuments, including the exquisite effigy of four-month-old Elizabeth Dacre Howard. The nave, with its soaring west front, is still in full use as the parish church.

Lanercost's cloisters include a beautiful vaulted 13th-century refectory undercroft. They partly owe their preservation to their conversion, after the priory's suppression, into the Tudor mansion of the Dacre family. The cloister west range includes the Dacre Hall, still displaying fragments of 16th-century wall-painting, as well as the four-storey Dacre Tower, adapted from the monastic kitchen.

Set beside a still-active farm, vicarage, and 'vicar's pele tower' (viewable only from outside), Lanercost Priory's extensive remains make an unforgettable ensemble. Information panels tell you about the priory and its later conversion into a grand mansion.

The parish church and Dacre Hall are not managed by English Heritage.

NON-MEMBERS

Adult	£3.40
Concession	£3.10
Child	£2.00

OPENING TIMES

1 Apr-30 Sep, daily	10am-5pm
1 Oct-4 Nov, Thu-Mon	10am-4pm
5 Nov-28 Mar, Sat-Sun	10am-4pm
24-26 Dec and 1 Jan	Closed

HOW TO FIND US

Direction: Off a minor road S of Lanercost; 2 miles NE of Brampton

Train: Brampton 3 miles

Bus: Alba/Classic Hadrian's Wall bus AD122 Apr-Nov. Otherwise Stagecoach/Arriva service 685 to within 2½ miles

Tel: 01697 73030

Lanercost tearoom and farm shop is open every day except 25 and 26 Dec. www.lanercost.co.uk Tel: 016977 41267 (not managed by English Heritage).

MAP Page 322 (4E)
OS Map 86, 315: NY556637

Piel Castle
Cumbria

The impressive ruins of a 14th-century castle with a massive keep, inner and outer baileys and towered curtain walls still standing. It was built by the Abbot of Furness on the south-eastern point of Piel Island, to guard the deep-water harbour of Barrow-in-Furness against pirates and Scots raiders.

OPENING TIMES
Any reasonable time. Access by ferry boat not managed by EH

HOW TO FIND US
Direction: Piel Island, 3¼ miles SE of Barrow-in-Furness

By small boat: Two ferries operate services to Piel Island (subject to tides and weather). Call Steve Chattaway on 07516 453784 or Alan Cleasby on 07798 794550. There is a small charge for this service

Train: Barrow-in-Furness 4 miles

Bus: Blueworks Taxis service 11 Barrow-in Furness – Ulverston

MAP Page 322 (7D)
OS Map 96, OL6: SD233636

Ravenglass Roman Bath House
Cumbria

The remains of the bath house of Ravenglass Roman fort, established in AD 130, are among the tallest Roman

Ravenglass Roman Bath House

structures surviving in northern Britain: the walls stand almost 4 metres (13 feet) high. The fort at Ravenglass (whose earthworks can be seen near the bath house) guarded what was probably a useful harbour, and there is evidence that soldiers stationed here served in Hadrian's fleet.

OPENING TIMES
Any reasonable time

HOW TO FIND US
Direction: ¼ mile E of Ravenglass, off minor road leading to A595

Train: Ravenglass (adjacent)

Bus: 3D Travel service 6 or AA Travel service X6

MAP Page 322 (6C)
OS Map 96, OL6: SD088959

Shap Abbey
Cumbria

The impressive full-height 15th-century tower and other remains of a remote abbey of Premonstratensian 'white canons'.

Information panels guide you round the abbey and illustrate daily monastic life.

OPENING TIMES
Any reasonable time

Shap Abbey

HOW TO FIND US
Direction: 1½ miles W of Shap, on the bank of the River Lowther

Train: Penrith 10 miles

Bus: Stagecoach in Cumbria/ Apollo 8/Grand Prix service 106 Penrith – Kendal within 1½ miles

Disabled access (limited views from outside the site).

Steep access road is unsuitable in wintry weather.

MAP Page 322 (6E)
OS Map 90, OL5: NY548152

St Ninian's, Brougham
Cumbria – CA10 2AD

© CCT

The originally Norman St Ninian's Church was rebuilt in the 17th century by Lady Anne Clifford, who inherited Brougham Castle. The simple interior is whitewashed, with clear glass windows, stone flagged floor, box pews, an elegant screen, and a three-decker pulpit.

Owned and managed by The Churches Conservation Trust.

OPENING TIMES
Open daily during daylight hours

HOW TO FIND US
Train: Nearest Penrith 3 miles

Bus: Routes 104/625

Nr Brougham Castle

MAP Page 322 (5E)
OS Map 90, OL05: NY557289

Stott Park Bobbin Mill

Cumbria – LA12 8AX

This extensive working mill was begun in 1835 to produce the wooden bobbins vital to the Lancashire spinning and weaving industries. Some 250 men and boys (some drafted in from workhouses) worked here over the years in often arduous conditions to produce a quarter of a million bobbins a week. Visitors can see demonstrations of the working machinery which still produces bobbins for sale today, and experience English Heritage's conservation of the traditional skills involved in this authentic Lakeland craft. Guided tours are included in the admission charge: the last tour begins ½ hour before closing.

NON-MEMBERS

Adult	£6.20
Concession	£5.60
Child	£3.70
Family	£16.10

OPENING TIMES

1 Apr-31 Oct, Mon-Fri	11am-5pm
1 Oct-28 Mar	Closed

Please call for details of steam days

HOW TO FIND US

Direction: Located 1½ miles N of Newby Bridge, off A590

Train: Grange-over-Sands 8 miles; Lakeside Station (Lakeside & Haverthwaite railway) ¾ mile

Bus: Lecks 538 (Thu). Alternatively Stagecoach service X35 or 618 to Newby Bridge and 1½ mile walk. Blueworks summer service X31 & X32

Ferry: Windermere ferry from Ambleside or Bowness to Lakeside, then 1 mile

Tel: 01539 531087

Local Tourist Information
Hawkshead: 01539 436525

🍴 E P 🚶 🚻 ♿ 🎁 📷 🎞 ⚠
OVP

Disabled access (ground floor only. Specific interpretation for visually impaired visitors).

Parking (lower car park).

Dogs welcome (restricted areas only).

MAP Page 322 (6D)
OS Map 96/97, OL7: SD372881

Wetheral Priory Gatehouse
Cumbria

Well-preserved 15th-century gatehouse, the sole survivor of a small Benedictine priory. A miniature 'pele-tower' containing two storeys of comfortable rooms, it later became a fortified vicarage, a defence against border raiders.

OPENING TIMES

1 Apr-30 Sep, daily	10am-6pm
1 Oct-28 Mar, daily	10am-4pm
24-26 Dec and 1 Jan	Closed

HOW TO FIND US

Direction: Near Wetheral village; 6 miles E of Carlisle, on B6263

Train: Wetheral ½ mile

Bus: Reay's/Stagecoach in Cumbria services 75 to Wetheral then short walk

MAP Page 322 (4E)
OS Map 86, 315: NY468541

Goodshaw Chapel
Lancashire

English Heritage's only Nonconformist place of worship, this atmospheric Baptist chapel displays a complete set of box-pews, galleries and pulpit dating from c. 1742 to 1809. A festival of hymns and sermons is held on the first Sunday in July.

OPENING TIMES
Please call the keykeeper for details. Tel: 01706 227333

HOW TO FIND US
Direction: In Crawshawbooth, 2 miles N of Rawtenstall via A682 (in Goodshaw Ave – turning off A682 opp. Jester public house). Chapel approx. 1½ miles from main road

Train: Burnley Manchester Road 4½ miles

Bus: Transdev Burnley & Pendle 'Witch Way' services X43/4

MAP Page 320 (4E)
OS Map 103, OL21: SD814261

Sawley Abbey
Lancashire

The remains of a Cistercian abbey founded in 1148, set on the banks of the Ribble against a backdrop of dramatic hills. After its dissolution in 1536, the monks were briefly returned to the abbey during the Pilgrimage of Grace. They remained in possession until the insurrection's collapse and the execution of their abbot.

Managed by the Heritage Trust for the North West.

OPENING TIMES
1 Apr-30 Sep, daily	10am-6pm
1 Oct-28 Mar, daily	10am-4pm
24-26 Dec and 1 Jan	Closed

HOW TO FIND US
Direction: Located at Sawley; 3½ miles N of Clitheroe, off A59

Train: Clitheroe 4 miles

Bus: Holmeswood service C2. Alternatively Transdev Lancashire United (of Blackburn) services 280 & X80 stop nearby

MAP Page 320 (4D)
OS Map 103, OL41: SD777464

Warton Old Rectory
Lancashire

A rare survival of a large 14th-century stone house with great hall and chambers. It served as a residence and courthouse for the wealthy and powerful rectors of Warton.

Managed by the Heritage Trust for the North West.

Warton Old Rectory

OPENING TIMES
1 Apr-30 Sep, daily	10am-6pm
1 Oct-28 Mar, daily	10am-4pm
24-26 Dec and 1 Jan	Closed

HOW TO FIND US
Direction: At Warton; 1 mile N of Carnforth, on minor road off A6

Train: Carnforth 1 mile

Bus: Stagecoach in Lancashire service 55; Kirby Lonsdale Minibuses L1, 430 & 435

MAP Page 320 (3D)
OS Map 97, OL7: SD499723

Whalley Abbey Gatehouse
Lancashire

The 14th-century gatehouse of the nearby Cistercian abbey, the second wealthiest monastery in Lancashire, beside the River Calder. The first floor was probably a chapel.

OPENING TIMES
Any reasonable time

HOW TO FIND US
Direction: In Whalley; 6 miles NE of Blackburn, on minor road off A59

Train: Whalley ¼ mile

Bus: From surrounding area

MAP Page 320 (4D)
OS Map 103, 287: SD729362

Associated attractions in the North West

These visitor attractions, all independent of EH, offer discounts to our members. Please call before you visit to confirm details. A valid EH membership card must be produced for each member.

Muncaster Castle
Cumbria CA18 1RQ

Historic haunted castle: extensive gardens, World Owl Centre with daily bird show and Heron Happy Hour. Indoor Meadow Vole Maze. Gift shops, café, playground. B&B available. Special events all year.

1hr approx from J36/M6
Tel: 01229 717614
www.muncaster.co.uk

| Group rate discount on entry | ▦ |

Norton Priory Museum & Gardens
Cheshire WA7 1SX

Explore the remains of the medieval priory, follow woodland paths and discover the beautiful Georgian Walled Garden. Museum offers tearoom, shop and family activities.

3 miles from J11 of M56
Tel: 01928 569895
www.nortonpriory.org

| £2 off ticket price | ▦ ᕮ3 |

Pendle Heritage Centre
Lancashire BB9 6JQ

Historic farmhouse, restored using traditional building skills. Exhibitions, 18th-century walled garden, shop and café.

Close to J13 of M65
Tel: 01282 677151
www.htnw.co.uk

| 50% discount on entry | ▦ ᕮ1 |

Smithills Hall
Greater Manchester BL1 7NP

Set in over 2200 acres of woodland, on the edge of the West Pennine Moors, Smithills Hall is one of the oldest and best preserved manor houses in the North West.

1 mile to Moss Bank Way A58
Tel: 01204 332377
www.boltonmuseums.org.uk

| 20% discount on entry | ▦ |

Stretton Watermill
Cheshire SY14 7HS

Step back in time and visit a working mill in beautiful rural Cheshire. See one of the country's best preserved demonstration water-powered corn mills.

9 miles from Beeston Castle
Tel: 01606 271640
www.strettonwatermill.blogspot.com

| 2 for 1 entry | ▦ OVP |

Weaver Hall Museum and Workhouse
Cheshire CW9 8AB

Discover the hidden history of Cheshire from the salt industry to archaeological treasures, all housed in a former Victorian workhouse.

14 miles from Beeston Castle
Tel: 01606 271640
www.weaverhallmuseum.org.uk

| 2 for 1 entry | ▦ OVP |

▦ EH Members   OVP OVP Holders   ᕮ? Discounted Child Places Included

Hadrian's Wall

Marching 73 miles from sea to sea across some of the wildest and most dramatic country in England, this celebrated World Heritage Site was the north-west frontier of the whole Roman Empire. Walk along the Wall to discover 2000 years of history at our many forts, museums, and even the High Street of a once-thriving Roman town.

HIGHLIGHTS OF THE WALL 2012/13

- **Birdoswald Roman Fort:** discover the life of a Roman in the museum.
- **Chesters Roman Fort & Museum:** the best-preserved Roman cavalry fort.
- **Housesteads Roman Fort:** dramatically sited fort with new exhibition this year.

Travel into the Past

English Heritage cares for 24 sites all along the Wall, from large forts with museums to lonely turrets and milecastles amid spectacular hill-country. The following section divides our frontier sites into three sections, beginning near Carlisle – whose mighty medieval castle (with new things to see this year) stands on a Roman site, and displays fascinating Roman finds.

Hare Hill ❶
Cumbria

A short length of Wall still stands 2.7 metres (8.8 feet) high.

HOW TO FIND US
Direction: ¾ mile NE of Lanercost

OS Map 86, 43: NY564646

Banks East Turret ❷
Cumbria

Imposing and well-preserved turret with adjoining stretches of Hadrian's Wall.

HOW TO FIND US
Direction: On minor road E of Banks village; 3½ miles NE of Brampton

🅿 ♿ ⚠

OS Map 86, 315: NY575647

Scotland

Carlisle Castle
See feature on page 258

Carlisle

Brampton

Birdoswald Roman Fort
See feature on page 274

Cumbria

Haltwhistle

Hexham

Corbridge

Northumberland

Birdoswald Roman Fort ❺

See feature on page 274

Harrow's Scar Milecastle and Wall ❻
Cumbria

A mile-long section of the Wall, rebuilt in stone later in Hadrian's reign. It is linked to Birdoswald Roman Fort (see p.274).

HOW TO FIND US
Direction: ¼ mile E of Birdoswald, on minor road off B6318

🅿

Parking at Birdoswald

OS Map 86, OL43: NY620664

Willowford Wall, Turrets and Bridge ❼
Cumbria

A fine 914 metre (2999 feet) stretch of Wall, including two turrets and impressive bridge remains beside the River Irthing. Linked by a bridge to Birdoswald Roman Fort (see p.274).

HOW TO FIND US
Direction: W of minor road, ¾ mile W of Gilsland

OS Map 86, OL43: NY627664

Brampton

From Hare Hill to Walltown Crags

The western section of the Wall – which began at Bowness on the Solway Firth – passes near Carlisle and Lanercost Priory before climbing onto the Whin Sill crags east of Birdoswald Roman Fort, with its 2000-year history.

Pike Hill Signal Tower **3**
Cumbria

The remains of one of a network of signal towers predating Hadrian's Wall, Pike Hill was later joined to the Wall at an angle of 45 degrees.

HOW TO FIND US

Direction: On minor road E of Banks village

🅿

OS Map 86, 315: NY577648

Leahill Turret and Piper Sike Turret **4** Cumbria

Turrets west of Birdoswald: Piper Sike has a cooking-hearth.

HOW TO FIND US

Direction: On minor road 2 miles W of Birdoswald Fort

OS Map 86, OL43/315: NY586652

22

Newcastle-upon-Tyne

23 **24**

Gateshead

Tyne and Wear

Durham

Poltross Burn Milecastle
Cumbria **8**

One of the best-preserved milecastles on Hadrian's Wall, Poltross includes an oven, a stair to the rampart walk, and the remains of its north gateway.

HOW TO FIND US

Direction: On minor road E of Banks village. Immediately SW of Gilsland village, by old railway station

🅿
Parking (near the Station Hotel).

OS Map 86, OL43: NY634662

Walltown Crags **9**
Northumberland

One of the best places of all to see the Wall, dramatically snaking and diving along the crags of the Whin Sill.

HOW TO FIND US

Direction: 1 mile NE of Greenhead, off B6318

OS Map 86/87, 43: NY674663

Haltwhistle

From Cawfields Roman Wall to Black Carts Turret

This central section of the Wall climbs and dives across often wild and rugged country, attaining its highest point at Winshields Wall before reaching the famous forts of Vindolanda and windswept Housesteads — which has a new exhibition this year.

Photo: © Roger Clegg

Cawfields Roman Wall Northumberland ⑩

A fine stretch of Hadrian's Wall on a steep slope, with turrets and an impressive milecastle, probably built by the Second Legion.

HOW TO FIND US

Direction: 1¼ miles N of Haltwhistle, off B6318

🚶 ♿ 🅿️

Parking not operated by EH. Parking charge applies (payable to Northumberland National Park).

OS Map 86/87, OL43: NY716667

Winshields Wall Northumberland ⑪

The highest point on the Wall, in rugged country with spectacular views.

HOW TO FIND US

Direction: W of Steel Rigg car park; on minor road off B6318

OS Map 86/87, 43: NY742676

Roman Vindolanda See Associated Attractions on page 279

Housesteads Roman Fort See feature on page 277

Scotland

Carlisle Castle See feature on page 258

① ② ③ ⑦ ⑧ ⑨ ⑩ ⑪ ⑬ ⑭ ⑮ ⑯ ⑰ ⑱

④ ⑤ ⑥   ⑫   ⑲ ⑳   ㉑

Brampton

Haltwhistle

Hexham

Corbridge

Carlisle   Cumbria   Northumberland

Near Carrawburgh fort stands a fascinating temple to the eastern god Mithras, with facsimiles of altars found during excavation. Sited like many Mithraic temples near a military base, it was founded in the 3rd century and eventually desecrated, probably by Christians. Nearby, but no longer visible, was the shrine of the water nymph Coventina.

HOW TO FIND US

Direction: 3¾ miles W of Chollerford, on B6318

🅿️ Parking charge payable to Northumberland National Park.

OS Map 87, 43: NY859711

Temple of Mithras, Carrawburgh Northumberland ⑮

The **Hadrian's Wall Bus (AD122)** runs throughout the spring and summer months between Newcastle, Hexham and Carlisle, and is an excellent way to see the stunning scenery in this part of England. It stops at Corbridge, Chesters, Housesteads, Vindolanda and Birdoswald Roman Sites – as well as main railway stations, market places, towns and villages along the way.

Roman Vindolanda 12
Northumberland

See Associated Attractions on page 279

Housesteads Roman Fort 13
Northumberland

See feature on page 277

Sewingshields Wall 14
Northumberland

A length of Wall with milecastle remains, impressively sited along the Whin Sill, commanding fine views of many prehistoric and later earthworks to the north.

HOW TO FIND US

Direction: N of B6318; 1½ miles E of Housesteads Fort

OS Map 86/87, OL43: NY805702

Newcastle-upon-Tyne

22 23 24

Gateshead

Tyne and Wear

Durham

Black Carts Turret 16
Northumberland

A 460-metre (1509 feet) length of Hadrian's Wall including one turret. **Please note:** It is not possible for visitors to park here.

HOW TO FIND US

Direction: On minor road E of Banks village; 3½ miles NE of Brampton

P 🅰 ⚠

OS Map 86, 315: NY575647

From Chesters Roman Fort to Benwell

Passing into gentler country, the Wall marches through Chesters Roman Fort in its beautiful riverside setting and north of amazingly-preserved Corbridge Roman Town, then on to Benwell – whence it once continued to its North Sea terminus at Wallsend.

Chesters Roman Fort and Museum 17

See feature on page 275

Chesters Bridge Abutment Northumberland 18

Close to Chesters Roman Fort are the remains of a bridge which carried Hadrian's Wall across the North Tyne. Visible on both river banks, they are most impressive on the eastern side.

HOW TO FIND US

Direction: ½ mile S of Low Brunton, on A6079

OS Map 87, 43: NY914701

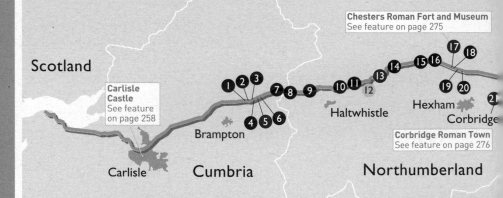

Scotland

Carlisle Castle
See feature on page 258

Brampton

Carlisle

Cumbria

Haltwhistle

Chesters Roman Fort and Museum
See feature on page 275

Hexham

Corbridge

Corbridge Roman Town
See feature on page 276

Northumberland

Planetrees Roman Wall Northumberland 20

A 15-metre (49 feet) length of narrow Wall on broad foundations, reflecting a change of policy concerning the thickness of the Wall during construction.

HOW TO FIND US

Direction: 1 mile SE of Chollerford on B6318

OS Map 87, OL43: NY929696

Corbridge Roman Town 21

See feature on page 276

Heddon-on-the-Wall Northumberland 22

A consolidated stretch of Wall, up to 2 metres (6½ feet) thick in places.

HOW TO FIND US

Direction: Immediately E of Heddon village; S of A69

OS Map 88, 316: NZ137669

Brunton Turret 19
Northumberland

Wall section and a surviving piece of turret 2½ metres (8.2 feet) high, built by men of the Twentieth Legion.

HOW TO FIND US

Direction: ¼ mile S of Low Brunton, off A6079

OS Map 87, OL43: NY922698

22

23 24

Newcastle-upon-Tyne

Gateshead

Tyne and Wear

Durham

Denton Hall Turret 23
Tyne and Wear

The foundations of a turret and a 65-metre (213 feet) length of Wall.

HOW TO FIND US

Direction: 4 miles W of Newcastle-upon-Tyne city centre, on A69

OS Map 88, 316: NZ198655

Benwell Roman Temple 24
Tyne and Wear

The remains of a small temple to the native god 'Antenociticus', in the 'vicus' (civilian settlement) which stood outside Benwell fort.

HOW TO FIND US

Direction: Temple located immediately S of A69, at Benwell in Broomridge Ave; Vallum Crossing in Denhill Park

OS Map 88, 316: NZ217647

Benwell Vallum Crossing 24
Tyne and Wear

A stone-built causeway, where the road from the south crossed the Vallum earthwork on its way to Benwell fort.

OS Map 88, 136: NZ216646

Birdoswald Roman Fort Cumbria – CA8 7DD

Birdoswald is one of the best places to gain an overview of Hadrian's Wall at one single site. A Roman fort, turret and milecastle can all be seen here, with nearby the longest continuous stretch of Wall visible today. The Visitor Centre illustrates the history of the Wall, and tells the story of Birdoswald and its people over the past 2000 years.

Known as 'Banna', Birdoswald likewise has the best preserved defences of any of the major Hadrian's Wall forts. Three main gates, perimeter walls, angle towers, granaries and drill hall are all still traceable.

Another distinctive feature is the traces of the buildings successively raised here after the Roman withdrawal: including a large 5th-century timber hall, perhaps for a local British chieftain; a medieval fortified tower; an Elizabethan 'bastle house', a defence against 'Border Reivers'; and finally the present turreted farmhouse. Adjacent buildings now house a tearoom, a shop and the displays.

The fort stands on the Hadrian's Wall Path National Trail. Guided tours for groups are available at a small additional fee. Please contact the site for details and bookings.

Accommodation

If you would like to stay within the walls of the fort, a 36-bed farmhouse can be booked for groups. Please call 01697 747602 or email birdoswald. accommodation@english-heritage.org.uk

NON-MEMBERS

Adult	£5.20
Concession	£4.70
Child	£3.10

Free to National Trust members

OPENING TIMES

1 Apr-30 Sep, daily	10am-5.30pm (last admission 5pm)
1 Oct-4 Nov, daily	10am-4pm
5 Nov-28 Mar, Sat-Sun	10am-4pm
24-26 Dec and 1 Jan	Closed

HOW TO FIND US

Direction: Bardon Mill 4 miles

Bus: Alba/Classic service AD122 (Apr-Oct); otherwise Telford service 185 or Wright Bros service 681

Tel: 01697 747602

Local Tourist Information
Hexham: 01434 652220

Disabled access (companion recommended). Limited access to site. 750-metre walk up a steep gradient. Disabled parking available at the top of the hill. Please enquire at the information centre in the bottom car park to arrange disabled parking.

Car park not operated by English Heritage (charge payable to Northumberland National Park).

MAP Page 322 (4E)
OS Map 86/87, OL43: NY790688

Chesters Roman Fort and Museum
Northumberland – NE46 4EU

Picturesquely set in the beautiful valley of the River North Tyne, Chesters is the best-preserved example of a Roman cavalry fort in Britain. The site also features a museum containing an amazing collection of archaeological discoveries.

Known as 'Cilurnum', Chesters was one of the series of permanent forts added during the construction of the Wall. It housed a garrison of some 500 troops, by the 3rd century a cavalry regiment originating from Asturias in northern Spain. There is much still to see, including remains of all four principal gates; the headquarters building with courtyard, hall and regimental shrine; and the elaborate and luxurious commandant's house.

Even better preserved, between the fort and the river, is the garrison's bath house. This still displays the complex of rooms which offered soldiers hot, cold or steam baths, as well as a changing-room-cum-clubhouse with niches for statues of gods.

Hundreds of Roman finds from the central section of the Wall – retrieved by the Victorian antiquarian, John Clayton – are crowded into Chesters' highly distinctive museum, which has been restored to its Victorian glory with its original colour-scheme and 'traditional' museum layout. Recent additions include a portrait of John Clayton, a tactile model of the site, ramped access to the museum and a viewing platform overlooking the river.

NON-MEMBERS

Adult	£5.20
Concession	£4.70
Child	£3.10

OPENING TIMES

1 Apr-30 Sep, daily	10am-6pm
1 Oct-4 Nov, daily	10am-4pm
5 Nov-28 Mar, Sat-Sun	10am-4pm
24-26 Dec and 1 Jan	Closed

HOW TO FIND US

Direction: ¼ mile W of Chollerford, on B6318

Train: Hexham 5½ miles

Bus: Alba/Classic service AD122 Carlisle – Hexham (Apr-Oct); also Tyne Valley/Snaith service 880 from Hexham

Tel: 01434 681379

Local Tourist Information
Hexham: 01434 652220

Disabled access (companion recommended). Disabled parking and toilets.

Dogs on leads (restricted areas only).

Tearoom (summer only; not managed by English Heritage).

Parking (pay and display. Charge refundable upon admission).

MAP Page 323 (4F)
OS Map 87, OL43: NY912702

Corbridge Roman Town Northumberland – NE45 5NT

Corbridge Roman Town is the only place in Britain where visitors can walk along the original surface of a Roman 'high street', flanked by the excavated remains of granaries, a fountain house, markets, workshops and temples.

Astride the intersection of the Roman Dere Street and Stanegate roads, Corbridge was initially the site of a series of important forts: but after Hadrian's Wall was fully commissioned it developed into a prosperous garrison town, a tempting leave-centre for off-duty Wall soldiers. Abandoned after the collapse of Roman rule in Britain, the site of the settlement moved to the present Corbridge town, the Saxon tower of whose church – partly built with recycled Roman masonry – can clearly be seen from the Roman site.

The Roman town centre has been systematically excavated, producing the fascinating array of finds now most attractively displayed in the site museum.

Covering every aspect of Roman life, the artefacts here include the tombstone of little Ertola, who 'lived most happily four years and sixty days', shown still playing with her ball; and the famous Corbridge lion carving, the recognised symbol of the site. His modern counterpart, Grricola the Roman lion, takes younger visitors on a trail around the museum, finding his favourite items.

NEW FOR 2012

New presentation of a buried cache of internationally important Roman armour and tools. Technology helps visitors to explore how the artefacts were found and examine them in detail.

NON-MEMBERS

Adult	£5.20
Concession	£4.70
Child	£3.10

OPENING TIMES

1 Apr-30 Sep, daily	10am-5.30pm
	(last admission 5pm)
1 Oct-4 Nov, daily	10am-4pm
5 Nov-28 Mar, Sat-Sun	10am-4pm
24-26 Dec and 1 Jan	Closed

HOW TO FIND US

Direction: ½ mile NW of Corbridge, on minor road, then signposted

Train: Corbridge 1¼ miles

Bus: Alba/Classic AD122 (Apr-Oct); Go North East 10, 684; Arriva/Stagecoach in Cumbria services 685; Wrights service 888

Tel: 01434 632349

Local Tourist Information 01434 652220

Dogs on leads (restricted areas only).

Disabled access (parking, toilet, audio tour, access to the museum and perimeter of site).

MAP Page 323 (4F)
OS Map 87, OL43: NY982648

Housesteads Roman Fort

Northumberland – NE47 6NN

Among the most popular sites on the Wall, Housesteads is also the most complete example of a Roman fort anywhere in Britain. It stands high on the wild Whin Sill escarpment, flanked by dramatic stretches of the Wall.

NEW FOR 2012

English Heritage is working in partnership with National Trust and Northumberland National Park Authority to improve the visitor experience at Housesteads Roman Fort. Phase one is a new multi-media exhibition in the museum, exploring life at the hilltop fortress and its people on the edge of the Roman Empire.

There will also be a re-displayed Roman collection, with many locally excavated artefacts returning to the fort for the first time in 200 years. Access to the museum building will be improved, and new interpretation panels will help visitors explore and understand the fort layout. The new Housesteads Museum re-opens in spring 2012.

Housesteads Roman Fort | continued

Begun in about AD 124 as one of twelve permanent forts supporting Hadrian's frontier system, Housesteads was known as 'Vercovicium', probably meaning 'the place of effective fighters'. It was garrisoned by around 1000 infantry (generally Tungrians from what is now Belgium), later reinforced by Germanic cavalry. The big five-acre fort displays the remains of four gateways and a turreted curtain wall: within are a host of clearly traceable buildings, including the headquarters, commandant's house, baths, hospital – and the renowned multi-seater communal latrines. Served by an ingenious sewage system, these even retain the channel used for washing the sponges employed for personal cleansing. Beyond them, outside the fort wall, are the excavated foundations of its attendant 'vicus' or civilian settlement.

A fascinating museum will re-open to the public this year, telling the story of the fort and its inhabitants. Visitors will see views of Housesteads as it once was in a new film, as well as a re-displayed collection of artefacts exploring all aspects of Roman life on the northerly edge of Hadrian's empire.

The fort stands uphill from the car park (via a fairly strenuous 10-minute walk, which also gives access to Hadrian's Wall Path National Trail). Owned by the National Trust, Housesteads is managed by English Heritage.

f www.facebook.com/ housesteadsromanfort

NON-MEMBERS

Adult	£6.00
Concession	£5.40
Child	£3.60

Free to National Trust members

OPENING TIMES

1 Apr-30 Sep, daily	10am-6pm
1 Oct-4 Nov, daily	10am-4pm
5 Nov-28 Mar, Sat-Sun	10am-4pm
24-26 Dec and 1 Jan	Closed

Free members' guided tours
26 Nov, 14 Dec, 23 Jan,
14 Feb, 12 Mar   10.30am & 1.30pm

HOW TO FIND US

Direction: Bardon Mill 4 miles

Bus: Alba/Classic service AD122 (Apr-Oct)

Tel: 01434 344363

Local Tourist Information
Hexham: 01434 652220

Disabled access (companion recommended). Limited access to site. 750-metre walk up a steep gradient. Disabled parking available at the top of the hill. Please enquire at the information centre in the bottom car park to arrange disabled parking.

Car park not operated by English Heritage (charge payable to Northumberland National Park).

MAP Page 323 (4F)
OS Map 86/87, OL43: NY790688

Associated attractions at Hadrian's Wall

These visitor attractions, all independent of EH, offer discounts to our members. Please call before you visit to confirm details. A valid EH membership card must be produced for each member.

Hexham Old Gaol
Northumberland NE46 2AZ

Built 1330-33, this is the earliest recorded purpose-built prison in England. This fully-accessible building introduces visitors to the history of the prisoners, and to the Border Reivers, warring Borders families of the 1500s.

3 miles to Corbridge Roman Town
Tel: 01434 652349
www.experiencewoodhorn.com/

2 for 1 entry   `⊞` `OVP` `†↟†6`

Roman Vindolanda
Northumberland NE47 7JN

Extensive Roman fort and settlement in the central section of Hadrian's Wall. Active archaeological programme and superb museum, plus open air museum set in charming gardens.

2 miles west of Housesteads
Tel: 01434 344277
www.vindolanda.com

10% discount on entry   `⊞`

Segedunum Roman Fort, Bath House and Museum
Tyne and Wear NE28 6HR

Segedunum is once again the gateway to Hadrian's Wall. It is the most excavated fort along the Wall, with a large interactive museum and a 35m high viewing tower, providing outstanding views across this World Heritage Site.

3 miles from A19
www.twmuseums.org.uk/segedunum

10% discount on entry   `⊞`

279

Tullie House Museum and Art Gallery
Cumbria CA3 8TP

Tullie House Museum and Art Gallery is an excellent choice for a great day out for all the family. It is recognised for its first class customer service and a varied and exciting events and exhibitions programme.

Close to Carlisle Castle
Tel: 01228 618718
www.tulliehouse.co.uk

2 for 1 entry   `⊞` `OVP`

The Hadrian's Wall Bus (AD122)
runs throughout spring and summer between Newcastle, Hexham and Carlisle
For timetable details* visit **www.hadrians-wall.org/bus**

*Information correct at time of going to press

`⊞` EH Members   `OVP` OVP Holders   `†↟†?` Discounted Child Places Included

Dunstanburgh Castle

NORTH EAST

PROPERTIES

North East properties consist of:

26	English Heritage
I	The Churches Conservation Trust
5	Associated Attractions

Remember to check opening times before you visit any of our properties www.english-heritage. org.uk/daysout

Details of local public transport information in England are available from Traveline www.traveline.org.uk or call 0871 200 2233.

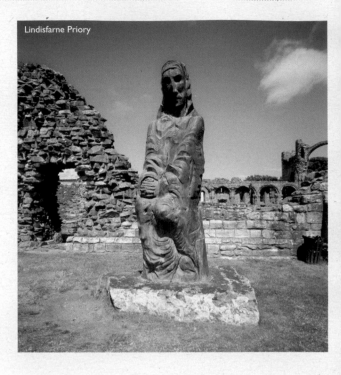
Lindisfarne Priory

Make the most of your membership and keep up to date with upcoming events, the latest news and special offers by subscribing to our e-newsletter. Register online now at **www.english-heritage.org.uk/newsletter**

DURHAM
Auckland Castle Deer House
Barnard Castle
Bowes Castle
Derwentcote Steel Furnace
Egglestone Abbey
Finchale Priory

NORTHUMBERLAND
Aydon Castle
Belsay Hall, Castle and Gardens
Berwick-upon-Tweed Barracks
Berwick-upon-Tweed Castle
Berwick-upon-Tweed Main Guard
Berwick-upon-Tweed Town Defences
Black Middens Bastle House
Brinkburn Priory
Dunstanburgh Castle
Edlingham Castle
Etal Castle
Lindisfarne Priory
Norham Castle
Prudhoe Castle
Warkworth Castle and Hermitage

REDCAR AND CLEVELAND
Gisborough Priory

TYNE AND WEAR
Bessie Surtees House
Hylton Castle
St Paul's Monastery, Jarrow
Tynemouth Priory and Castle

HADRIAN'S WALL
See page 267

NORTH EAST

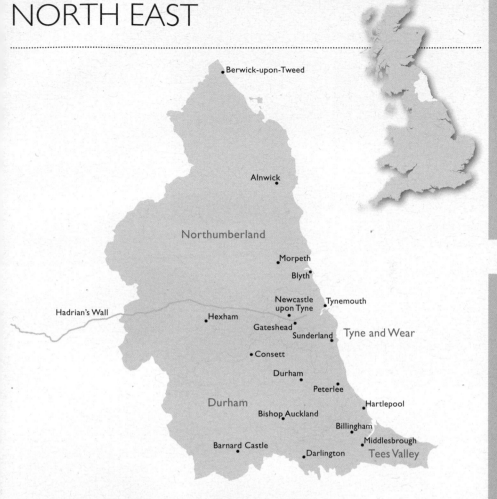

- Berwick-upon-Tweed
- Alnwick

Northumberland

- Morpeth
- Blyth
- Newcastle upon Tyne
- Tynemouth
- Hexham
- Gateshead
- Sunderland

Hadrian's Wall

Tyne and Wear

- Consett
- Durham
- Peterlee
- Hartlepool

Durham

- Bishop Auckland
- Billingham
- Middlesbrough
- Barnard Castle
- Darlington

Tees Valley

HIGHLIGHTS FOR 2012/13 IN THE NORTH EAST

- **Belsay Hall, Castle & Gardens:** Medieval castle, Greek Revival villa & extensive gardens.
- **Tynemouth Priory:** set on a headland overlooking the North Sea.
- **Hadrian's Wall:** new exhibition at Housesteads opens this year.

DURHAM

Auckland Castle Deer House
Durham

A charming Gothic Revival 'eyecatcher' built in 1760 in the park of the Bishops of Durham. It provided deer with shelter and food, and had grounds for picnics and rooms for enjoying the view.

Managed by the Church Commissioners for England.

OPENING TIMES

Park

1 Apr-30 Sep, daily	10am-6pm
1 Oct-28 Mar, daily	10am-4pm
24-26 Dec and 1 Jan	Closed

HOW TO FIND US

Direction: Located in Auckland Park, Bishop Auckland; N of town centre on A68

Train: Bishop Auckland 1 mile

Bus: Arriva services 2A, 6, 35, 36, 36a, 56, X24; Go Ahead X20, X21; Aabat Taxis 104

MAP Page 323 (5G)
OS Map 93, 305: NZ216304

Go 'Behind Closed Doors' at the Bowes Museum this June with the Head of Conservation

For full details of our programme of exclusive members' events go to www.english-heritage.org.uk/events

---

Barnard Castle
Durham – DL12 8PR

Barnard Castle is spectacularly set on a high rock above the River Tees, on the fringe of an attractive market town. Taking its name from its 12th-century founder, Bernard de Balliol, this huge and imposing fortress was later developed by the Beauchamp family and Richard III. Richard's boar emblem is carved above a window in the inner ward, the castle's chief strength: here loyalist forces were besieged during the 1569 Northern Rising against Queen Elizabeth I, before surrendering to 5000 rebels. There are fine views over the Tees Gorge, and a 'sensory garden' of scented plants and tactile objects.

NON-MEMBERS

Adult	£4.40
Concession	£4.00
Child	£2.60

OPENING TIMES

1 Apr-30 Sep, daily	10am-6pm
1 Oct-28 Mar, Sat-Sun	10am-4pm
24-26 Dec and 1 Jan	Closed

HOW TO FIND US

Direction: In Barnard Castle town

Bus: Arriva services 75, 76, 88, 95, 96; Classic service 352; Central service 70, 71, 72; Alston Road service 73; Hodgson services 79 & 79X; Cumbria Classic 572

Barnard Castle

Tel: 01833 638212

OVP

Parking (pay and display in town centre).

MAP Page 323 (6G)
OS Map 92, OL31: NZ049165

Bowes Castle
Durham

The impressive ruins of Henry II's 12th-century keep, on the site of a Roman fort guarding the approach to strategic Stainmore Pass over the Pennines.

OPENING TIMES

Any reasonable time

HOW TO FIND US

Direction: In Bowes Village off A66; 4 miles W of Barnard Castle town

Bus: Central 72; Hodgsons 79X; Cumbria Classic 572; Classic services 352

MAP Page 323 (6F)
OS Map 92, OL30/31: NY992135

Derwentcote Steel Furnace
Durham

Derwentcote Steel Furnace

Built in the 1730s, Derwentcote is the last surviving cementation steel-making furnace in Britain. It produced high-grade steel for springs and cutting tools.

OPENING TIMES

Any reasonable time (Grounds only – no access to Furnace)

24-26 Dec and 1 Jan	Closed

HOW TO FIND US

Direction: 10 miles SW of Newcastle, on A694; between Rowland's Gill and Hamsterley

Train: Metro Centre, Gateshead, 7 miles

Bus: Go North East Red Kite services 45/6 Newcastle-upon-Tyne – Consett

Tel: 01661 881636 (Sat-Sun)

Dogs on leads (restricted areas only).

Parking across main road from site.

MAP Page 323 (4G)
OS Map 88, 307: NZ130566

Egglestone Abbey
Durham

The charming ruins of a small monastery of Premonstratensian 'white canons', picturesquely set above a bend in the River Tees near Barnard Castle (see left). Remains include much of the 13th-century church and a range of living quarters, with traces of their ingenious toilet drainage system.

OPENING TIMES

1 Apr-28 Mar, daily	10am-6pm
24-26 Dec and 1 Jan	Closed

Egglestone Abbey

HOW TO FIND US

Direction: 1 mile S of Barnard Castle, on a minor road off B6277

Bus: Hodgsons service 79 & 79X then 2 mile walk

Parking (pay and display).

Tearoom (not managed by EH).

MAP Page 323 (6G)
OS Map 92, OL31: NZ062151

Finchale Priory
Durham – DH1 5SH

The very extensive remains of a 13th-century priory, founded on the site of the retired pirate St Godric's hermitage. Part of it later served as a holiday retreat for the monks of Durham Cathedral. Beautifully sited by the River Wear, with delightful riverside walks nearby.

OPENING TIMES

1 Apr-28 Mar, daily	10am-5pm
24-26 Dec and 1 Jan	Closed

HOW TO FIND US

Direction: 3 miles NE of Durham; on minor road off A167

Train: Durham 5 miles

Bus: Arriva services 7, 7A & 63 from Durham to HMP Frankland and then 2 mile walk

Parking (fee applies; not managed by EH).

Tearoom (not managed by EH).

MAP Page 323 (4G)
OS Map 88, 308: NZ296471

NORTHUMBERLAND

Aydon Castle
Northumberland – NE45 5PJ

One of the finest and most unaltered examples of a 13th-century English manor house, Aydon Castle stands in a secluded woodland setting. It was originally built as an undefended residence, but almost immediately fortified on the outbreak of Anglo-Scottish warfare. Nevertheless it was pillaged and burnt by the Scots in 1315, seized by English rebels two years later and again occupied by Scots in 1346. In the 18th century Aydon became a farmhouse, remaining so until 1966.

NON-MEMBERS

Adult	£3.90
Concession	£3.50
Child	£2.30

OPENING TIMES

1 Apr-30 Sep, Thu-Mon	10am-5pm
1 Oct-28 Mar	Closed

HOW TO FIND US

Direction: 1 mile NE of Corbridge, on minor road off B6321 or A68

Train: Corbridge 4 miles – approach via bridle path from W side of Aydon Road, immediately N of Corbridge bypass

Bus: Classic service AD122 April – November. Otherwise closest is Corbridge served by Go North East 10, 684; Arriva X85; Stagecoach/Arriva 685 and Wrights 888

Tel: 01434 632450

OVP

Disabled access (ground floor only).

Dogs on leads (restricted areas only).

MAP Page 323 (4F)
OS Map 87, 316: NZ001663

Belsay Hall, Castle and Gardens Northumberland – NE20 0DX

Belsay has something for everyone. A fine medieval castle, enlarged into a Jacobean mansion; the imposing Greek Revival villa that succeeded it; and the outstanding plant-rich gardens linking the two buildings.

Level paths and short grass make the gardens suitable for wheelchairs and there are plenty of seats. The tearoom, in the original Victorian kitchens, provides a perfect setting for a break during your visit.

The whole ensemble is the creation of the Middleton family over more than seven centuries. First came the castle, still dominated by its massive 14th-century defensive 'pele tower'. Built as a refuge at a time of Anglo-Scottish warfare, it was also designed to impress: it still displays rare traces of elaborate medieval wall-paintings. In more peaceful times a Jacobean mansion wing was added: here the family lived until Christmas Day 1817, when they moved into Belsay Hall.

Belsay Hall is an elegant Classical Greek Revival villa, now displayed without furnishings to reveal the fine craftsmanship of its construction. Begun in 1807, it was designed by Sir Charles Monck (formerly Middleton), a man inspired by Ancient Greece and the buildings he had seen on his honeymoon in Athens. Despite its austere façade, it had a comfortable interior, arranged round its amazing central 'Pillar Hall.'

The vast gardens which provide a magnificent setting for the castle and hall are also largely Sir Charles's work. His romantic Quarry Garden, created where stone was cut for his hall, has ravines and sheer rock faces inspired by Sicilian quarries. His grandson Sir Arthur Middleton, likewise a pioneering plantsman, further embellished the Quarry with the exotic species which thrive in its micro-climate and added the Winter Garden, Yew Garden, and Magnolia Terrace. Pre-booked tours of the garden are now available, led by the Head Gardener. At whatever time of the year you visit, there is always something in flower.

www.english-heritage.org.uk/belsayhall

Spring

A white carpet of thousands of Snowdrops, followed by a riot of colour from Daffodils, Spring Snowflakes and Dog's Tooth Violets. Rhododendrons and large Magnolias.

Summer

Rhododendrons (May & June). Giant Himalayan Lilies up to nine feet tall, and other species of lilies. A NCCPG National Collection of Iris can be seen, as well as the Pocket Handkerchief Tree.

Autumn

Amazing autumn colours of red, yellow and orange foliage. The fallen leaves of Cercidiphyllum Japonicum smell of burnt sugar!

Winter

Spectacular Rhododendrons flower, and frosted spiders' webs frame the topiary in the Yew Garden. Scented Viburnums and Jasmines and the appropriately titled Christmas Box (Sarcococca) can be found in the Winter Garden.

www.facebook.com/belsayhall

NON-MEMBERS

Adult	£7.70
Concession	£6.90
Child	£4.60
Family	£20.00

OPENING TIMES

1 Apr-30 Sep, daily	10am-5pm
1 Oct-4 Nov, daily	10am-4pm
5 Nov-17 Feb, Sat-Sun	10am-4pm
18-22 Feb, daily	10am-4pm
23 Feb-28 Mar, Sat-Sun	10am-4pm
24-26 Dec and 1 Jan	Closed

Free members' guided tours
23 Nov, 17 Dec, 22 Jan,
14 Feb, 13 Mar   10.30am & 1.30pm

HOW TO FIND US

Direction: In Belsay; 14 miles NW of Newcastle, on A696

Train: Morpeth 10 miles

Bus: Arriva 508 from Newcastle 🚃 Sun and Bank Hols only, (Jun-Oct); Arriva Sun and Bank Hol service 714 Belsay village; Snaith's 808 from Newcastle and Munro's 131 Newcastle – Jedburgh

Tel: 01661 881636

Local Tourist Information
Morpeth: 01670 500700

Disabled access (grounds, tearoom and ground floor only; toilets).

Dogs on leads (grounds only not halls).

Tearoom (open daily Apr-Oct, Sat-Sun in Mar).

MAP Page 323 (3G)
OS Map 88, 316: NZ086785

287

Berwick-upon-Tweed Barracks and Main Guard
Northumberland – TD15 1DF

Berwick Barracks, among the first in England to be purpose-built, were begun in 1717, adapting a design by the distinguished architect Nicholas Hawksmoor. Today the barracks host a number of attractions, including *By Beat of Drum* – an exhibition on the life of the British infantryman. While there, visit the King's Own Scottish Borderers Museum, the Berwick Gymnasium Art Gallery and the Berwick Borough Museum.

The Main Guard is a Georgian Guard House near the quay: it displays *The Story of a Border Garrison Town* exhibition.

The Main Guard is managed by Berwick Civic Society. The Gymnasium Gallery is operated by The Maltings.

NON-MEMBERS

Barracks

Adult	£3.90
Concession	£3.50
Child	£2.30

OPENING TIMES

Barracks

1 Apr-30 Sep, Mon-Fri	10am-5pm
1 Oct-28 Mar	Closed

Main Guard
Please call for details

HOW TO FIND US

Direction: On the Parade, off Church St in town centre

Berwick-upon-Tweed Barracks and Main Guard

Train: Berwick-upon-Tweed ¼ mile

Bus: From surrounding areas

Tel: 01289 304493

Disabled access (Main Guard).

Dogs on leads (restricted areas only).

Parking: pay and display (in town).

MAP Page 323 (1F) OS Map 75, 346
Barracks: NU001531
Main Guard: NU000525

Berwick-upon-Tweed Castle and Town Defences
Northumberland – TD15 1DF

The remains of a medieval castle crucial to Anglo-Scottish warfare, superseded by the most complete and breathtakingly impressive bastioned town defences in England, mainly Elizabethan but updated in the 17th and 18th centuries. Surrounding the whole historic town, their entire circuit can be walked, guided by interpretation panels.

OPENING TIMES

Any reasonable time

HOW TO FIND US

Direction: The castle is adjacent to Berwick-upon-Tweed railway station. The ramparts surround the town (accessed at various points)

Train: Berwick-upon-Tweed, adjacent

Bus: From surrounding areas

Disabled access (Ramparts).

Parking: pay and display (in town).

Note: Steep hidden drops. Dangerous after dark.

MAP Page 323 (1F)
OS Map 75, 346 Castle: NT993534
Ramparts: NU003530

Black Middens Bastle House
Northumberland

A fortified farmhouse with thick stone walls, of a type distinctive to the troubled 16th-century Anglo-Scottish borders. The living quarters were only accessible at first floor level. Set in splendid walking country, on the Reivers Route cycle trail.

OPENING TIMES

Any reasonable time

HOW TO FIND US

Direction: 180 metres N of minor road, 7 miles NW of Bellingham; or along a minor road from A68

Bus: Arriva service 714 (summer Sun only) serves Lanehead (3 miles). Otherwise nearest bus service is Snaith's/Tyne Valley service 880 which links Hexham and Bellingham (7 miles).

MAP Page 323 (3F)
OS Map 80, OL42: NY773900

Brinkburn Priory
Northumberland – NE65 8AR

The beautiful 12th-century church of the Augustinian priory of Brinkburn survives completely roofed and restored. Picturesquely set by a bend in the River Coquet, it is reached by a scenic 10-minute walk from the car park. Parts of the monastic buildings are incorporated into the elegant adjacent manor house.

Brinkburn Priory

NON-MEMBERS

Adult	£3.40
Concession	£3.10
Child	£2.00

OPENING TIMES

1 Apr-30 Sep, Thu-Mon	11am-4pm
1 Oct-28 Mar	Closed

HOW TO FIND US

Direction: 4½ miles SE of Rothbury, off B6344

Train: Acklington 10 miles

Bus: Arriva service 144 Morpeth – Thropton (passing ⇌ Morpeth)

Tel: 01665 570628

🐕 💻 🅿 📷 📷 ⚠ OVP

Picnic area (⅓ mile).

MAP Page 323 (3G)
OS Map 92, 325: NZ116983

Dunstanburgh Castle
Northumberland – NE66 3TT

Dramatic Dunstanburgh Castle was built at a time when relations between King Edward II and his most powerful baron, Earl Thomas of Lancaster, had become openly hostile. Lancaster began the fortress in 1313 and the latest archaeological research carried out by English Heritage indicates that he built it on a far grander scale than was hitherto

Dunstanburgh Castle

recognised, perhaps more as a symbol of his opposition to the king than as a military stronghold. The innovative gatehouse, for instance, competed with the new royal castles in Wales.

The earl failed to reach Dunstanburgh when his rebellion was defeated, and was taken and executed in 1322. Thereafter the castle passed eventually to John of Gaunt, who strengthened it against the Scots by converting the great twin towered gatehouse into a keep. The focus of fierce fighting during the Wars of the Roses, it was twice besieged and captured by Yorkist forces, but subsequently fell into decay. Its impressive ruins now watch over a headland famous for seabirds.

Owned by the National Trust, maintained and managed by English Heritage.

NON-MEMBERS

Adult	£4.00
Concession	£3.60
Child	£2.40
Free to National Trust members	

OPENING TIMES

1 Apr-30 Sep, daily	10am-5pm
1 Oct-4 Nov, daily	10am-4pm
5 Nov-28 Mar, Sat-Sun	10am-4pm
24-26 Dec and 1 Jan	Closed

HOW TO FIND US

Direction: 8 miles NE of Alnwick; on footpaths from Craster or Embleton – 1½ miles rugged coastal walk

Train: Chathill, not Sun, 5 miles from Embleton, 7 miles from Castle; Alnmouth, 7 miles from Craster, 8¼ miles from Castle

Bus: Arriva service 501; Travelsure 401. Alight Craster and take coast walk, 1½ miles

Tel: 01665 576231

Dunstanburgh Castle

Local Tourist Information
Craster: 01665 576007

🐕 💻 📷 📷 ⚠ OVP

Parking (in Craster village; approx 1½ miles walk. A charge is payable).

Nearest toilets located at car park in Craster Village.

MAP Page 323 (2G)
OS Map 75, 332: NU257219

Edlingham Castle
Northumberland

The riverside ruins, principally the solar tower, of a manor house progressively fortified against the Scots during the 14th century.

Managed by the Parochial Church Council of St John the Baptist, Edlingham, with Bolton Chapel.

OPENING TIMES

Any reasonable time

HOW TO FIND US

Direction: At E end of Edlingham village, on minor road off B6341; 6 miles SW of Alnwick

Train: Alnmouth 9 miles

Bus: Travelsure 473 to Banktop then 2 mile walk

🐕 ⚠

Note: waterproof footwear is recommended.

MAP Page 323 (2G)
OS Map 81, 332: NU116092

Etal Castle Northumberland – TD12 4TN

Etal Castle was begun in the early 14th century by Robert Manners as a tower house, in a strategic position by a ford over the River Till on the Anglo-Scottish border. Thus intensely vulnerable to attack by raiders, it was soon provided with a curtain wall with corner towers and a large gatehouse.

In 1513 the castle was suddenly thrust into the forefront of history when captured by James IV of Scotland, during his invasion of England in support of his French allies. But almost immediately afterwards the invaders were routed at the nearby Battle of Flodden – whose 500th anniversary falls on 9 Sep 2013 – where James himself was killed along with the flower of his nobility.

An award-winning exhibition tells the story of Flodden – the most comprehensive defeat ever inflicted by the English on the Scots – and the long border warfare between the two nations.

NON-MEMBERS

Adult	£3.90
Concession	£3.50
Child	£2.30
Family	£10.10

OPENING TIMES

1 Apr-30 Sep, daily	11am-4.30pm
1 Oct-4 Nov, daily	11am-4.30pm
5 Nov-28 Mar, Sat-Sun	10am-4pm
24-26 Dec and 1 Jan	Closed

HOW TO FIND US

Direction: In Etal village, 10 miles SW of Berwick

Train: Berwick-upon-Tweed 10½ miles

Bus: Glen Valley 267 Berwick-upon-Tweed – Wooler

Tel: 01890 820332

Dogs on leads (restricted areas only).

Toilets (in village).

MAP Page 323 (1F)
OS Map 74/75, 339: NT925393

Lindisfarne Priory
See feature – Page 292

Norham Castle
Northumberland – TD15 2JY

Commanding a strategic ford over the River Tweed, Norham was a border stronghold of the Bishops of Durham. It was a frequent target for the Scots and was besieged at least 13 times, gaining a reputation as a very dangerous place. But even its powerful great tower and massive walls could not resist James IV's cannon, and it fell to him in 1513, shortly before his defeat at Flodden. Quickly recaptured, it was extensively rebuilt and by the 1520s was a powerful artillery fortress, its new gun towers still traceable today.

OPENING TIMES

1 Apr-30 Sep, daily	10am-5pm
1 Oct-28 Mar	Closed

Norham Castle

HOW TO FIND US

Direction: In Norham village; 6 miles SW of Berwick-upon-Tweed, on minor road off B6470 (from A698)

Train: Berwick-upon-Tweed 7½ miles

Bus: Perryman's 67 ⊠ Berwick-upon-Tweed – Galashiels

Disabled access (excluding keep).

MAP Page 323 (1F)
OS Map 74/75, 339: NT906476

St Andrew's Church, Bywell
Northumberland – NE43 7AD

© CCT

The tall Saxon tower of St Andrew's dates from about 850, and its massive walls are 5m thick. The body of the church is 13th century, but the mosaic sanctuary floor, glittering reredos and fine stained glass were restored in 1871. There are also some boldly carved medieval grave slabs.

Owned and managed by The Churches Conservation Trust.

OPENING TIMES

Open daily during daylight hours

HOW TO FIND US

Train: Nearest ⊠ Stocksfield 1 mile

Bus: Routes 416/508

10 mins from Prudhoe Castle (or 15 mins from Corbridge Roman Town)

MAP Page 323 (4G)
OS Map 87, 316: NZ048614

Prudhoe Castle   Northumberland – NE42 6NA

Begun between 1100 and 1120 to defend a strategic crossing of the River Tyne against Scottish invaders, Prudhoe Castle has been continuously occupied for over nine centuries. After two sieges during the 1170s – the Scots attackers reportedly declaring 'as long as Prudhoe stands, we shall never have peace' – the mighty stone keep and a great hall were added, followed in about 1300 by two strong towers. Passing from its original Umfraville owners to the powerful Percy family in 1398, it was again updated with a fashionable new great hall.

Even after its last military action against the Scots in 1640, Prudhoe's importance as the centre of a great landed estate continued. Early in the 19th century the Percys restored it, building a fine new manor house within its walls. All these developments are now vividly interpreted in a family-friendly exhibition including site finds, helping visitors to explore and understand the extensive remains of this formidable and long-lived fortress.

NON-MEMBERS

Adult	£4.40
Concession	£4.00
Child	£2.60

OPENING TIMES

1 Apr-30 Sep,
Thu-Mon   10am-5pm

HOW TO FIND US

Direction: In Prudhoe, on minor road off A695

Train: Prudhoe ¼ mile

Bus: Go North East 10, 11, 686

Tel: 01661 833459

Dogs on leads (restricted areas only).
Toilets with disabled access on site.

MAP Page 323 (4G)
OS Map 88, 316: NZ091634

Lindisfarne Priory Northumberland – TD15 2RX

Still a place of pilgrimage today, Lindisfarne Priory on Holy Island was one of the most important centres of early Christianity in Anglo-Saxon England. The dramatic approach to the island across the causeway only emphasises the serene appeal of this atmospheric site.

Eadfrith. Among England's greatest artistic and religious treasures, the Gospels are due to return from London to Durham Cathedral in 2013.

The fascinating museum offers a clear interpretation of the story of St Cuthbert and the 1300 year history of Lindisfarne Priory.

www.english-heritage.org.uk/lindisfarnepriory

NON-MEMBERS

Adult	£4.90
Concession	£4.40
Child	£2.90

OPENING TIMES

1 Apr-30 Sep, daily	9.30am-5pm
1 Oct-4 Nov, daily	9.30am-4pm
5 Nov-17 Feb, Sat-Sun	10am-4pm
18-22 Feb, daily	10am-4pm
23 Feb-28 Mar, Sat-Sun	10am-4pm
24-26 Dec and 1 Jan	Closed

The causeway floods at high tide, so it is very important to check the tide times before crossing.

HOW TO FIND US

Direction: On Holy Island, only reached at low tide across causeway; tide tables at each end, or from Tourist Information Centre

Train: Berwick-upon-Tweed 14 miles, via causeway

Bus: Perrymans service 477 from Berwick-upon-Tweed (passes close Berwick-upon-Tweed ≋). Times vary with tides

Tel: 01289 389200

Tourist Information Centre 01289 330733

🐕 ▣ 🚻 ♿ 🅿️ 🖼️ 🎫 🛗 ⚠ OVP

Dogs on leads (restricted areas only).

Parking and toilets in the village. Parking pay and display operated by Berwick Borough Council.

Access (limited in some areas of priory grounds).

MAP Page 323 (1G)
OS Map 75, 340: NU126417

293

Founded in AD 635 and still a place of pilgrimage today, Lindisfarne Priory on Holy Island was one of the most important centres of early Christianity in Anglo-Saxon England. The dramatic approach to the island across the causeway only emphasises the serene appeal of this atmospheric site.

St Cuthbert, Prior of Lindisfarne, is the most celebrated of the priory's many holy men. After ten years seeking peace as a hermit on lonely Inner Farne Island, he reluctantly became Bishop before retiring to die on Inner Farne in 687. Buried in the priory, his remains were transferred to a pilgrim shrine. After eleven years his coffin was opened and his body found

to be undecayed – a sure sign of sanctity.

From the end of the 8th century, the rich monastery was easy prey for Viking raiders. In 875 the monks left, carrying Cuthbert's remains, which after long wanderings were enshrined in Durham Cathedral in 1104, where they still rest. Only after that time did Durham monks re-establish a priory on Lindisfarne. The evocative ruins of the richly decorated priory church they built in c. 1150 still stand, with their famous 'rainbow arch' – a vault-rib of the now-vanished crossing tower.

The priory is likewise renowned for the Lindisfarne Gospels, produced there in the late 7th or early 8th century by Bishop

Warkworth Castle and Hermitage

Northumberland — NE65 0UJ

The magnificent cross-shaped keep of Warkworth, crowning a hilltop rising steeply above the River Coquet, dominates one of the largest, strongest and most impressive fortresses in northern England. The castle's most famous owners were the Percy family, whose lion badge can be seen carved on many parts of their stronghold. Wielding almost kingly power in the North, their influence reached its apogee under the first Percy Earl of Northumberland and his son 'Harry Hotspur', hero of many Border ballads as the bane of Scots raiders and a dominant character in Shakespeare's *Henry IV*. Having helped to depose Richard II, these turbulent 'kingmakers' both fell victim to Henry IV: the next three Percy earls likewise died violent deaths.

Still roofed and almost complete, the uniquely-planned keep dates mainly from the end of the 14th century. It presides over the extensive remains of a great hall, chapel, fine gatehouse and a virtually intact circuit of towered walls.

Half a mile from the castle, tucked away by the Coquet and accessible only by boat, stands a much more peaceful building: the late medieval cave Hermitage and chapel of a solitary holy man.

The Duke's Rooms and the Hermitage are open on Wed, Sun and Bank Holidays from 1 April to 30 September.

www.english-heritage.org.uk/ warkworthcastle

NON-MEMBERS

Castle:

Adult	£4.90
Concession	£4.40
Child	£2.90
Family	£12.70

Hermitage:

Adult	£3.30
Concession	£3.00
Child	£2.00

OPENING TIMES

Castle:

1 Apr-30 Sep, daily	10am-5pm
1 Oct-4 Nov, daily	10am-4pm
5 Nov-17 Feb, Sat-Sun	10am-4pm
18-22 Feb, daily	10am-4pm
23 Feb-28 Mar, Sat-Sun	10am-4pm
24-26 Dec and 1 Jan	Closed

Hermitage:

1 Apr-30 Sep, Wed, Sun & Bank Hols	11am-5pm
1 Oct-28 Mar	Closed

HOW TO FIND US

Direction: In Warkworth; 7½ miles S of Alnwick, on A1068

Train: Alnmouth 3½ miles

Bus: Arriva 518 Newcastle – Alnwick & Travelsure 472

Tel: 01665 711423

Local Tourist Information Amble: 01665 712313

Audio tours (also available for the visually impaired and those with learning difficulties).

Disabled access (limited access).

Dogs on leads (restricted areas only).

Parking (Charge payable, which is refundable on admission).

MAP Page 323 (2G)
OS Map 81, 332: NU247058

REDCAR AND CLEVELAND

Gisborough Priory
Redcar and Cleveland

The ruins of an Augustinian priory founded by the Bruce family, afterwards Kings of Scotland. They are dominated by the dramatic skeleton of the 14th-century church's east end.

Managed by Redcar and Cleveland Borough Council.

NON-MEMBERS

Adult	£1.80
Concession	90p
Child	90p
Family	£3.60

OPENING TIMES

1 Apr-30 Sep, Wed-Sun	10am-4pm
1 Oct-31 Mar, Wed-Sun	10am-3pm
24 Dec-1 Jan	Closed

HOW TO FIND US

Direction: In Guisborough town, next to the parish church

Train: Marske 4½ miles

Bus: Arriva services 5, 5A, X5, 26, 28, 81, 93, X93, 707, 708; Moorsbus M1, M2, M4, M12 (service 28 actually passes by)

Tel: 01287 633801

Toilets and parking (in town).

MAP Page 323 (6H)
OS Map 94, OL26/306: NZ617160

TYNE AND WEAR

Bessie Surtees House
Tyne and Wear – NE1 3JF

These two five-storey, 16th- and 17th-century merchants' houses – which now also house English Heritage's regional office – are fine examples of Jacobean domestic architecture, with some splendid period interiors. The Surtees house is best known as the scene of the elopement of Bessie with John Scott, later Lord Chancellor of England. An exhibition illustrating the history of the houses is on the first floor.

OPENING TIMES

All year round, Mon-Fri	10am-4pm
Bank Hols & 24 Dec-2 Jan	Closed

HOW TO FIND US

Direction: 41-44 Sandhill, Newcastle-upon-Tyne

Train: Newcastle ½ mile

Metro: Central ½ mile

Bus: From surrounding areas

Tel: 0191 269 1200

MAP Page 323 (4G)
OS Map 88, 316: NZ256338

Hylton Castle
Tyne and Wear

The distinctive and highly decorative gatehouse-tower of a castle built by the wealthy Sir William Hylton shortly before 1400. Originally containing four floors of self-contained family accommodation, its entrance front displays royal and family heraldry, including Richard II's white hart badge.

OPENING TIMES

1 Apr-28 Mar, daily	10am-4pm
Grounds only – no access to Castle	
24-26 Dec and 1 Jan	Closed

Hylton Castle

HOW TO FIND US

Direction: 3¾ miles W of Sunderland

Train: Seaburn Metro (2½ miles) then bus 99; Pallion Metro then bus 29, 29A, 39 or 39A

Bus: Stagecoach services 3, 13; Go North East services 26, 56, X88

Dogs on leads.
Disabled access (grounds only).

MAP Page 323 (4H)
OS Map 88, 308: NZ358588

St Paul's Monastery, Jarrow
Tyne and Wear

The home of the Venerable Bede, chronicler of the beginnings of English Christianity, Jarrow has become one of the best-understood Anglo-Saxon monastic sites. The Anglo-Saxon church – with the oldest dedication stone in the country, dated AD 685 – partly survives as the chancel of the parish church. A free downloadable audio tour is available from the English Heritage website.

OPENING TIMES

Monastery ruins any reasonable time

HOW TO FIND US

Direction: In Jarrow, on minor road N of A185; follow signs for Bede's World

Metro: Bede ¾ miles

Bus: Go North East 16 and The Crusader services 27

Tel: 0191 489 7052

MAP Page 323 (4H)
OS Map 88, 316: NZ339652

Tynemouth Priory and Castle
Tyne and Wear – NE30 4BZ

Set in an almost impregnable position on a steep headland between the river and the North Sea, Tynemouth has always been as much a fortress as a religious site.

Here stood a 7th-century Anglian monastery, burial place of Oswin, sainted King of Northumbria. After its destruction by Danish raiders, the present Benedictine priory was founded on its site in c. 1090.

The towering east end of the priory church, built in c. 1200 with slender lancet windows and soaring arches, still survives almost to its full height, dominating the headland. Beyond it stands a small but complete and exceptionally well-preserved chapel, with a rose window and an ornately sculpted roof vault. This was built in the mid-15th century as a chantry for the souls of the powerful Percy family, Earls of Northumberland.

Enclosing both headland and monastery, and still surviving in part, were the strong medieval walls which once made Tynemouth among the largest fortified areas in England, and

an important bastion against the Scots.

When the priory's 19 monks surrendered Tynemouth to Henry VIII in 1539, it was immediately adopted as a royal castle. Thereafter the fortress headland continued to play an important role in coastal defence from Elizabethan times until the end of the Second World War.

The interactive *Life in the Stronghold* exhibition takes visitors on a journey from Tynemouth's beginnings as an Anglo-Saxon settlement, via its medieval monastery and Tudor fortification, right up to its importance as a Second World War coastal gun battery.

Conservation works have been carried out on the coastal gun battery and magazine, restored to look as they did during World War I. Replica uniforms hang on the walls, alongside the special magazine clothes which soldiers changed into before handling explosive material. Visitors can explore the space in which soldiers worked underground to prepare ammunition for the guns.

www.english-heritage.org.uk/tynemouthpriory

⬛ Available for corporate and private hire

NON-MEMBERS
Adult	£4.60
Concession	£4.10
Child	£2.80
Family	£12.00

OPENING TIMES
1 Apr-30 Sep, daily	10am-5pm
1 Oct-4 Nov, Thu-Mon	10am-4pm
5 Nov-28 Mar, Sat-Sun	10am-4pm
24-26 Dec and 1 Jan	Closed

Gun Battery: Access limited, please ask site staff for details

HOW TO FIND US
Direction: In Tynemouth, near North Pier

Metro: Tynemouth ½ mile

Bus: Arriva services 306

Tel: 0191 257 1090

Dogs on leads.
Disabled access (priory only).
Toilets with disabled access on site.
Limited disabled parking avaiable.

MAP Page 323 (4H)
OS Map 88, 316: NZ373694

Associated attractions in the North East

These visitor attractions, all independent of EH, offer discounts to our members. Please call before you visit to confirm details. A valid EH membership card must be produced for each member.

Alnwick Castle and The Alnwick Garden
NE66 1NQ

From poisonous plants to Potter-inspired magic, Alnwick Castle and The Alnwick Garden bring together a castle rich in history and one of the country's most surprising gardens, creating an experience full of the unexpected.

Between Warkworth Castle and Dunstanburgh Castle

Tel: 01665 511350

www.alnwickcastle.com or www.alnwickgarden.com

20% discount on full price adult day tickets ⌗

Bamburgh Castle
Northumberland NE69 7DF

Home to the Kings of Northumbria, with fourteen public rooms and over 2000 artefacts, including arms, furniture, paintings and china. Armstrong and Aviation Artefacts Museum.

16½ miles from Lindisfarne Priory

Tel: 01668 214515

www.bamburghcastle.com

20% discount on entry ⌗ OVP 👪 6

The Bowes Museum
County Durham DL12 8NP

Has undergone a major transformation to create a stunning 21st century attraction in beautiful grounds. An inspirational day out for all the family, with fascinating collections, romantic history, fine dining and shopping.

Near Barnard Castle

Open daily 10am–5pm

Tel: 01833 690606

www.thebowesmuseum.org.uk

£1 off admission ⌗ OVP 👪 4

Killhope – The North of England Lead Mining Museum
Durham DL13 1AR

A multi-award winning Victorian Mining Museum, and a grand day out. Accompany a guide on a mine tour. Our enthusiastic team will ensure you have a day to remember.

Open Apr–Oct 10.30am–5pm

Tel: 01388 537505

www.killhope.org.uk

25% off ticket ⌗ OVP 👪 6

Tanfield Railway
County Durham NE16 5ET

The world's oldest railway. Take a 6 mile return trip behind locally built steam engines hauling vintage carriages. 18th-century Causey Arch adjacent. Operates Sundays & Bank Holiday Mondays.

15 mins from J63 A1M

Tel: 0845 4634938

www.tanfield-railway.co.uk

2 for 1 train ticket only ⌗ OVP 👪 2

Give the gift of membership

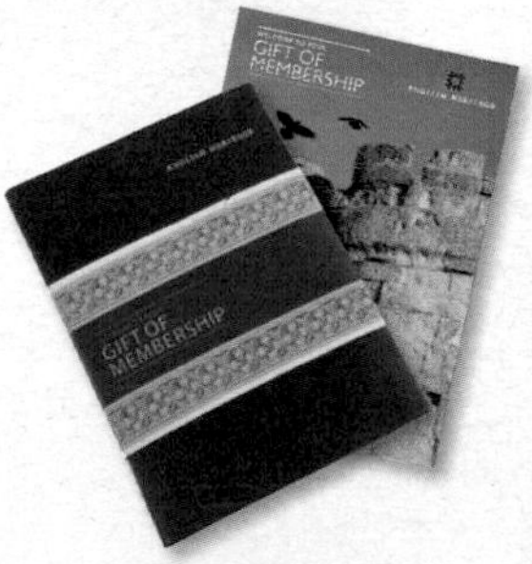

English Heritage Gift of Membership makes the ideal present – a whole year of fantastic days out at over 400 properties including historic houses, castles and gardens.

Call 0870 333 1182 or visit **www.english-heritage.org.uk/gift** for more details.

⌗ EH Members OVP OVP Holders 👪 ? Discounted Child Places Included

Associated Attractions

English Heritage members can gain **half-price** admission to Cadw attractions during the first year of membership and **free** entry in subsequent years.

Cadw

Conwy Castle © Crown Copyright

Beaumaris Castle, Anglesey
LL58 8AP
Tel: 01248 810361

Blaenavon Ironworks,
Nr Pontypool, Torfaen NP4 9RN
Tel: 01495 792615

Caerleon Roman Fortress,
Caerleon, Newport NP18 1AE
Tel: 01633 422518

Caernarfon Castle, Caernarfon,
Gwynedd LL55 2AY
Tel: 01286 677617

Caerphilly Castle, Caerphilly
CF83 1JD
Tel: 029 2088 3143

Carreg Cennen Castle, Nr Trapp,
Carmarthenshire SA19 6TS
Tel: 01558 822291

Castell Coch, Cardiff CF15 7JS
Tel: 029 2081 0101

Chepstow Castle, Chepstow,
Monmouthshire NP16 5EY
Tel: 01291 624065

Cilgerran Castle, Nr Cardigan,
Pembrokeshire SA43 2SF
Tel: 01239 621339

Conwy Castle, Conwy LL32 8AY
Tel: 01492 592358

Criccieth Castle, Criccieth,
Gwynedd LL52 0DP
Tel: 01766 522227

Dolwyddelan Castle, Dolwyddelan,
Gwynedd LL25 0JD
Tel: 01690 750366

Harlech Castle, Harlech,
Gwynedd LL46 2YH
Tel: 01766 780552

Kidwelly Castle, Kidwelly,
Carmarthenshire SA17 5BQ
Tel: 01554 890104

Laugharne Castle, Laugharne,
Carmarthenshire SA33 4SA
Tel: 01994 427906

Oxwich Castle, Oxwich,
Swansea SA3 1NG
Tel: 01792 390359

Plas Mawr, Conwy LL32 8DE
Tel: 01492 580167

Raglan Castle, Raglan,
Monmouthshire NP15 2BT
Tel: 01291 690228

Rhuddlan Castle, Rhuddlan,
Denbighshire LL18 5AD
Tel: 01745 590777

Rug Chapel and Llangar Church,
Corwen, Denbighshire LL21 9BT
Tel: 01490 412025

St Davids Bishop's Palace,
St Davids, Pembrokeshire
SA62 6PE
Tel: 01437 720517

Strata Florida Abbey,
Pontrhydfendigaid, Ceredigion
SY25 6ES
Tel: 01974 831261

Tintern Abbey, Tintern,
Monmouthshire NP16 6SE
Tel: 01291 689251

Tretower Court and Castle,
Tretower, Powys NP8 1RD
Tel: 01874 730279

Valle Crucis Abbey, Nr Llangollen,
Denbighshire LL20 8DD
Tel: 01978 860326

Weobley Castle, Nr Llanrhidian,
Swansea SA3 1HB
Tel: 01792 390012

White Castle, Nr Abergavenny,
Monmouthshire NP7 8UD
Tel: 01600 780380

**For more details about Cadw,
write to: Plas Carew,
Unit 5/7 Cefn Coed, Parc
Nantgarw, Cardiff CF15 7QQ
Please call 01443 336000
or visit the Cadw website at
www.cadw.wales.gov.uk**

Associated Attractions

English Heritage members can gain **half-price** admission to Historic Scotland attractions during the first year of membership and **free** entry in subsequent years.

Historic Scotland

Urquhart Castle

Kinnaird Head Lighthouse

Fort George

Skara Brae

Stirling Castle

All images © Historic Scotland

Cardoness Castle, Nr Gatehouse of Fleet, Dumfries and Galloway
Tel: 01557 814427

Castle Campbell, Dollar Glen, Central
Tel: 01259 742408

Corgarff Castle, Nr Strathdon, Grampian
Tel: 01975 651460

Craigmillar Castle, Edinburgh and Lothians
Tel: 0131 661 4445

Craignethan Castle, Lanark, Greater Glasgow
Tel: 01555 860364

Crichton Castle, Nr Pathhead, Edinburgh and Lothians
Tel: 01875 320017

Crossraguel Abbey, Nr Maybole, Greater Glasgow
Tel: 01655 883113

Dallas Dhu Historic Distillery, Nr Forres, Grampian
Tel: 01309 676548

Dirleton Castle and Gardens, Dirleton, East Lothian
Tel: 01620 850330

Doune Castle, Doune, Central
Tel: 01786 841742

Dryburgh Abbey, Nr Melrose, Borders
Tel: 01835 822381

Duff House, Banff, Grampian
Tel: 01261 818 181

Dumbarton Castle, Dumbarton, Greater Glasgow
Tel: 01389 732167

Dunblane Cathedral, Dunblane, Central
Tel: 01786 823 388

Dundonald Castle, Dundonald, Greater Glasgow
Tel: 01563 851489

Dundrennan Abbey, Nr Kirkcudbright, Dumfries and Galloway
Tel: 01557 500262

Aberdour Castle and Garden, Aberdour, Fife
Tel: 01383 860519

Arbroath Abbey, Angus
Tel: 01241 878756

Argyll's Lodging, Stirling, Central
Tel: 01786 450000

Balvenie Castle, Dufftown, Grampian
Tel: 01340 820121

Bishop's and Earl's Palaces, Kirkwall, Orkney
Tel: 01856 871918

The Black House, Arnol, Lewis, Western Isles
Tel: 01851 710395

Blackness Castle, Firth of Forth, Edinburgh and Lothians
Tel: 01506 834807

Bonawe Historic Iron Furnace, Taynuilt, Argyll
Tel: 01866 822432

Bothwell Castle, Bothwell, Greater Glasgow
Tel: 01698 816894

Broch of Gurness, Aikerness, Orkney
Tel: 01856 751414

Brough of Birsay, NW of Kirkwall, Orkney
Tel: 01856 841 815

Caerlaverock Castle, Nr Dumfries, Dumfries and Galloway
Tel: 01387 770244

Cairnpapple Hill, Torphichen, Edinburgh and Lothians
Tel: 01506 634622

Historic Scotland

Stirling Castle

© Historic Scotland

Dunfermline Palace and Abbey,
Dunfermline, Fife
Tel: 01383 739026

Dunstaffnage Castle, Nr Oban,
Argyll
Tel: 01631 562465

Edinburgh Castle,
Edinburgh and Lothians
Tel: 0131 225 9846

Edzell Castle and Garden,
Edzell, Angus
Tel: 01356 648631

Elcho Castle, Nr Bridge of Earn,
Perthshire
Tel: 01738 639998

Elgin Cathedral, Elgin, Highlands
Tel: 01343 547171

Fort George, Nr Ardersier village,
Highlands
Tel: 01667 460232

Glasgow Cathedral, Glasgow
Tel: 0141 552 6891

Glenluce Abbey, Nr Glenluce,
Dumfries and Galloway
Tel: 01581 300541

Hackness Martello Tower and
Battery, Hoy, Orkney
Tel: 01856 701727

Hermitage Castle,
Nr Newcastleton, Borders
Tel: 01387 376222

Huntingtower Castle, Nr Perth,
Perthshire
Tel: 01738 627231

Huntly Castle, Huntly, Grampian
Tel: 01466 793191

Inchcolm Abbey, Firth of Forth,
Fife
Tel: 01383 823332

Inchmahome Priory,
Lake of Menteith, Central
Tel: 01877 385294

Iona Abbey and Nunnery,
Island of Iona, Argyll
Tel: 01681 700512

Jarlshof Prehistoric and Norse
Settlement, Sumburgh Head,
Shetland
Tel: 01950 460112

Jedburgh Abbey and Visitor
Centre, Jedburgh, Borders
Tel: 01835 863925

Kildrummy Castle, Nr Alford,
Grampian
Tel: 01975 571331

Kinnaird Head Castle,
Lighthouse and Museum,
Fraserburgh, Grampian
Tel: 01346 511022

Kisimul Castle, Isle of Barra,
Western Isles
Tel: 01871 810313

Linlithgow Palace, Linlithgow,
West Lothian
Tel: 01506 842896

Loch Leven Castle, Lochleven,
Perthshire
Tel: 01577 862670

MacLellan's Castle, Kirkcudbright,
Dumfries and Galloway
Tel: 01557 331856

Maeshowe Chambered Cairn,
Nr Kirkwall, Orkney
Tel: 01856 761606

Meigle Sculptured Stone Museum,
Meigle, Angus
Tel: 01828 640612

Melrose Abbey, Melrose,
Borders
Tel: 01896 822562

New Abbey Corn Mill, New Abbey,
Dumfries and Galloway
Tel: 01387 850260

Newark Castle, Port Glasgow,
Greater Glasgow
Tel: 01475 741858

Rothesay Castle,
Rothesay, Isle of Bute
Tel: 01700 502691

St Andrews Castle,
St Andrews, Fife
Tel: 01334 477196

St Andrews Cathedral,
St Andrews, Fife
Tel: 01334 472563

St Serf's Church and Dupplin
Cross, Dunning, Perthshire
Tel: 01764 684497

St Vigeans Sculptured Stones,
Nr Arbroath, Angus
Tel: 01241 433739

Seton Collegiate Church,
Nr Cockenzie, East Lothian
Tel: 01875 813334

Skara Brae and Skaill House,
Nr Kirkwall, Orkney
Tel: 01856 841815

Smailholm Tower, Near
Smailholm, Borders
Tel: 01573 460365

Spynie Palace, Nr Elgin, Grampian
Tel: 01343 546358

Stanley Mills, North of Perth
Tel: 01738 828268

Stirling Castle, Stirling, Central
Tel: 01786 450000

Sweetheart Abbey, New Abbey,
Dumfries and Galloway
Tel: 01387 850397

Tantallon Castle, Nr North
Berwick, East Lothian
Tel: 01620 892727

Threave Castle, Nr Castle Douglas,
Dumfries and Galloway
Tel: 07711 223101

Tolquhon Castle, Nr Aberdeen,
Grampian
Tel: 01651 851286

Urquhart Castle,
Drumnadrochit, Highlands
Tel: 01456 450551

**For more details on Historic
Scotland, write to:
Longmore House, Salisbury Place,
Edinburgh EH9 1SH**

**Please call 0131 668 8999, email:
hs.members@scotland.gsi.gov.uk
or visit the Historic Scotland
website at www.historic-
scotland.gov.uk**

Associated Attractions

English Heritage members can gain **half-price** admission to Manx National Heritage attractions during their first year of membership and **free** entry in subsequent years.

Manx National Heritage

Rushen Abbey

Members must present a valid membership card on admission (Manx National Heritage permit free admission to the member only and children aged 4 years and under). Admission charges apply for special events. Travel connections between the Isle of Man's heritage sites are available through the Victorian Steam Railway, Manx Electric Railway, Horse Tram and Bus Vannin. **To book travel visit www.visitisleofman.com**

Isle of Man

Castle Rushen – Castletown

The National Folk Museum – Cregneash

The Grove – Museum of Victorian Life – Ramsey

House of Manannan – Peel

Laxey Wheel and Mines Trail – Laxey

Manx Museum – Douglas

Nautical Museum – Castletown

Niarbyl Restaurant & Visitor Centre – Dalby

Old Grammar School – Castletown

Old House of Keys – Castletown

Peel Castle – Peel

Rushen Abbey & Abbey Restaurant – Ballasalla

The Sound Café and Visitor Centre – near Cregneash

For more details, please contact: Manx National Heritage, Kingswood Grove, Douglas, Isle of Man IM1 3LY.

Please call 01624 648000 or visit the Manx National Heritage website at www.manxnationalheritage.im

Laxey Wheel

Portcullis at Castle Rushen

All images © Manx National Heritage

Associated Attractions

English Heritage members can gain **free** admission to New Zealand Historic Places Trust attractions from the first year of membership.

New Zealand Historic Places Trust

New Zealand's built heritage may be considered young in world terms, but many of the properties cared for by the New Zealand Historic Places Trust (NZHPT) are physical reminders of the birth and development of this South Pacific nation and its enduring connection to Great Britain.

Old St Paul's

Alberton

Fyffe House

Totara Estate

Kerikeri Mission Station

English Heritage members have free standard entry to the 48 properties the NZHPT cares for nationwide – from the Kerikeri Mission Station in Northland dating from 1821-22 and New Zealand's oldest standing building, to Hayes Engineering Works in the gold mining region of Central Otago. Please understand that charges may apply for special events and exhibitions.

There are a range of heritage properties and sites to visit where you can learn about the people and places that make New Zealand what it is today. These include impressive homesteads, centres of industry and innovation, battle sites and so much more.

Among them are:

The Kerikeri Mission Station and Stone Store in Northland – the Mission Station is New Zealand's oldest standing building, built in 1821-22, while the nearby Stone Store is one of the country's most photographed buildings.

Alberton and Highwic in Auckland – impressive dwellings that were home to two prominent businessmen and their families in colonial New Zealand.

Old St Paul's in Wellington – where stunning stained glass windows help illuminate the glorious native timber interior of this 19th century Gothic Revival church, a home away from home for US servicemen during World War Two.

Fyffe House in Kaikoura – where a whale of a time is guaranteed, the property built as part of the early whaling industry and partly on whale vertebrae foundations.

Totara Estate in South Canterbury – British dinner tables have featured our finest cuts of meat over many years, and Totara Estate is where New Zealand's billion dollar frozen meat industry began.

More information on heritage sites to visit can be found on the NZHPT's website www. historicplaces.org.nz. Our staff look forward to welcoming you.

The Friends of Friendless Churches

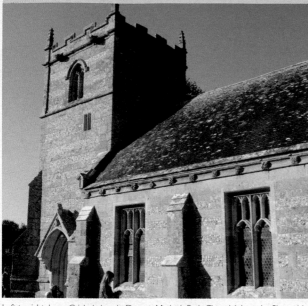

Left to right: Long Crichel church, Dorset. Matlock Bath Chapel (photo by Simon Harpur) and Ayshford Chapel, Devon (photo by Apex Photo Agency).

The Friends own redundant but beautiful places of worship that would otherwise have been demolished or left to ruin.

Founded by proud Welshman Ivor Bulmer-Thomas in 1957, we now own 46 Grade II* and Grade I buildings in England and Wales. In the last 12 months we have taken a record number of new churches into care. Our six new vestings include the long-redundant Long Crichel (see top left). We are about to embark on a major conservation campaign at the chapel of St John the Baptist, at Matlock Bath, Derbs (see top right) on the back of a significant grant from English Heritage.

We are a small, voluntary organisation that works in partnership, sharing an office and staff with the Ancient Monuments Society, a statutory consultee on listed building consent in England and Wales.

We warmly welcome visitors to our churches, but do not claim sophistication in terms of parking, toilets, attendants or shops, and access may require approach to a key-holder. Our churches are places for quiet study and contemplation, preserved for posterity as beautiful historic buildings.

FRIENDS OF FRIENDLESS CHURCHES

CONTACT

St Ann's Vestry Hall
2 Church Entry, London EC4V 5HB
Tel: 020 7236 3934
Email: office@friendsoffriend
lesschurches.org.uk
**www.friendsoffriendlesschurches.
org.uk**
Registered charity no: 1113097

The Historic Chapels Trust

Wainsgate Baptist Church   Photo: Geoff Matthews

Preserving places of worship in England

The Trust was established to take into ownership redundant chapels and other places of worship in England that are of outstanding architectural and historic interest. Our mission is to secure for public benefit their preservation, repair and regeneration.

To the right are 20 of the chapels in our care that you can visit. Please call the keyholder before you make plans.

London
The Dissenters' Chapel, Kensal Green Cemetery, London
Tel: 020 8969 3181

St George's German Lutheran Church, Tower Hamlets, London
Tel: 020 7481 0533

South East
Cote Baptist Chapel, Oxfordshire
Tel: 020 7481 0533

South West
Penrose Methodist Chapel, St Ervan, Cornwall
Tel: 01841 540737

Salem Chapel, East Budleigh, Devon
Tel: 01395 445236/446189

Strict Baptist Chapel, Grittleton, Wiltshire
Tel: 01454 218036

East of England
Chantry Chapel, Thorndon Park, Nr Brentwood, Essex
Tel: 020 7481 0533

Walpole Old Chapel, Suffolk
Tel: 01986 798308

West Midlands
Bethesda Methodist Chapel, Stoke-on-Trent, Staffordshire
Tel: 01782 856810

Umberslade Baptist Church, Tanworth-in-Arden, Warwickshire
Tel: 0121 704 2694

Longworth RC Chapel, Bartestree, Herefordshire
Tel: 01432 853200

Yorkshire
Farfield Friends Meeting House, West Yorkshire
Tel: 01756 710587

Todmorden Unitarian Church, West Yorkshire
Tel: 01706 815407

Wainsgate Baptist Church, West Yorkshire
Tel: 01422 843315

North West
Shrine of Our Lady of Lourdes, Blackpool, Lancashire
Tel: 01253 865770

St Benet's Chapel, Netherton, Merseyside
Tel: 0151 520 2600

Wallasey Unitarian Church, Merseyside
Tel: 0151 639 9707

North East
Biddestone RC Chapel, Northumberland
Tel: 01665 574420/01669 630270/ 01669 620230

Coanwood Friends Meeting House, Northumberland
Tel: 01434 321316

Westgate Methodist Chapel, Co. Durham
Tel: 01388 517727

For further information please visit our website www.hct.org.uk or telephone 020 7481 0533.

English Heritage is unique

We are the government's statutory adviser on the historic environment but we are also a members' organisation. This means our funding comes in part from the Department for Culture, Media & Sport (DCMS) and partly from memberships, donations and fundraising. Increasingly, we depend on you, our members, not just financially but in our work to care for the historic environment. Our remit is broad. We advise on what should be protected; we offer grants; provide training, education and information; we maintain the national archive and, crucially, we look after more than 400 sites – all of which are free to visit for all our members and their families.

We are a non-profit organisation, so every penny of your membership goes towards maintaining the properties in our care. We are overseen by a Commission of up to 17 Commissioners appointed by the Secretary of State. Day to day management is delegated to our Chief Executive, Dr Simon Thurley, supported by an Executive Board comprising the Executive Directors of English Heritage's four operational groups.

HERITAGE GIVES US A SENSE OF BELONGING

The built environment has shaped our history and touches all of us – every day. We are convinced that our lives would be so much poorer if we allowed our heritage to ebb away on a tide of indifference. From stately homes to princely castles and from industrial buildings to modest terraced houses, shops and offices, our heritage belongs to us all, and we all have a responsibility to preserve and care for it for future generations to enjoy. We also know that England's historic environment is paramount to our tourist industry, contributing hugely to the country's prosperity.

DESIGNATION

Where possible we want to see historic buildings come to life, rather than being preserved as museum pieces. We also wish to ensure that any changes to buildings are in keeping with their historic roots. To this end, we work with local authorities on designating listed buildings. Most listed buildings date from before 1840 but we also designate some later buildings. There are three grades of listing : Grade 1, Grade II* and Grade II.

We also designate monuments and landscapes, and help local authorities in establishing Conservation Areas. For more information on listing, visit **www.english-heritage.org.uk/ listing**

Battlefields are important sources of archaeological and historic interest and over 40 are on our Register of Historic Battlefields. We also oversee a similar Register of Parks and Gardens. Visit **www.english-heritage.org.uk/conservation**

OUR PARTNERSHIP WITH MEMBERS

We are determined to work closely with our members, and firmly believe we should join together to protect our nation's heritage. Please contact us on 0870 333 1182/**members@ english-heritage.org.uk** at any time if you have any comments or need our assistance. We endeavour to answer calls within 15 seconds, emails and letters within 5 working days, and will always protect your personal information.

INTERPRETATION

How we show our properties and the information we provide to visitors is essential. We use the latest technology to enhance your visit, but we do not want our properties only to be discovered through the prism of multi-media presentations. A large number of our sites now have audio guides and our new web resource, Portico, provides more comprehensive and scholarly information on properties curated by English Heritage. And our guidebooks, written by experts in their field, are renowned for their motivating content and illustration.

VOLUNTEERING

We welcome volunteers who are keen to share their passion and interest in the historic environment with others. Activities include room stewarding, gardening, curatorial cleaning and assisting with our education programme at selected properties. Find out more about this rewarding work by visiting **www.english-heritage.org.uk/volunteering**

OUR WIDER WORK

Supporting the heritage sector sits at the heart of everything we do, and our broad remit encompasses a range of initiatives connected to this.

We administer the **blue plaques** scheme in London and also advise other groups and local authorities on putting up commemorative plaques. To find out more about the scheme, visit **www.english-heritage.org.uk/blueplaques**

English Heritage gives **grants** to individuals, local authorities and voluntary organisations to help conserve and enhance England's historic environment. These are targeted where there is greatest risk of loss of historic significance as identified in our Heritage at Risk Register. We also advise the Heritage Lottery Fund. To find out more, visit **www.english-heritage.org.uk/ grants**

We are the national archaeology service for England and we implement the statutory protection of England's 19,750 Scheduled Monuments. Visit **www.english-heritage.org. uk/archaeology**. We are also responsible for all **English maritime archaeological** sites up to 12 nautical miles off-shore. Designated Wrecks range from Bronze Age cargoes to early submarines. We advise the government on installations and extraction works at sea, which potentially can damage maritime archaeology.

Our **Research and Training** programmes increase understanding of the historic environment and help us guide its management in an informed and sustainable way. The pressures on capacity and skills are intense. We are working to address skills shortages within the traditional crafts and built heritage sector to ensure there is a continuing source of craftspeople to care for England's half a million listed buildings.

As part of our **statutory remit**, we advise local authorities and owners on proposals to change historic sites, ensuring the impact on historic significance is managed constructively. To find out more, visit **www.english-heritage.org.uk/your-property/planning-advice**

Another key responsibility is to develop robust **policies** to protect and promote the historic environment. We publish the evidence to support these policies annually as Heritage Counts (**www.heritagecounts.org.uk**). We also work closely with **UNESCO**, advising on the designation and management of World Heritage Sites in England.

If you share our passion for England's historic environment and want to help us make the past part of our future, view our current vacancies or register for our job alerts at **www.english-heritage.org.uk/jobs**

ENGLISH HERITAGE ARCHIVES

Our archives, formerly part of the National Monuments Record (NMR), hold more than 12 million photographs, drawings and reports covering England's archaeology, architecture, social and local history.

Visit us online, at **www.english-heritage.org.uk/archive** to see:
- **1 million** descriptions of historical photographs and documents
- **90,000** historic photographs of England from the 1850s to the present day
- Over **320,000** contemporary colour photographs of England's listed buildings
- Thousands of historic **aerial photos** from 1919 onwards

Or contact us at: Archive Services, The Engine House, Fire Fly Avenue, Swindon SN2 2EH
Tel: 01793 414600 Fax: 01793 414606
Email: **archives@english-heritage.org.uk**

Opening Times: Public Search Room Tues-Fri 9.30am-5pm

307

English Heritage is a not-for-profit organisation, and all the proceeds from our admissions, fundraising and commercial activities are invested back into our properties to help protect them for future generations to enjoy.

308

books & gifts

When you've whetted your appetite for information looking around our properties, make sure you visit our shop on site, where you'll find a huge range of fascinating books and unique gifts.

117 CASTLES & FORTS
OUTHOUSES & HALLS I COLD WAR BUNKER
6 HISTORIC BRIDGES
5 CONDUIT HOUSES
56 STATUES & MONUMENTS
54 ROMAN SITES
I DEER HOUSE I FISH HOUSE
6 INDUSTRIAL SITES
90 ECCLESIASTICAL SITES

HOW TO ORDER

If you can't visit one of our properties, you can still see our range at our online shop, **www.english-heritageshop.org.uk** or call **01761 452 966.**

Scan & click

Members can receive a copy of the English Heritage Publishing Catalogue by calling **0870 333 1181** or online at **www.english-heritage.org.uk/publications**

Products sold are subject to availability.

Events that bring history to life

From family fun days, craft fairs and exhibitions to spectacular battle displays and exclusive members' events, you'll find something for everyone to enjoy in our events calendar. In fact, we have the largest historical events programme in Europe, and so you'll have hundreds of activities to choose from throughout the year.

FESTIVAL OF HISTORY

An action-packed weekend for the whole family to enjoy. Spanning 2,000 years of history and featuring over 50 shows each day, over 1,000 performers, costumed intepreters and re-enactors bring the story of England to life.

Kelmarsh Hall, Northamptonshire, 14-15 July

BIG BATTLE SPECTACULARS

If you enjoy huge historical re-enactments then 'our 'tour de force' events could be just for you.

St George's Day Festival, Wrest Park, 21-22 April
Battle of Hastings 13-14 October

TIME TRAVELLERS GO...

Armed with their very own passport, children can learn centuries-old skills and earn prizes by completing tasks and collecting stickers at our properties.

Visit www.english-heritage.org. uk/timetravellersgo

PERFORMING ARTS

We've got a great variety of music and theatre events throughout the year – both indoors and out.

EXCLUSIVE MEMBERS' EVENTS

Go behind the scenes, learn a new skill and discover the secrets concealed by some of the most intriguing properties in England. We hold over 100 events throughout the year, which are available exclusively to members. See *Heritage Today* for details.

HOLIDAY COTTAGES

South East

Dover Castle, Kent
The Sergeant Major's House
and Peverell's Tower

Walmer Castle, Kent
The Garden Cottage and
The Greenhouse Apartment

Battle Abbey, East Sussex
South Lodge

Carisbrooke Castle,
Isle of Wight
The Bowling Green Apartment

Osborne House,
Isle of Wight
Pavilion Cottage

East

Audley End House, Essex
Cambridge Lodge

Hardwick Old Hall, Derbyshire
East Lodge

Kirby Hall, Northamptonshire
Peacock Cottage

South West

Pendennis Castle, Cornwall
The Custodian's House
and Callie's Cottage

St Mawes Castle, Cornwall
Fort House

West

Witley Court, Worcestershire
Pool House Cottage

Yorkshire

Mount Grace Priory,
North Yorkshire
Prior's Lodge

Rievaulx Abbey,
North Yorkshire
Refectory Cottage

www.facebook.com/
englishheritageholidaycottages

Reservations 0870 333
1187 or visit **www.english-
heritage.org.uk/book-and-
buy/holiday-cottages**

Stay & celebrate with us

Location is one of the key principles behind the development of English Heritage holiday cottages and properties to hire for a celebration or corporate event. All are positioned at the heart of an historic property – where history, discovery and enjoyment are just on the doorstep.

Wellington Arch

Wrest Park

Eltham Palace

Bolsover Castle

Main image: Dover Castle

PROPERTIES FOR HIRE ⊤

Properties available for hire are marked with a ⊤ throughout the handbook. Those also licensed for civil ceremonies are marked with a ▲.

London
Eltham Palace ▲
020 8294 2577

Kenwood 020 7973 3416

Marble Hill House ▲
020 7973 3416

Ranger's House ▲
020 8294 2577

Wellington Arch
020 7973 3416

South East
Osborne House, Isle of Wight
01983 203055

East
Bolsover Castle, Derbyshire ▲
01246 856456

Wrest Park, Bedfordshire ▲
01525 863704

South West
Old Wardour Castle,
Wiltshire ▲ 01305 820868

Pendennis Castle, Cornwall ▲
01326 310106

Portland Castle, Dorset ▲
01305 820868

St Mawes Castle, Cornwall ▲
01326 310106

West
Kenilworth Castle and ▲
Elizabethan Garden,
Warwickshire
01926 857 482

For more information on exclusive hire, please contact the Hospitality Managers on the property telephone numbers above, or visit **www.english-heritage.org.uk/hospitality**

SOUTH WEST

Bristol
Cornwall
Devon
Dorset
Gloucestershire
Isles of Scilly
Somerset
Wiltshire

⊞ English Heritage Sites
▲ Associated Attractions
⌂ The Churches Conservation Trust

A   B   C   D   E

1
2
3
4
5
6
7

Isles of Scilly

King Charles's Castle
Cromwell's Castle
Old Blockhouse
Bant's Carn Burial Chamber & Halangy Down Ancient Village
Innisidgen Burial Chambers
Porth Hellick Down Burial Chamber
Garrison Walls
Harry's Walls

Map labels

Cardigan
Cilgerran Castle
Fishguard
Newport (Pembs.)
Newcastle Emlyn
Lampeter
Llandovery
Carmarthen
Carreg Cennen Castle
Llandeilo
Haverfordwest
St. Clears
Laugharne Castle
Milford Haven
Kilgetty
Kidwelly
Kidwelly Castle
Pont Abraham
Pembroke
Saundersfoot
Tenby
Llanelli
Carmarthen Bay
Weobley Castle
Rhossili
Oxwich Castle
The Mumbles
Port Talbot

Ilfracombe
Combe Martin
Lynton
Lundy Island
Woolacombe
Lynmouth
Croyde
Hartland Point
Braunton
Barnstaple
Bideford
South Molton
Great Torrington
DEVON
Bude
Holsworthy
Hatherleigh
Penhallam Manor
Okehampton
Okehampton Castle
Tintagel Castle
Boscastle
Lydford Castle & Saxon Town
Grimspound
Launceston Castle
Launceston
Hound Tor Deserted Medieval Village
The Arthurian Centre
Tintagel
CORNWALL
Camelford
Merrivale Prehistoric Settlement
Ashburton
Padstow
Wadebridge
Hurlers Stone Circles
Tavistock
Dupath Well
Upper Plym Valley
St Breock Downs Monolith
King Doniert's Stone
Bodmin & Wenford Railway
Bodmin
Trethevy Quoit
Totnes Castle
Newquay
Liskeard
PLYMOUTH
Ivybridge
To
Perranporth
Wheal Martyn
Restormel Castle
Fowey
Looe
Royal Citadel
Modbury
St Austell
St Catherine's Castle
Talland Bay
Kingsbridge
Truro
Salcombe
St Ives
Redruth
St Mawes Castle
Chysauster Ancient Village
Falmouth
St Mawes
Start Point
Ballowall Barrow
St Just
Penzance
Helston
Pendennis Castle
National Maritime Museum Cornwall
Carn Euny Ancient Village
Tregiffian Burial Chamber
Land's End
Halliggye Fogou
Porthcurno Telegraph Museum
Lizard
Lizard Point

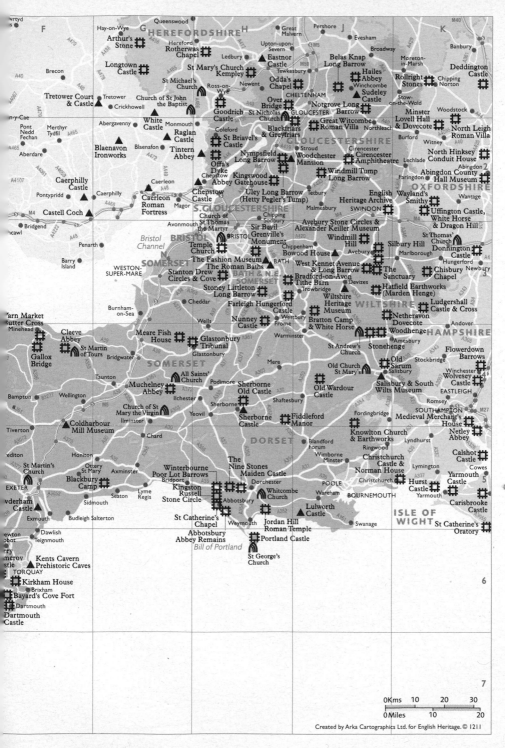

Created by Arka Cartographics Ltd. for English Heritage. © 1211

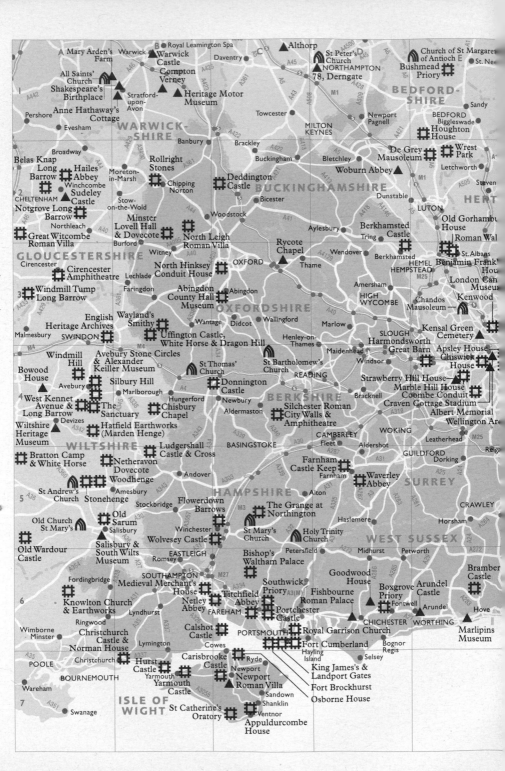

A Mary Arden's Farm
Royal Leamington Spa
Warwick
Warwick Castle
Compton Verney
Daventry
Althorp
St Peter's Church
NORTHAMPTON
78, Derngate
Church of St Margaret of Antioch
St Nec
Bushmead Priory
BEDFORD-SHIRE

All Saints' Church
Shakespeare's Birthplace
Stratford-upon-Avon
Anne Hathaway's Cottage
Heritage Motor Museum
Towcester
MILTON KEYNES
Newport Pagnell
BEDFORD
Biggleswade
Houghton House
Sandy

Pershore
Evesham
Banbury
Brackley
Buckingham
Bletchley
De Grey Mausoleum
Woburn Abbey
Letchworth
Wrest Park
HERT

Broadway
Belas Knap Long Barrow
Hailes Abbey
Winchcombe
Sudeley Castle
Moreton-in-Marsh
Rollright Stones
Chipping Norton
Deddington Castle
BUCKINGHAMSHIRE
Dunstable
LUTON
Stev
A605

CHELTENHAM
Notgrove Long Barrow
Northleach
Great Witcombe Roman Villa
Stow-on-the-Wold
Minster Lovell Hall & Dovecote
Burford
North Leigh Roman Villa
Woodstock
Bicester
Aylesbury
Tring
Berkhamsted Castle
Berkhamsted
Old Gorhambu House
Roman Wal
St Albans

GLOUCESTERSHIRE
Cirencester
Cirencester Amphitheatre
Lechlade
North Hinksey Conduit House
OXFORD
Rycote Chapel
Thame
Wendover
HEMEL HEMPSTEAD
Benjamin Frank' Hou
London Can Museu

Windmill Tump Long Barrow
Faringdon
Abingdon County Hall Museum
Abingdon
OXFORDSHIRE
Amersham
HIGH WYCOMBE
Chandos Mausoleum
Kenwood

Malmesbury
SWINDON
English Heritage Archives
Wayland's Smithy
Uffington Castle, White Horse & Dragon Hill
Wantage
Didcot
Wallingford
Henley-on-Thames
Marlow
SLOUGH
Harmondsworth
Great Barn
Kensal Green Cemetery

Windmill Hill
Avebury Stone Circles & Alexander Keiller Museum
St Thomas' Church
St Bartholomew's Church
READING
Maidenhead
Windsor
Apsley House
Chiswick House

Bowood House
Avebury
Silbury Hill
Marlborough
Donnington Castle
Newbury
BERKSHIRE
Bracknell
Strawberry Hill House
Marble Hill House
Coombe Conduit
Craven Cottage Stadium

West Kennet Avenue & Long Barrow
The Sanctuary
Devizes
Hungerford
Chisbury Chapel
Aldermaston
Silchester Roman City Walls & Amphitheatre
WOKING
Albert Memorial
Wellington Ar

Wiltshire Heritage Museum
Hatfield Earthworks (Marden Henge)
WILTSHIRE
Ludgershall Castle & Cross
BASINGSTOKE
CAMBERLEY
Fleet
GUILDFORD
Leatherhead
Reiga

Bratton Camp & White Horse
Netheravon Dovecote
Woodhenge
Andover
A30
Farnham Castle Keep
Farnham
Waverley Abbey
Aldershot
SURREY
Dorking

St Andrew's Church
Stonehenge
Amesbury
Stockbridge
Flowerdown Barrows
Alton
Haslemere
CRAWLEY

Old Church St Mary's
Old Sarum
Salisbury
HAMPSHIRE
The Grange at Northington
Holy Trinity Church
Horsham

Salisbury & South Wilts Museum
Winchester
Wolvesey Castle
St Mary's Church
WEST SUSSEX
Midhurst
Petworth

Old Wardour Castle
Fordingbridge
EASTLEIGH
Romsey
Bishop's Waltham Palace
Petersfield

Knowlton Church & Earthworks
Ringwood
Lyndhurst
Medieval Merchant's House
SOUTHAMPTON
Titchfield Abbey
Southwick Priory
Fishbourne Roman Palace
Goodwood House
Boxgrove Priory
Fontwell
Arundel Castle
Arundel
Bramber Castle
Hove

Christchurch Castle & Norman House
Lymington
Netley Abbey
FAREHAM
Portchester Castle
CHICHESTER
Royal Garrison Church
WORTHING
Marlipins Museum

Wimborne Minster
Wareham
Christchurch
Calshot Castle
PORTSMOUTH
Fort Cumberland
Bognor Regis
Selsey

POOLE
BOURNEMOUTH
Hurst Castle
Yarmouth
Yarmouth Castle
Carisbrooke Castle
Newport
Newport Roman Villa
Cowes
Ryde
Hayling Island
King James's & Landport Gates
Fort Brockhurst
Osborne House

Swanage
ISLE OF WIGHT
St Catherine's Oratory
Ventnor
Appuldurcombe House
Sandown
Shanklin

LONDON AND SOUTH EAST

Berkshire
Buckinghamshire
East Sussex
Hampshire
Isle of Wight
Kent
Oxfordshire
Surrey
West Sussex

English Heritage Sites
Associated Attractions
The Churches Conservation Trust

EAST OF ENGLAND

Bedfordshire
Cambridgeshire
Essex
Hertfordshire
Norfolk
Suffolk

⚓ English Heritage Sites
▲ Associated Attractions
🏛 The Churches Conservation Trust

316

Mansfield

Rufford Abbey
Papplewick Pumping Station
NOTTINGHAMSHIRE
NOTTINGHAM
West Bridgford
Loughborough

Newark-on-Trent
Grantham
Melton Mowbray

Woodhall Spa
Coningsby
Tattershall College
Sleaford
Spalding

LEICESTERSHIRE RUTLAND
Kirby Muxloe Castle LEICESTER
Jewry Wall
Oakham Rutland Water
Lyddington Bede House
Kirby Hall
Longthorpe Tower
PETERBOROUGH
Apethorpe Hall
CAMBS.
Stamford
Burghley House

WEST MIDLANDS
WOLVERHAMPTON
WALSALL
TAMWORTH
Bosworth Battlefield
Hinckley
Market Harborough
Rockingham Castle
St Peter's Church
Corby
Eleanor Cross
Chichele College
Oundle
Huntingdon

DUDLEY
Merry Hill
BIRMINGHAM
SOLIHULL
Halesowen Abbey
Bromsgrove
NUNEATON
COVENTRY
RUGBY
Lutterworth
Rushton Triangular Lodge
Kelmarsh Hall
Kettering
St Andrew's Church
NORTHAMPTON-SHIRE

JW Evans Silver Factory

Kenilworth Castle & Elizabethan Garden
Kenilworth
Stoneleigh Abbey
Royal Leamington Spa
Wellingborough
St Peter's Church
NORTHAMPTON
78, Derngate
Church of St Margaret of Antioch St Nec.
Bushmead Priory
BEDFORD-SHIRE
Sandy

WORCS.
Droitwich Spa
Mary Arden's Farm
Warwick
Warwick Castle
Daventry
Althorp

All Saints' Church
Shakespeare's Birthplace
Stratford-upon-Avon
Compton Verney
Heritage Motor Centre
Towcester
Newport Pagnell
BEDFORD
Biggleswade
Houghton House

Pershore
Evesham
WARWICK-SHIRE
Anne Hathaway's Cottage
Banbury
Brackley
MILTON KEYNES
Buckingham
Bletchley
De Grey Mausoleum
Woburn Abbey
Wrest Park
Letchworth
Dunstable
Stevenage

Belas Knap Long Barrow
Hailes Abbey
Winchcombe
Sudeley Castle
Moreton-in-Marsh
Rollright Stones
Chipping Norton
Stow-on-the-Wold
Deddington Castle
Bicester
BUCKINGHAMSHIRE
LUTON

Broadway

CHELTENHAM
Notgrove Long Barrow
Great Witcombe Roman Villa
Northleach
Minster Lovell Hall & Dovecote
Burford
Witney
North Leigh Roman Villa
Woodstock
Rycote Chapel
Thame
Aylesbury
Tring
Wendover
Berkhamsted Castle
Berkhamsted
HEMEL HEMPSTEAD
Old Gorhambury House
Roman Wa
St Albans
Benjamin Frankli Hous

GLOUS.
Cirencester
Cirencester Amphitheatre
Lechlade
North Hinksey Conduit House
OXFORD
London Cana Museum
Kenwood

Windmill Tump Long Barrow
Faringdon
Abingdon County Hall Museum
Abingdon
Amersham
HIGH WYCOMBE
Chandos Mausoleum

English Heritage Archives
SWINDON
Wayland's Smithy
Wantage Didcot Wallingford
Uffington Castle, White Horse & Dragon Hill
Marlow
Henley-on-Thames
Maidenhead
SLOUGH
Harmondsworth Great Barn
Kensal Green Cemetery

Malmesbury
Windmill Hill
Avebury Stone Circles & Alexander Keiller Museum
St Thomas' Church
St Bartholomew's Church
READING
Windsor
Apsley House
Chiswick House

Bowood House
Avebury
Silbury Hill
Hungerford
Marlborough
West Kennet Avenue & Long Barrow
The Sanctuary
Donnington Castle
Newbury
Chisbury Chapel
Aldermaston
Bracknell
BERKSHIRE
Marble Hill House
Strawberry Hill House
Craven Cottage Stadium
Coombe Conduit
Albert Memorial
Wellington Arc

Created by Arka Cartographics Ltd. for English Heritage. © 12/11

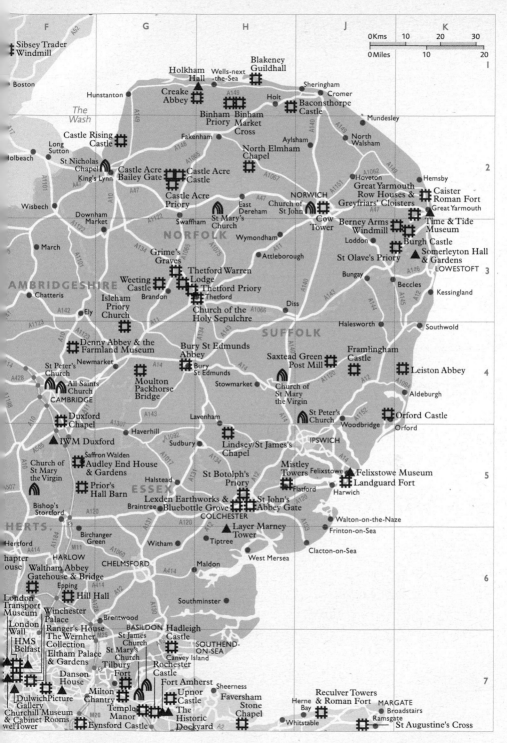

F

Sibsey Trader Windmill
Boston

The Wash

Hunstanton

Long Sutton
Holbeach

Castle Rising Castle

St Nicholas Chapel
King's Lynn

Wisbech

Downham Market

AMBRIDGESHIRE

Chatteris

March

Ely

Islham Priory Church

Denny Abbey & the Farmland Museum

Newmarket

St Peter's Church
All Saints Church
CAMBRIDGE

Duxford Chapel

IWM Duxford

Church of St Mary the Virgin

Saffron Walden
Audley End House & Gardens

Prior's Hall Barn

Halstead

Bishop's Stortford

HERTS.

Hertford

Birchanger Green
Witham

HARLOW

CHELMSFORD

hapter
ouse
Waltham Abbey
Gatehouse & Bridge

Epping

Hill Hall

London Transport Museum
London Wall
HMS Belfast

Winchester Palace
Ranger's House
The Wernher Collection
Eltham Palace & Gardens

Danson House

Dulwich Picture Gallery
Churchill Museum & Cabinet Rooms
welTower

G

Holkham Hall
Creake Abbey

Binham Priory
Binham Market Cross

Fakenham

Castle Acre Bailey Gate
Castle Acre Priory
Castle Acre Castle

Swaffham

St Mary's Church

NORFOLK

Grime's Graves

Weeting Castle
Brandon

Thetford Warren Lodge
Thetford Priory
Thetford

Church of the Holy Sepulchre

Bury St Edmunds Abbey
Bury St Edmunds

Moulton Packhorse Bridge

Stowmarket

Lavenham

Haverhill

Sudbury

Lindsey/St James's Chapel

Lexden Earthworks & Bluebottle Grove
COLCHESTER

Layer Marney Tower

Tiptree

Maldon

Southminster

Brentwood

BASILDON
St James Church
St Mary's Church
Tilbury Fort

Milton Chantry
Temple Manor
Eynsford Castle

Hadleigh Castle

SOUTHEND-ON-SEA
Canvey Island

Rochester Castle
Fort Amherst
Upnor Castle
The Historic Dockyard

H

Wells-next-the-Sea
Blakeney Guildhall

Holt

North Elmham Chapel

East Dereham

Wymondham

Attleborough

Diss

SUFFOLK

Saxtead Green Post Mill

Church of St Mary the Virgin

St Peter's Church

Woodbridge

IPSWICH

Mistley Towers
Flatford

Harwich

St Botolph's Priory

St John's Abbey Gate

Walton-on-the-Naze
Frinton-on-Sea

Clacton-on-Sea

West Mersea

Sheerness

Faversham
Stone Chapel

Herne Bay
Whitstable

J

Sheringham
Cromer

Baconsthorpe Castle

Mundesley

Aylsham
North Walsham

Hoveton

NORWICH
Church of St John
Cow Tower

Berney Arms Windmill
Loddon

St Olave's Priory

Bungay

Beccles

Halesworth

Framlingham Castle

Aldeburgh

Orford Castle
Orford

Felixstowe
Landguard Fort

Felixstowe Museum

K

0 Kms 10 20 30
0 Miles 10 20

Great Yarmouth Row Houses & Greyfriars' Cloisters
Hemsby
Caister Roman Fort
Great Yarmouth
Time & Tide Museum
Burgh Castle
Somerleyton Hall & Gardens
LOWESTOFT

Kessingland

Southwold

Leiston Abbey

Reculver Towers & Roman Fort
MARGATE
Broadstairs
Ramsgate
St Augustine's Cross

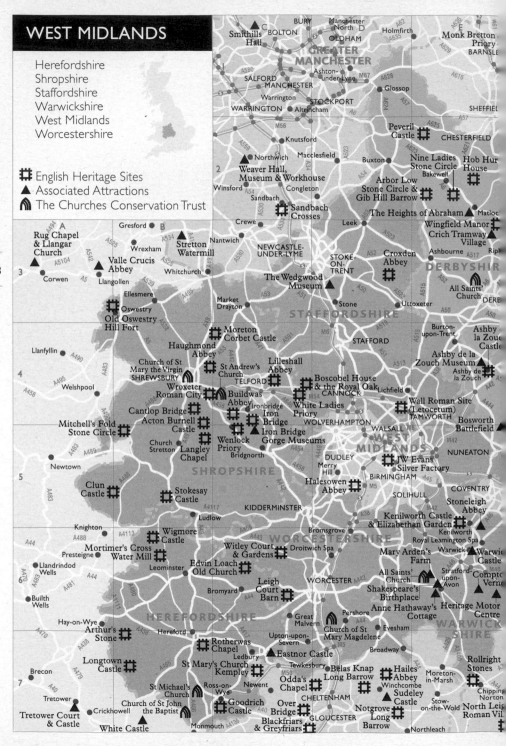

F   SCUNTHORPE   G   GRIMSBY   J   K

Brodsworth Hall & Gardens
DONCASTER
Cleethorpes

0Kms   10   20   30
0Miles   10   20

OUTH YORKS.
Brigg

NORTH EAST LINCOLNSHIRE

Conisbrough Castle
Gainsthorpe Medieval Village
Caistor

A1(M)

ROTHERHAM
A613
Gainsborough Old Hall
Market Rasen

Roche Abbey
Gainsborough
Louth

LINCOLNSHIRE
Mablethorpe

Mattersey Priory
Retford

Worksop
Wragby
A157
Sutton-on-Sea

Creswell Crags

Bolsover Cundy House
Milton Mausoleum
Ollerton
LINCOLN
St George's Church
Horncastle
Alford

Bolsover Castle
Lincoln Medieval Bishops' Palace
Woodhall Spa
Bolingbroke Castle
Ingoldmells

Rufford Abbey
Mansfield
Skegness

Hardwick Old Hall
Tattershall College
Coningsby

Newark-on-Trent

utton carsdale Hall

Papplewick Pumping Station
Sibsey Trader Windmill

NOTTINGHAMSHIRE
Sleaford
Boston

NOTTINGHAM
West Bridgford
Grantham

The Wash

Hunstanton

Castle Rising Castle

Melton Mowbray
Spalding
Holbeach
Long Sutton
St Nicholas Chapel
King's Lynn
Castle Acre Bailey Gate

Loughborough

Castle Acre Priory

LEICESTERSHIRE   **RUTLAND**
Wisbech
Downham Market

Kirby Muxloe Castle
Oakham
Rutland Water
Stamford
Burghley House

LEICESTER
Jewry Wall
Lyddington Bede House
Longthorpe Tower
Kirby Hall
PETERBOROUGH
March
Weeting Castle

Rockingham Castle
Apethorpe Hall
Flag Fen Bronze Age Centre
Brandon

Market Harborough
St Peter's Church
Corby
Oundle
CAMBRIDGESHIRE

Rushton Triangular Lodge
Eleanor Cross
Chatteris
Isleham Priory Church

Kettering
St Andrew's Church
Ely

Kelmarsh Hall
Huntingdon

NORTHAMPTONSHIRE
Chichele College

Althorp
Wellingborough
Church of St Margaret of Antioch

St Peter's Church
NORTHAMPTON
Bushmead Priory
St. Neots

78,Derngate

BEDFORD-SHIRE
Sandy

Towcester
Newport Pagnell
BEDFORD
Biggleswade

MILTON KEYNES

Houghton House

Bletchley
De Grey Mausoleum
Wrest Park

Deddington Castle
Buckingham
Woburn Abbey

BUCKINGHAMSHIRE
Dunstable

Bicester
LUTON

Woodstock
Aylesbury

Created by Arka Cartographics Ltd. for English Heritage © 12/11

319

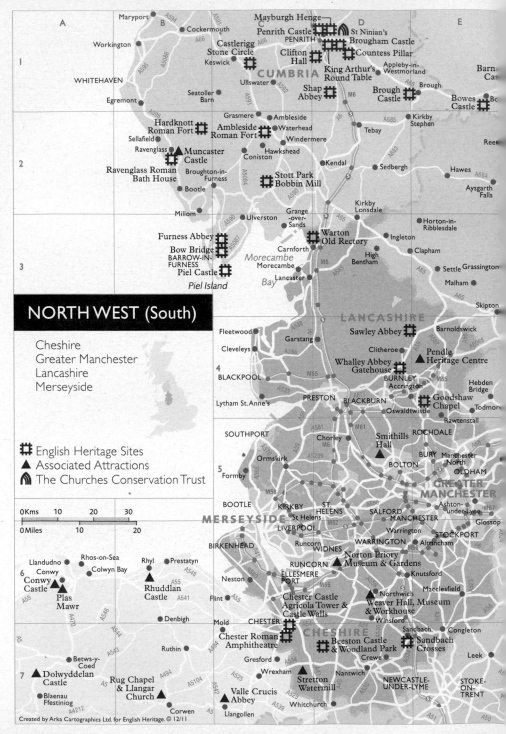

320

NORTH WEST (South)

Cheshire
Greater Manchester
Lancashire
Merseyside

⌗ English Heritage Sites
▲ Associated Attractions
⌂ The Churches Conservation Trust

| 0 Kms | 10 | 20 | 30 |
| 0 Miles | 10 | 20 | |

Maryport
Workington
WHITEHAVEN
Egremont
Cockermouth
Penrith Castle
PENRITH
Castlerigg
Stone Circle
Keswick
Clifton
Hall
Mayburgh Henge
St Ninian's
Brougham Castle
Countess Pillar
King Arthur's
Round Table
Appleby-in-
Westmorland
Barna
Cas
CUMBRIA
Ullswater
Shap
Abbey
Brough
Castle
Brough
Bowes
Castle Bo
Seatoller
Barn
Grasmere
Ambleside
Waterhead
Windermere
Tebay
Kirkby
Stephen
Hardknott
Roman Fort
Ambleside
Roman Fort
Sellafield
Ravenglass
Muncaster
Castle
Coniston
Hawkshead
Kendal
Sedbergh
Hawes
Aysgarth
Falls
Ree
Ravenglass Roman
Bath House
Broughton-in-
Furness
Bootle
Millom
Stott Park
Bobbin Mill
Grange
-over-
Sands
Kirkby
Lonsdale
Horton-in-
Ribblesdale
Ingleton
Clapham
Settle
Grassington
Malham
Skipton
Ulverston
Furness Abbey
Bow Bridge
BARROW-IN-
FURNESS
Piel Castle
Piel Island
Carnforth
Warton
Old Rectory
Morecambe
Morecambe
Lancaster
Bay
High
Bentham
LANCASHIRE
Fleetwood
Cleveleys
Garstang
Sawley Abbey
Barnoldswick
Clitheroe
Whalley Abbey
Gatehouse
Pendle
Heritage Centre
BLACKPOOL
Lytham St.Anne's
PRESTON
BLACKBURN
BURNLEY
Accrington
Oswaldtwistle
Hebden
Bridge
Todmor
Goodshaw
Chapel
Rawtenstall
SOUTHPORT
Chorley
Smithills
Hall
ROCHDALE
BURY Manchester
North
OLDHAM
Ormskirk
BOLTON
GREATER
MANCHESTER
Formby
BOOTLE
KIRKBY
St Helens
ST.
HELENS
SALFORD
MANCHESTER
Ashton-
under-Lyne
Glossop
MERSEYSIDE
LIVERPOOL
Warrington
WARRINGTON
STOCKPORT
Altrincham
BIRKENHEAD
WIDNES
RUNCORN
Runcorn
Norton Priory
Museum & Gardens
Knutsford
Macclesfield
Neston
ELLESMERE
PORT
Northwich
Weaver Hall, Museum
& Workhouse
Winsford
Flint
Mold
CHESTER
Chester Castle
Agricola Tower &
Castle Walls
CHESHIRE
Sandbach
Sandbach
Crosses
Congleton
Leek
Chester Roman
Amphitheatre
Gresford
Beeston Castle
& Woodland Park
Crewe
Nantwich
NEWCASTLE-
UNDER-LYME
STOKE-
ON-
TRENT
Llandudno
Rhos-on-Sea
Rhyl
Prestatyn
Conwy
Castle
Colwyn Bay
Rhuddlan
Castle
Plas
Mawr
Denbigh
Wrexham
Stretton
Watermill
Betws-y-
Coed
Dolwyddelan
Castle
Ruthin
Valle Crucis
Abbey
Whitchurch
Blaenau
Ffestiniog
Rug Chapel
& Llangar
Church
Corwen
Llangollen
Created by Arka Cartographics Ltd. for English Heritage. © 12/11

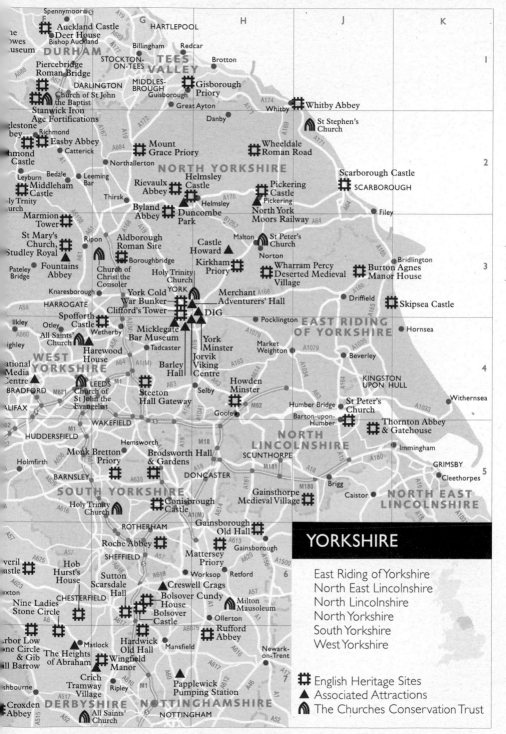

Spennymoor
Auckland Castle
Deer House
Bishop Auckland
DURHAM
Piercebridge
Roman Bridge
DARLINGTON
Church of St John
the Baptist
Stanwick Iron
Age Fortifications
Richmond
Easby Abbey
Catterick
Leyburn
Bedale
Leeming
Bar
Middleham
Castle
Thirsk
Marmion
Tower
Ripon
St Mary's
Church,
Studley Royal
Aldborough
Roman Site
Boroughbridge
Pateley
Bridge
Fountains
Abbey
Church of
Christ the
Consoler
Knaresborough
HARROGATE
Spofforth
Castle
Wetherby
Ilkley
Otley
All Saints'
Church
Harewood
House
WEST
YORKSHIRE
Steeton
Hall Gateway
 national
Media
Centre
BRADFORD
LEEDS
Church of
St John the
Evangelist
HALIFAX
WAKEFIELD
HUDDERSFIELD
Holmfirth
Monk Bretton
Priory
Hemsworth
BARNSLEY
SOUTH YORKSHIRE
Holy Trinity
Church
Conisbrough
Castle
ROTHERHAM
Roche Abbey
SHEFFIELD
Mattersey
Priory
Gainsborough
Old Hall
Gainsborough
Hob
Hurst's
House
Sutton
Scarsdale
Hall
CHESTERFIELD
Creswell Crags
Worksop
Retford
Nine Ladies
Stone Circle
Bolsover Cundy
House
Bolsover
Castle
Milton
Mausoleum
Ollerton
Rufford
Abbey
Arbor Low
one Circle
& Gib
ill Barrow
Matlock
The Heights
of Abraham
Hardwick
Old Hall
Wingfield
Manor
Mansfield
Newark-
on-Trent
Crich
Tramway
Village
Ripley
Papplewick
Pumping Station
Croxden
Abbey
DERBYSHIRE
NOTTINGHAMSHIRE
All Saints'
Church
NOTTINGHAM

HARTLEPOOL
Billingham
Redcar
STOCKTON-
ON-TEES
TEES
VALLEY
Brotton
MIDDLES-
BROUGH
Gisborough
Priory
Guisborough
Great Ayton
Whitby
Whitby Abbey
Danby
St Stephen's
Church
Mount
Grace Priory
Northallerton
Wheeldale
Roman Road
NORTH YORKSHIRE
Rievaulx
Abbey
Helmsley
Castle
Helmsley
Pickering
Castle
Pickering
Scarborough Castle
SCARBOROUGH
Byland
Abbey
Duncombe
Park
North York
Moors Railway
Filey
Castle
Howard
Malton
St Peter's
Church
Norton
Kirkham
Priory
Wharram Percy
Deserted Medieval
Village
Bridlington
Burton Agnes
Manor House
Holy Trinity
Church
York Cold
War Bunker
Merchant
Adventurers' Hall
Driffield
Skipsea Castle
Clifford's Tower
YORK
DIG
Pocklington
EAST RIDING
OF YORKSHIRE
Hornsea
Micklegate
Bar Museum
York
Minster
Jorvik
Viking
Centre
Market
Weighton
Beverley
KINGSTON
UPON HULL
Barley
Hall
Tadcaster
Selby
Howden
Minster
Withernsea
Goole
Humber Bridge
St Peter's
Church
Barton-upon-
Humber
Thornton Abbey
& Gatehouse
Brodsworth Hall
& Gardens
SCUNTHORPE
NORTH
LINCOLNSHIRE
Immingham
DONCASTER
Gainsthorpe
Medieval Village
Brigg
Caistor
GRIMSBY
Cleethorpes
NORTH EAST
LINCOLNSHIRE

YORKSHIRE

East Riding of Yorkshire
North East Lincolnshire
North Lincolnshire
North Yorkshire
South Yorkshire
West Yorkshire

English Heritage Sites
Associated Attractions
The Churches Conservation Trust

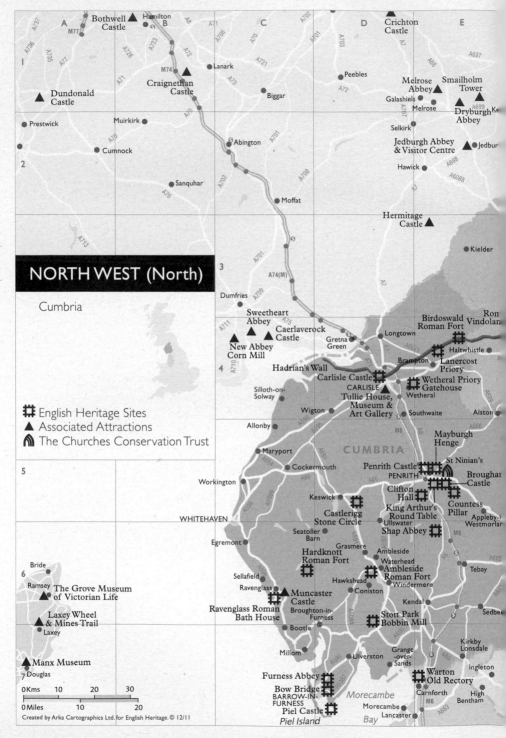

NORTH WEST (North)

Cumbria

English Heritage Sites
▲ **Associated Attractions**
🜱 **The Churches Conservation Trust**

A — B — C — D — E

I

Bothwell Castle ▲ Hamilton
M77
Craignethan Castle ▲
M74 ● Lanark
A723
Dundonald ▲ Castle
● Prestwick
● Muirkirk
● Cumnock
● Sanquhar

Crichton ▲ Castle
● Peebles
● Biggar
Melrose ▲ Abbey Smailholm ▲ Tower
Galashiels ● ● Melrose
Dryburgh ▲ Abbey K
● Selkirk
Jedburgh Abbey ▲ Jedbur
& Visitor Centre
● Hawick

Hermitage ▲ Castle

● Kielder

2

3
● Abington
● Moffat
● Dumfries
A74(M)
A74

Sweetheart ▲ Abbey
Caerlaverock ▲ Castle
New Abbey ▲ Corn Mill
Hadrian's Wall
● Silloth-on-Solway
● Wigton
● Allonby

Birdoswald ▲ Ron
Roman Fort Vindolan
● Longtown
● Gretna Green
● Haltwhistle
● Brampton Lanercost 🜱 Priory
Carlisle Castle 🜱 Wetheral Priory 🜱 Gatehouse
CARLISLE ● Wetheral
Tullie House, ▲ Museum & Art Gallery
● Southwaite ● Alston

4

5
● Maryport
● Cockermouth
● Workington

CUMBRIA
M6
Mayburgh 🜱 Henge
Penrith Castle 🜱 St Ninian's 🜱
PENRITH Brougha 🜱 Castle
Clifton 🜱 Hall Countess 🜱 Pillar
● Appleby-i Westmorlan

WHITEHAVEN
● Keswick
Castlerigg 🜱 Stone Circle
● Seatoller Barn
● Egremont

King Arthur's 🜱 Round Table
● Ullswater
Shap Abbey 🜱
● Grasmere
● Waterhead
● Ambleside Ambleside 🜱 Roman Fort
Hardknott 🜱 Roman Fort ● Windermere
● Hawkshead ● Coniston ● Kendal
Tebay ●
A685

6
● Bride
● Ramsey
The Grove Museum ▲ of Victorian Life
Laxey Wheel ▲ & Mines Trail
● Laxey
Sellafield ●
● Ravenglass
Muncaster ▲ Castle
Ravenglass Roman Bath House 🜱
● Bootle
● Broughton-in-Furness
Stott Park 🜱 Bobbin Mill
● Sedbe
Kirkby Lonsdale
● Ingleton

7
Manx Museum ▲
Douglas
● Millom
● Ulverston
● Grange-over-Sands
Furness Abbey 🜱
Bow Bridge 🜱
BARROW-IN-FURNESS
Piel Castle 🜱
Piel Island
Morecambe Bay
● Morecambe ● Lancaster
Warton 🜱 Old Rectory
● Carnforth High Bentham ●

0 Kms 10 20 30
0 Miles 10 20

Created by Arka Cartographics Ltd. for English Heritage. © 12/11

NORTH EAST

County Durham
Northumberland
Tyne & Wear
Tees Valley

English Heritage Sites

▲ **Associated Attractions**

The Churches Conservation Trust

323

F
Berwick-upon-Tweed Barracks & Main Guard
A6105
erwick-upon-Tweed
Berwick-upon-Tweed Castle & Town Defences
orham Castle
dstream
Etal Castle
Belford
G
Lindisfarne Priory
Bamburgh Castle
Seahouses
H
I

Adderstone

Wooler

Dunstanburgh Castle
Craster

Alnwick Castle & Gardens
Alnwick

2

Edlingham Castle
Warkworth Castle & Hermitage
Rothbury
Amble

NORTHUMBERLAND
ck Middens
stle House
Brinkburn Priory

Otterburn

J   **K**

ngham
Morpeth
ASHINGTON
Newbiggin-by-the-Sea
3

Belsay Hall Castle & Gardens
Blyth
esters Roman
t & Museum
Bessie Surtees House
Whitley Bay
Tynemouth Priory & Castle
Chesters Bridge Abutment
NEWCASTLE UPON TYNE
Segedunum Roman Fort
useteads
nan Fort
Aydon Castle
Prudhoe Castle
St Paul's Monastery
ydon
idge
Hexham
Prudhoe
TYNE & WEAR
Hexham
Old Gaol
Derwentcote Steel Furnace
SUNDERLAND
Hylton Castle
4
Corbridge Roman Town
St Andrew's Church
Beamish
Killhope - The North of England Lead Mining Museum
Tanfield Railway
Finchale Priory
Consett
A689
Stanhope
DURHAM
A1(M)
Peterlee
DURHAM
Spennymoor
HARTLEPOOL
Auckland Castle Deer House
5
Bishop Auckland
Billingham
Redcar
The Bowes Museum
Piercebridge Roman Bridge
STOCKTON-ON-TEES
Brotton
Barnard Castle
DARLINGTON
MIDDLES-BROUGH
Gisborough Priory
TEES VALLEY
Guisborough
Bowes Castle
Bowes
Church of St John the Baptist
Great Ayton
Danby
Whitby
Whitby Abbey
ough
stle
rkby
phen
Egglestone Abbey
Stanwick Iron Age Fortifications
St Stephen's Church
6
Reeth
Richmond
Wheeldale Roman Road
Easby Abbey
Catterick
Richmond Castle
Northallerton
Mount Grace Priory
Scarborough Castle
Hawes
Aysgarth Falls
NORTH YORKSHIRE
Leyburn
Bedale
Leeming Bar
Rievaulx Abbey
Helmsley Castle
Pickering Castle
SCARBOROUGH
Holy Trinity Church
Middleham Castle
Thirsk
Helmsley
Pickering
Filey
Horton-in-Ribblesdale
Marmion Tower
Byland Abbey
Duncombe Park
North York Moors Railway
7
lapham
St Mary's Church, Studley Royal
Ripon
Aldborough Roman Site
Easingwold
Castle Howard
Malton
St Peter's Church
Burton Agnes Manor House
Fountains Abbey
Settle
Grassington
Pateley Bridge
Church of Christ the Consoler
Boroughbridge
Kirkham Priory
Wharram Percy Deserted Medieval Village
Malham

Details of OS LandRanger and Explorer map references are provided for easy location of each property, with specific map numbers (LandRanger; Explorer) followed by the grid reference.

NB. All maps in this handbook are created using Ordnance Survey mapping. Unless otherwise credited, they are © Crown Copyright and database right 2012. All rights reserved. Ordnance Survey Licence number 100019088.

English Heritage Members' & Visitors' Handbook 2012/13

For English Heritage:
Gaynor Hemingway-Gibbs, Kathryn Steele-Childe, Tersia Boorer, Charles Kightly.

Design and Publishing:
Ledgard Jepson Ltd.

For Ledgard Jepson Ltd:
David Exley, Bev Turbitt, Andrea Rollinson.

Print: Wyndeham Roche Ltd

Transport Information:
John Burch, CPT.

Please support us

Many of the projects that improve and enhance our properties would not be possible without the generous support we receive each year from donors. There are many ways you can help, from making a donation or volunteering your time, to leaving a gift in your will for the future. You can also make a donation when you renew your membership.

England is famous for its gardens and landscapes, but it is only at Wrest Park that you can follow the evolution of landscape gardening over the last 300 years. The site has been completely revitalised over the last couple of years, with the restoration of the Italian and Rose gardens; the re-instatement of miles of historic pathways; and vivid new interpretation inside the mansion. This and many other projects have been made possible by generous donations from our members and visitors, together with other charitable funders.

English Heritage Foundation, registered charity 1140351

ENGLISH HERITAGE
STEP INTO ENGLAND'S STORY

To find out about current fundraising projects and how you can help, please email foundation@english-heritage.org.uk, telephone 020 7973 3797 or visit **www.english-heritage.org.uk/supportus**